D0903242

Conway, B E
Theory and
principles of
electrode
processes.

B. E. CONWAY is Professor of Chemistry at the University of Ottawa. He received his Ph.D. from the Imperial College of Science and Technology, University of London and the degree of D.Sc. from the same University on published research. Dr. Conway has also taught at the University of Pennsylvania and previously served as Research Associate with the Chester Beatty Research Institute, University of London. He is the author of over 100 publications in the field of electrochemistry and general physical chemistry and was the recipient of the Noranda Lecture Award in 1964 from the Chemical Institute of Canada.

MODERN CONCEPTS IN CHEMISTRY

EDITORS

Bryce Crawford, Jr., University of Minnesota
W. D. McElroy, Johns Hopkins University
Charles C. Price, University of Pennsylvania

THEORY AND PRINCIPLES OF
ELECTRODE
PROCESSES

B. E. CONWAY

UNIVERSITY OF OTTAWA

THE RONALD PRESS COMPANY · NEW YORK

Library of Congress Catalog Card Number: 65–17090

Preface

Electrochemical kinetics comprises a rapidly developing branch of the study of kinetics of chemical reactions—a branch of considerable importance since the reactions concerned are heterogeneous ones, and, uniquely, their rates can be controlled through variation of the free energy of activation by changes of applied potential and measured by determination of currents. Despite the formulation of such effects for some forty years, these aspects of kinetics are rarely presented in general textbooks of physical chemistry; however, if only from a pedagogical point of view in the theory of absolute rates of reaction, they have value in illustrating the role of free energy of activation in reactions and the importance of adsorption of reactants and intermediates in surface reactions.

The present volume presents the essential features of the modern theory of electrochemical reactions and related problems of electrochemical adsorption which are complementary to the kinetic theory and together constitute the subject of electrocatalysis. The treatment of the subject is at a moderately advanced level suitable either for the graduate student studying in the fields of electrochemistry and kinetics or for the specialist; however, basic concepts have been treated in some detail where appropriate. After the presentation of the theory and principles of electrochemical adsorption and kinetics of electrode processes, a lengthy chapter on fundamental applications examines selected topics in the field of electrode processes in the light of the theory presented in Chapters 2 to 7. The concluding chapter deals with electrochemical problems at the gas-metal interface, including field emission and field ionisation.

The choice of topics examined and the relative degrees of emphasis placed on the various aspects of the subject of electrode processes which are presented necessarily reflect the Author's personal interests in the field and his desire to present the selected aspects in some depth rather than to cover a wider field of topics more superficially. An attempt has been made to give a reasonably full compilation of references with the aim of quoting both historically important papers and more modern ones which have added to the development of the subject in significant ways in recent years. Also, in a number of sections, some original presentations of theory are given. It is hoped that the present book may be of value not only to the general student of electrode processes but to the specialist in related fields of pure and applied electrochemistry and catalysis.

Grateful acknowledgment is made to several of my previous students—Drs. E. Gileadi, P. L. Bourgault, R. G. Barradas and H. Angerstein-Kozlowska—for discussions which, in recent years, have led to some of the ideas and work presented in this volume. Finally the Author's thanks are due to Professor K. J. Laidler, Chairman of the Department of Chemistry at the University of Ottawa, for his encouragement and cooperation in the use of the facilities of his Department during the preparation of this book and during the execution of some of the original work of the Author referred to in the text.

B. E. Conway

Ottawa, Ontario, Canada
June, 1964

Contents

CHAPTER   PAGE

I   Introduction   3

    Structure of Electrochemistry · The Nature of Elec-
    trode Reactions

2   Potential Differences at Interfaces   13

    Introduction · Types of Potential Difference at the
    Metal-Solution Interface · Thermodynamics of Poten-
    tials at Electrodes

3   Distribution of Ions and Molecules at Electrode Interfaces:
    The Ionic Double-Layer   25

    Introduction · Ion Distribution · Capacity · Stern's
    Treatment · Other Modifications · Dielectric Constant
    and Electrostriction in the Double-Layer · Solvent
    Orientation Theory of the Double Layer

4   Determination of Reactant Adsorption at Electrodes: Ionic
    Species   44

    Electrocapillary Method · Components of Charge from
    the Capacity Method · Use of Data on Components of
    Charge · Components of Charge When Ionic Equilibria

v

CHAPTER   PAGE

Are Involved—Adsorption of Organic Bases and Their
Ions · Other Methods · Significance of Potential of
Zero Charge

5   Adsorption Behaviour of Neutral Molecules and Ions .   .   69

Introduction · Theories of Adsorption · General Electrostatic Theory of Neutral Molecule Adsorption · Isotherms for Reactant Ions and Molecules at Electrodes ·
Electrochemical Isotherms for Ion Adsorption · Electrochemical Isotherms for Neutral Molecules at
Electrodes

6   Electrochemical Kinetic Principles   92

Basic Factors in Ion Discharge · Over-All Kinetic Rate
Equation · Heats of Activation and Frequency Factors ·
Treatment for Consecutive and Alternative Processes ·
Kinetics Under Temkin-Type Adsorption Conditions ·
Kinetic Equations Under Temkin Conditions When
Several Adsorbed Intermediates Are Involved · Ki-
netic Equations Arising for a Priori Heterogeneity ·
Energetics of Irreversible Processes

7   Adsorbed Intermediates at Electrodes   136

Introduction · Conditions for Intermediate Coverage
$(0.8 > \theta > 0.2)$ · Relation between Coverage, Charge
and Capacitance Associated with Intermediates · Adsorption Pseudocapacitance from Kinetic Equations ·
Chemical Factors · Methods for Study of Intermediates

8   Applications to Selected Problems 170

The Hydrogen Evolution Reaction · The Oxygen
Evolution Reaction · Corrosion and Passivity · Metal
Deposition and Dissolution · Ionic Redox Reactions ·

CHAPTER   PAGE

Rapid Electrochemical Reactions · Organic Electrode
Processes · Anodic Film Growth and Kinetics at Oxide
Film Electrodes · Stoichiometric Numbers

9 Electrochemical Field Effects at the Gas-Metal Interface   . 273

Apparatus · Field Emission of Electrons · Applications
to Adsorption · Field Ionisation

Appendix: Basic Types of Mechanisms for Organic
           Electrode Processes   283

References   285

Index   297

THEORY AND PRINCIPLES OF
ELECTRODE PROCESSES

I

Introduction

1. STRUCTURE OF ELECTROCHEMISTRY

In order to place the subject of electrode processes in its proper context, it is appropriate first to review briefly the structure of the field of electrochemistry. The origin of the subject can be traced back to the discoveries of Nicholson (1) and Faraday (2) regarding the electrical decomposition of aqueous solutions, and to the observations of Galvani (3) and Volta (4) on the chemical effects of electricity and the electrochemical generation of electricity. These observations complementarily laid the foundation of concepts regarding the electrical nature of matter and the nature of electrical phenomena, the study of which occupied much of the activities of chemists and physicists, respectively, in the nineteenth century. The studies of Faraday, Berthelot and Daniell, and later Arrhenius and Kohlrausch, provided a basis for more modern concepts of current flow and conduction in electrolyte solutions, and facilitated the understanding of the nature of the processes occurring at the electrode interfaces. At that time, the problems of current conduction in the solution and the electrochemical reactions occurring at the electrodes were regarded as more closely connected than would now be considered the case. For example, Faraday regarded the passage of current as causing the dissociation of the electrolyte solute into charged species, and thus in a formal way anticipated the dissociation field effect in which high fields do in fact cause enhanced dissociation of

3

potential electrolytes (e.g. acetic acid) or associated ion pairs. The precise nature of the process of neutralisation of ions which occurred at the electrodes could not at that time be formulated in any exact manner, and the concept of the unit charge, named the "electron" at the suggestion of Johnstone-Stoney (5) in his work on electrolysis, and later characterised by J. J. Thompson (6) in 1897 in the gas phase, was yet to be published. The early work in electrochemistry was thus characterised by a close relation between the phenomenology of electrode processes and the nature of electrolytic solutions. However, in later work following the theory of Arrhenius on incomplete electrolytic dissociation, and the experimental work on conductance of solutions by Kohlrausch and on thermodynamics of salt solutions by Lewis and others, the subject tended to separate into two streams: (a) the electrochemistry of ionic solutions (and fused salts), or "ionics," as it may be called, and (b) the electrochemistry of heterogeneous charge-transfer processes at electrode interfaces, or "electrodics" (7). This separation has indeed been maintained in a large degree to the present time.

In the "ionics" branch of the subject, which will not be examined in any detail in the present work, the principal lines of approach have been concerned with the nature of ions in solution (e.g. the extent of dissociation of true salts and potential electrolytes such as HCl, CH_3COOH which give ionic solutions by an acid-base reaction with the solvent), the study of hydration or solvation of such ions (8,9,10) and the examination of long-range interactions of ions leading to thermodynamic non-ideality of their solutions and to concentration-dependent conductance, diffusion behaviour and rheological properties.

In the "electrodics" branch of the subject, several principal areas of interest may be distinguished. First, the field of diffusion-controlled processes (11,12,13) involves reactant diffusion to the electrode as the step limiting the rate of the over-all electrochemical reaction. This field is mainly the province of the subjects of polarography and electroanalytical chemistry, and the development of this branch of the subject has been concerned largely with solutions of complex diffusion problems under d.c. and a.c. conditions. Secondly, there has been involved the development of instrumentation for the study of electrode processes in which the rate of the over-all reaction is controlled by some heterogeneous electrochemical or chemical step at the electrode-solution interface, for example, ion discharge to form an intermediate adsorbed species, or heterogeneous desorption of such species by some chemical or electrochemical reaction at the surface. Such rate-limiting steps may be termed "activation-controlled" in order to be distinguished from diffusion-controlled reactions, where the rate of reactant transfer to the surface is the step that limits the rate of the over-all process. In some cases, both types of process may be significant in determining the electrochemical kinetic behaviour of a system, e.g. for certain fast irreversible reductions. Within the subdivision (b) above, the fields of electro-inorganic chemistry and electro-organic chemistry may be distinguished. Although much significant work had been done in the latter subject (e.g., see 14) before the end of the nineteenth century, most of it was concerned with qualitative synthetic problems. Not until recently, when controlled potential techniques have begun to be more widely used, have there been attempts to put the subject of electro-organic chemistry on a sounder fundamental basis.

While the study of ionic solutions had progressed far by 1923 (the date of the formulation of the Debye-Hückel theory), and much concentrated experimental work continued particularly on the study of conductance and activities of salts in solution until the 1940's and later until the present time, the corresponding study of electrode processes was rather slower. Thus, although the phenomenology of electrolysis was already familiar in 1840, the basic kinetic treatment was not formulated until 1924 by Butler (15), or developed in a correct fashion until 1930 by Erdey-Gruz and Volmer (16), Baars (17) and Gurney (18), with subsequent important improvements to include ion distribution effects [Frumkin, 1933 (19)] and adsorption of adsorbed intermediates [Horiuti and Polyani, 1934 (20); Butler, 1936 (21)].

TABLE I-I

Structure of Electrochemistry

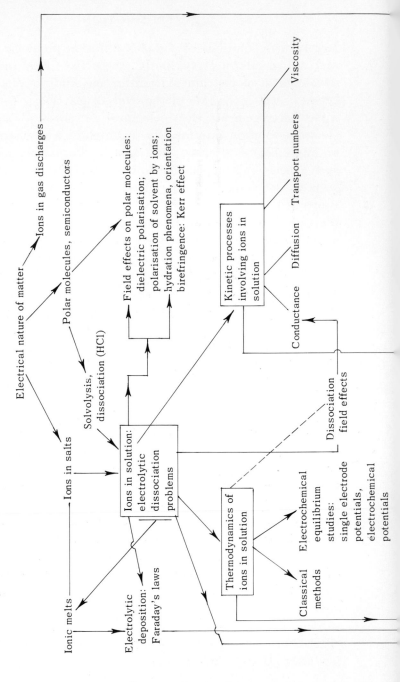

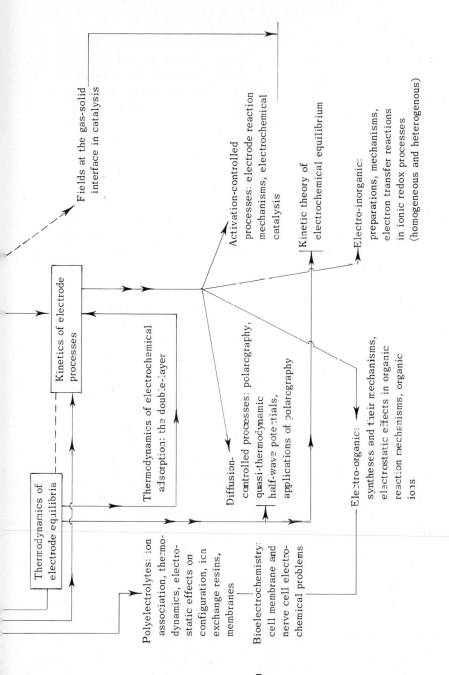

Fields at the gas-solid
interface in catalysis

Activation-controlled
processes: electrode reaction
mechanisms, electrochemical
catalysis

Kinetic theory of
electrochemical equilibrium

Electro-inorganic:
preparations, mechanisms,
electron transfer reactions
in ionic redox processes
(homogeneous and heterogenous)

Kinetics of electrode
processes

Thermodynamics of electrochemical
adsorption: the double-layer

Diffusion-
controlled processes: polarography,
quasi-thermodynamic
half-wave potentials,
applications of polarography

Electro-organic:
syntheses and their mechanisms,
electrostatic effects in organic
reaction mechanisms, organic
ions

Thermodynamics of
electrode equilibria

Polyelectrolytes: ion
association, thermo-
dynamics, electro-
static effects on
configuration, ion
exchange resins,
membranes

Bioelectrochemistry:
cell membrane and
nerve cell electro-
chemical problems

The relations between various branches of the subject, including those concerned with electrolytic solutions, are shown in Table 1–1. The scope of the present book will be concerned largely with the treatment of activation-controlled electrode processes indicated at the bottom right-hand corner of the scheme, and the problem of electrochemical adsorption of reactants and intermediates at the electrode interface.

2. THE NATURE OF ELECTRODE REACTIONS

Electrode reactions are characterised by charge transfer to or from ions or neutral molecules at an interface which can act as a controllable electron source (cathode) or sink (anode).   In certain cases, both the reactants and the products are ions, e.g. in redox reactions such as

$$Fe^{+++} + e_M \rightarrow Fe^{++} \tag{1}$$

and the electron designated as e_M is provided by the metal, e.g. Pt.   A similar electron interchange can occur homogeneously and has been the subject of recent study (22,23):

$$Fe_I^{++} + Fe_{II}^{+++} \rightarrow Fe_I^{+++} + Fe_{II}^{++} \tag{2}$$

where the subscripts I and II indicate the identity of the particular ions in the two valence states.   In this case, no electron interchange with the metal is involved.   However, reaction 1 can be set up at equilibrium at an electrode, and the latter then acts both as an electron source and sink for the conjugate redox pair (24). In the simple ionic redox case, no adsorbed intermediates are involved.   For most electrochemical reactions proceeding in a net direction, however, either atomic or free radical intermediates are formed, which are adsorbed at the interface as in the gas evolution reactions, or when phase growth occurs.   Examples of the latter process are metal deposition and oxide film formation on the baser metals.   In reactions where continuous formation of a new phase occurs, e.g. in metal deposition, intermediates may also be involved.   In all these reactions, the following types of steps may be distinguished and will be examined in detail in following chapters.

(i) Diffusion of Reactant ions or Molecules in a Gradient of Chemical or Electrochemical Potential Towards the Surface. Usually net diffusion can occur if a concentration gradient is set up by the electrode reaction itself on account of consumption of reactant at the interface. This is the condition in polarography. Alternatively, field-assisted diffusion (i.e. electrolytic migration) may occur if the reacting substance is ionic and not present with excess non-reacting salt ions, i.e., if its electrolytic transference number $t_\pm$ is significant and has a normal value of, say, $0.2 < t_\pm < 0.8$. Under such conditions, the reacting ions may move under the combined influence of a gradient of chemical and electrical potential, and the diffusion current density for a cation of valence z is

$$i_+ = \frac{zFD}{t_-}\frac{dc}{dx}$$

where D is the diffusion constant and dc/dx is the mean concentration gradient normal to the surface.

In the present volume, diffusion-controlled processes will not be examined in any detail, as the treatments involved are concerned more with problems arising in consideration of the transfer of the electrochemically reacting ions or molecules *to* a region of the solution close to the surface than with reactions *at* the electrode interface. However, the kinetics of some fast reactions cannot be properly examined without regard to diffusion effects, for example, particularly in a.c. impedance and d.c. transient studies.

(ii) Adsorption at the Interface. Following the diffusion or electrolytic migration of the electrochemically reactive particle to the electrode, an adsorption equilibrium is ideally set up between particles at the interface (i.e. within several Å of the "electronic surface" of the metal) and those in the solution. The standard free energy determining the distribution of the particles between the interfacial region at the electrode surface and the bulk of the solution will be determined by several distinguishable factors: (a) the electrostatic energy of the particle with respect to that for a typical position in the solution, (b) any chemical or polarisation energy involved in the interaction of the particle with the metal surface, and (c) any change of solvation energy of the particle in entering a region at the electrode surface where symmetrical interactions characteristic of the bulk solvent phase are necessarily absent. Normally, equilibrium between the reacting particle at the surface and the bulk solution is assumed for ions and molecules, but this may be significantly disturbed when finite currents pass (25), or if large molecules or ions are involved; in the latter case, adsorption equilibrium can be quite slow.

(iii) **Charge Transfer Involving Ions and Molecules.** The basic kinetic step in most electrochemical reactions is the transfer of electrons to or from ions or molecules. Formally these processes are equivalent as in the discharge step in hydrogen or oxygen evolution reaction ("h.e.r." and "o.e.r.") which proceed, over all, as follows:

$$2H_3O^+ + 2e \rightarrow H_2 + 2H_2O; \qquad 2H_2O + 2e \rightarrow 2OH^- + H_2$$

or

$$4OH^- \rightarrow O_2 + 2H_2O + 4e; \qquad 2H_2O \rightarrow O_2 + 4H^+ + 4e$$

by either ion discharge or charge transfer involving molecules, depending on the pH. While electron transfer is usually regarded as the charge-transfer step, it is also possible that proton transfer in the opposite direction (e.g. by tunneling; 26,27) may be the process by which charge is transferred, e.g. in the h.e.r. or in some organic reductions or inorganic oxidations such as that of hydrated nickel oxide.

(iv) **Following Reactions and Desorption Steps.** Most reactions not involving simply changes of valence of inorganic ions proceed by at least two consecutive steps, e.g. in the cases of the h.e.r. and o.e.r. referred to above and in most organic electrochemical reactions. In cases such as these, adsorbed free radical intermediates are involved and a heterogeneous desorption step (or steps), electrochemical or chemical in nature, is required before final product formation occurs.

TABLE 1-2

Types of Successive Steps in Electrochemical Reactions with Approximate Transfer Distances Shown

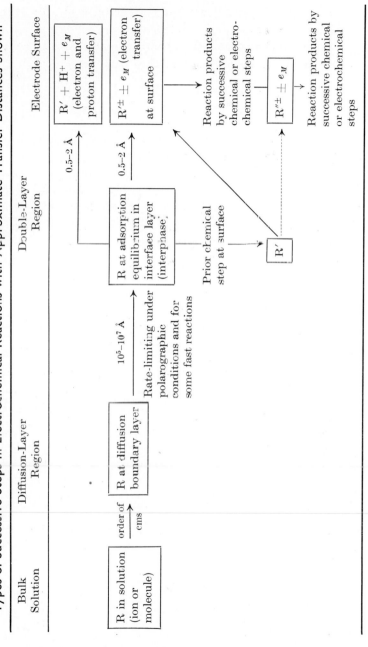

(v) Prior Chemical Reactions. In some cases, for example in hydrogen ionisation and electrocatalytic oxidation of organic substances, an heterogeneous chemical reaction can occur before electrochemical charge transfer takes place, e.g.

$$H_2 + M \rightarrow 2MH$$
$$2MH \rightarrow 2H^+ + 2e + M$$

or with some organic substances, dissociative chemisorption may have to precede electrochemical ionisation.

Details of these processes will be treated in following chapters. A scheme of the types of successive transfer processes involved in electrochemical reactions is given in Table 1–2, where R' and R'' are general representations for intermediates formed in the charge-transfer step. An anodic reaction has been considered for convenience, but similar principles apply to cathodic processes.

2
Potential Differences at Interfaces

I. INTRODUCTION

Both the adsorption of reactant ions and molecules at electrode interfaces and the rates of electrode reactions depend on the magnitude and profile of the potential difference between the inside of the metal and the bulk of the solution. The nature and origin of such potential differences is hence basic to the understanding of electrode kinetics, electrochemical thermodynamics and electrochemical adsorption.

2. TYPES OF POTENTIAL DIFFERENCE AT THE METAL-SOLUTION INTERFACE

Usually, experimentally significant potential differences are those measured between two pieces of metal of identical composition, e.g., with regard to the p.d. between two electrodes in solution determined by means of a potentiometer constructed with a wire resistance of homogeneous composition. While this case will be considered in more detail below, it is first convenient to discuss the significance of potential difference between a point X in a real substance and a charge-free reference point R at infinity (Fig. 1), according to the definitions of Lange (28,29). The change of energy (work done) in bringing a charged particle from R to inside the phase at the point X is defined as the *electrochemical*

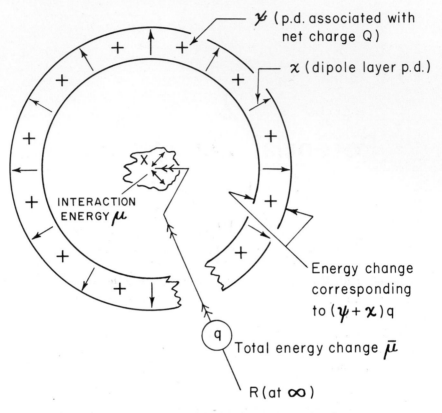

Fig. 1. Potential contributions to energy of a charge q inside a charged phase with dipolar surface region. (After Parsons, 30.)

potential $\bar{\mu}$ of this particle at X. The term "electrochemical" is used in order to signify that the work done may formally be regarded as arising from the sum of (a) energies of interactions of a *chemical* type between the particle and the material of the phase at X and (b) *electrical* energies associated with interaction of the particle with any net coulombic charge Q on the phase, plus (c) any energy involved in the passage of the particle across the interface of the phase where surface dipoles or a surface field may exist. The process of bringing the charge q from R to X can be represented (30) in terms of a spherical model bearing a net charge

Q and an array of surface dipoles (Fig. 1).   The energy of bringing the charged particle into the real sphere can be imagined to be equivalent to (a) bringing it into an uncharged sphere with no surface dipoles with the performance of work W, which will be identical with the chemical potential μ of the particle in the medium (amongst other similar particles at some definite concentration) since W arises only from local interactions between the particle and the bulk of the substance; and (b) bringing it into a hollow sphere having the same net charge and surface dipole configuration as the real sphere.   The work done in the latter case for a charge q is $q\phi$ when ϕ is the *electrical* p.d. between X and R.   Then,

$$\bar{\mu} - \mu + q\phi \tag{3}$$

The convenience of using "electrochemical potentials," $\bar{\mu}$, in electrochemical equilibria was first recognised by Butler (31), and the term $\mu + q\phi$ was termed the "electrochemical potential" by Guggenheim (31), who pointed out, however, that since single values of $\bar{\mu}$ could not be determined, a division into terms μ and $q\phi$ was not possible except in a formal way.   However, the concept is convenient and meaningful when differences of $\bar{\mu}$ are considered.   Also ϕ can be represented in terms of a net charge contribution ψ given (assuming unit dielectric constant) by

$$\psi = \frac{Q}{r} \tag{4}$$

if Q is the net charge on the sphere of radius r, and a surface dipole contribution χ, i.e.

$$\bar{\mu} = \mu + q\phi = \mu + (\psi + \chi)q \tag{5}$$

The potential difference χ will normally be made up of the sum of resolved contributions from any asymmetry of the distribution of electrons and nuclei at the metal interface and from orientation of molecular dipoles (e.g., of solvent or adsorbed gas) at the surface of the phase (32) (Fig. 2).   If the component of moment of such dipoles normal to the surface is m, χ due to dipoles (χ_d) is given by

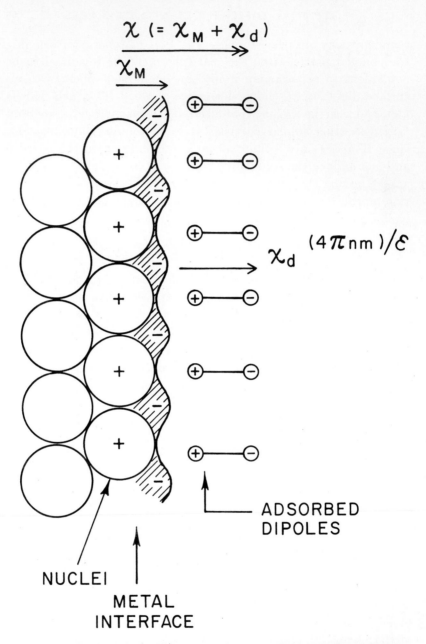

Fig. 2. Origin of dipole potentials at a metal interface showing effects due to electron overlap χ_M and adsorbed molecular dipoles χ_d.

16

the Helmholtz relation

$$\chi_d = -\frac{4\pi nm}{\epsilon_s} \tag{6}$$

(negative sign for positive ends of dipoles directed outwards) for n dipoles per square centimeter of surface with a surface layer dielectric constant ϵ_s. Normally m decreases as n increases, because of mutual depolarisation of dipoles* of similar orientation and close juxtaposition as n approaches the value for full coverage. According to Lange's terminology, ϕ will be called the inner potential (since it corresponds to the electrical p.d. between R and the *inside* of the spherical region), ψ the outer potential and χ the *surface* potential of the body. Frequently ϕ is called the Galvani potential and ψ the Volta potential. Since the term ψ can be experimentally measured, another term

$$\alpha = \mu + \chi q \tag{7}$$

is sometimes defined (*cf.* 30) as the *real potential* of the particle in the phase, i.e. the total potential energy change associated with entry of the charged particle from infinity into the medium when the latter is in an uncharged state; this follows since

$$\bar{\mu} = \mu + \chi q = \alpha$$

when $\psi = 0$, a condition which arises when $Q = 0$. Examples of real potentials are the negative of the electronic work function of

---

* Thus if m_θ is the effective dipole moment at coverage θ, and m_0 that of the isolated dipole ($\theta = 0$), then

$$m_\theta = \frac{m_0}{1 + k\theta}$$

where $k = 9\alpha_0/a^3$, and a is the distance between nearest neighbor dipoles at $\theta = 1$, and α_0 is the polarisability. The surface potential is then

$$\chi_\theta = \frac{4\pi n m_0}{1 + k\theta}$$

and n can also be expressed in terms of θ by $n = \theta n_{\theta=1}$.

a metal and the free energy of solvation* of ions from the vapor phase. Usually the difference of inner potentials $\Delta\phi$ (the Galvani p.d.) cannot be measured except in the case of two identical electrodes of the same composition. Thus, from Equation 5, for two electrical states, *1* and *2*, of the system,

$$\bar{\mu}_1 - \bar{\mu}_2 = q(\phi_1 - \phi_2) \tag{8}$$

Since $\mu_1 = \mu_2$ for identical composition, then $\bar{\mu}_1 - \bar{\mu}_2$ or $\Delta\phi_{1,2}$ can be measured by means of a potentiometer.

The outer, or Volta, potential will normally correspond to the energy of interaction of the charged particle with the charged body and will vary with distance r of the particle from the body according to $\psi = Q/r$ (or $Q/\epsilon r$ in a medium of dielectric constant ϵ). Volta potential differences are normally susceptible to experimental measurement (30). At short distances, of the order of 10–100 Å or less, the image potential associated with induction of opposite charges at the surface of the body† by the approaching charge can become important and is determined by the relation

$$\psi_i = \frac{q}{4r} \tag{9}$$

for a charge q at distance r from a plane metal surface. At very close distances, this simple law may break down as discussed by Bardeen (36), Sacks and Dexter (37) and Seitz (38). Thus, at short distances r from a surface, the image energy function $V(r)$ is given (38) approximately by

$$V(r) = \frac{q^2}{4r + q^2/W} \quad (r > 0) \quad \text{or} \quad V(r) = W \quad (r < 0)$$

* This quantity will differ from what is often calculated theoretically (33,34) by the energy of passage of the ion across the liquid-vapor interface of the solution where a surface potential will usually exist because of oriented surface dipoles and any asymmetric hydration of ions present in the solution. Such surface potentials have been discussed by Randles (35).

† The distribution of induced charges at the interface corresponds electrostatically to an imaginary charge equal and opposite to that causing the induction and existing at a position equivalent to that of the mirror image of the charge with respect to the surface plane of the metal.

where W is the interaction energy of the charged particle when it is *in* the surface, i.e., when $r < 0$. The image potential associated with ions near electrode interfaces can be significant with regard to their interactions in two dimensions laterally across the surface (see below), and to some extent with the surface itself. Usually the magnitude of the image potential is small at electrode-solution interfaces, but in processes at the gas-solid interface (see Chapter 9), it can be an important factor in determining rates of ionisation and electron emission in fields (39).

Surface potentials are not susceptible to direct measurement and may only be estimated theoretically. *Changes* of surface potential can, however, be determined, for example, by measuring changes of electronic work-function at metals upon which varying fractional coverages of adsorbed gas are established. Usually these changes $\Delta\chi$ of surface potential are determined for significant coverages θ, when $0.2 < \theta < 1$. Usually Equation 6 will refer to surface dipoles of adsorbed substance so that $\chi_d \to 0$, as $n \to 0$ ($\theta \to 0$). The total χ, however, will not necessarily tend to zero as $n \to 0$ (or $m = 0$) since an appreciable surface potential contribution χ_M (Fig. 2) probably already exists at the metal-vacuum interface (32) on account of asymmetry of the distribution of nuclei and electrons at the interface.

3. THERMODYNAMICS OF POTENTIALS AT ELECTRODES

(i) Single Electrode Potentials. The single metal-solution p.d. between the inside of a single metal electrode and the bulk of an electrolyte solution cannot of course be measured. It is, however, instructive to examine what factors determine its value since it is a quantity including the difference of two such "single" potential differences that is normally measured at a reversible or an irreversible electrode at which net current is passing. The equilibrium between a metal M and its ions M^{z+} in solution may be considered, i.e.

$$M \rightleftharpoons M^{z+} + ze_M \qquad (10)$$

with z excess electrons in the metal. Normally such a process will spontaneously proceed from left to right when any element is placed in a solution or solvent not initially containing any of its ions. The process will continue until the electric potential set up between M and the solution is just sufficient to prevent any further charge transfer. Under these conditions, the *electrochemical* potentials $\bar{\mu}$ of the species on the left and right of Equation 10 just become equal and the process is at equilibrium (*cf.* the equality of *chemical* potentials of components in a chemical equilibrium). Then,

$$\bar{\mu}_M = \bar{\mu}_{M^{z+}} + z\bar{\mu}_{e_M} \tag{11}$$

Expressing the $\bar{\mu}$ quantities in terms of μ and the inner potentials ϕ_M and ϕ_S for the bulk metal and solution phases, respectively, then gives (since "M" particles in the metal are uncharged)

$$\mu_M = \mu^0_{M^{z+}} + RT \ln a_{M^{z+}} + ze\phi_S - z\mu_{e_M} - ze\phi_M$$

If the metal M and the electrons in M are in their standard states, it follows directly that

$$\Delta\mu^0 + RT \ln a_{M^{z+}} = ze(\phi_M - \phi_S) \tag{12}$$

where $\Delta\mu^0 = \mu^0_{M^{z+}} - z\mu_{e_M} - \mu^0_M$, the standard chemical potential change in the single electrode reaction. Equation 12 is in fact a form of the Nernst equation for an electrochemical equilibrium but written for a single interface reaction. The terms involved are not accessible to experimental measurement, e.g., neither the single ion activity nor the $\Delta\mu^0$ term could be measured and there is no feasible electrical method whereby $\phi_M - \phi_S$ could be determined without introduction of other interfaces and associated potential differences.

The physical quantities that determine $\Delta\mu^0$ in Equation 12, and hence $\phi_M - \phi_S$, may be shown by reference to the following free-energy cycle:

$$
\begin{array}{ccc}
\mathrm{M}_g & \xrightarrow{\ I_z\ } & \mathrm{M}_g^{z+} + ze_g \\
\Big\uparrow \Delta G_{\mathrm{sub}}^0 & \Delta G_{M^{z+},s}^0 & \Big\downarrow -ze\Phi_e \\
\mathrm{M} & \underset{\ \ \ \ }{\overset{\Delta\mu^0}{\rightleftharpoons}} & \mathrm{M}_s^{z+} + ze_M \\
 & (a_{M^{z+}}) &
\end{array}
\tag{13}
$$

where $\Delta G_{\mathrm{sub}}^0$ is the standard free energy of sublimation of the metal lattice to gaseous M particles (M_g), I_z is the total ionisation potential to the state M^{z+}, $\Delta G_{M^{z+},s}^0$ is the standard free energy of solvation (33,34) of the ions in the solution and Φ_e is the electronic work function of the metal M. Although the above cycle is written for thermodynamic convenience of expressing formally the factors which determine $\Delta\mu^0$, there will be no physical transfer of electrons across the gas-solution interfaces. However, there will be a real charge transfer at the metal-solution interface so that Φ_e should refer to the value of the electronic work function in the presence of any adsorbed solvent dipoles at the metal interface. From Cycle 13 it is clear that

$$
\Delta\mu^0 = \Delta G_{\mathrm{sub}}^0 + I_z + \Delta G_{M^{z+},s}^0 - ze\Phi_e
\tag{14}
$$

and $\Delta G_{M^{z+},s}^0$ will normally be a large negative quantity. The right-hand side of Equation 14 hence defines $ze(\phi_M - \phi_S)$ for a given $a_{M^{z+}}$. It will be noted that the electronic work function of the metal enters in a primary way into the determination of $\Delta\mu^0$ and hence of $\phi_M - \phi_S$ (Equation 12) for a *single* electrode process such as that represented in Equation 10.

(ii) Differences of Single Metal-Solution Potential Differences. Normally, in electrochemical measurements, two electrode-solution interfaces are involved. Denoting the relevant equilibria by

$$
\mathrm{M}_1 \rightleftharpoons \mathrm{M}_1^{z+} + ze ; \qquad \mathrm{M}_2 \rightleftharpoons \mathrm{M}_2^{z+} + ze
$$

for the two electrodes (but not necessarily implying that these equilibria refer only to metal species) and other quantities by the

corresponding subscripts, application of Equation 12 gives

$$\Delta\mu_1^0 - \Delta\mu_2^0 + RT \ln \frac{a_{M_1^{z+}}}{a_{M_2^{z+}}} = ze(\phi_{M_1} - \phi_S) - ze(\phi_{M_2} - \phi_S)$$

$$(15)$$

$$= ze\,\Delta_{1,2}(\Delta\phi_{M,S}) \qquad (16)$$

where $\Delta_{1,2}(\Delta\phi_{M,S})$ is the difference of single metal-solution p.d.'s at the two electrode interfaces. It is clear, using Equation 14, that $\Delta_{1,2}(\Delta\phi_{M,S})$ will be determined by the differences of ΔG_{sub}^0, I_z and $\Delta G_{M^{z+},s}^0$ for the two M species as well as by the differences of work functions $\Phi_{e,1}$ and $\Phi_{e,2}$. Also, in the most general case, the valencies z may not be identical.

The quantity $\Delta_{1,2}(\Delta\phi_{M,S})$, however, is not what is measured potentiometrically as the e.m.f. E between two electrodes at equilibrium. Such a measurement by means of a compensating potentiometer, or any other device such as a high impedance electrometer, necessarily involves at least one contact between two wires of the substances M_1 and M_2 in the circuit. Thus, if the potentiometer is constructed with wire of M_1, the measuring circuit of Fig. 3 is involved.

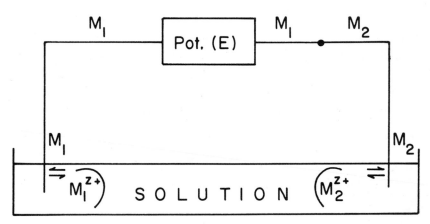

Fig. 3. Circuit for electrochemical equilibrium between metals, M_1, M_2 and their respective ions with equilibrium-measured potential E.

The condition for zero current in the circuit, when M_1 and M_2 are at equilibrium, is that the algebraic sum of all p.d.'s around the circuit is zero, i.e.

$$E + \Delta\phi_{2,1} + \Delta\phi_{S,M_2} + \Delta\phi_{M_1,S} = 0 \qquad (17)$$

Since the contact p.d. $\Delta\phi_{2,1}$ is the difference of work functions $-(\Phi_{e,2} - \Phi_{e,1})$, then

$$-E = \Phi_{e,1} - \Phi_{e,2} - \frac{\Delta\mu_2^0}{ze} - \frac{RT}{zF} \ln a_{M_2^{z+}} + \frac{\Delta\mu_1^0}{ze} + \frac{RT}{zF} \ln a_{M_1^{z+}}$$

$$(18)$$

From Equation 14, the $\Delta\mu^0$ terms involve Φ_e for M_1 and M_2, so that in Equation 18 the terms in Φ_e cancel out and the measured potential E is *independent* of the work function of the two metals. This result is to be stressed, since in early work (43, *cf.* 40) on the significance of electrode potentials, some disagreement arose with regard to the role of differences of ionisation potential and work function, in determining the differences of electrode potentials of elements. It is clear that a single metal-solution potential difference which cannot be measured must involve the relevant Φ_e directly, but the *differences* of such metal-solution potentials as *measured* on a potentiometer are independent of the work functions of the two elements concerned, since these terms must cancel in the metal-metal contact p.d. somewhere in the external circuit. This appears contrary to views expressed in earlier discussions of this problem (40,41), where it was concluded that the transfer of electrons across the contact potential difference constitutes a major component of the energy of the whole cell reaction. While this statement is strictly true, an equal and opposite energy change is involved at each interface with the solution so that the net effect is zero and measured reversible e.m.f. values should *not* show a relation to contact p.d.'s. That such a relation appears to exist is to be explained by a relation rather to ionisation potentials than to work function differences. Generally the variation of ionisation potentials from one metal to another parallels that of the work functions (e.g., the periodic relations of I and Φ_e to atomic number are similar). The above discussion has been made in some detail since, in a following chapter, a related examination will be made of the dependence of irreversible potentials (overpotentials and corresponding currents) for certain electrode processes on properties of the metal such as the electronic work function. However, this will logically be best considered in the chapter on basic kinetic principles (Chapter 6) after the equilibrium distribution of ions and molecules at electrode interfaces has been examined.

3

Distribution of Ions and Molecules at Electrode Interfaces: The Ionic Double-Layer

I. INTRODUCTION

Since electrochemical reactions are field-dependent hetero-genous processes, an important factor determining their rates will be the local concentration of reacting and other particles at the charged interface. This local concentration (or activity) will be determined with reference to the bulk concentration (or activity) by the standard electrochemical free energy (*cf.* 42) of adsorption, which formally will contain chemical and electrical contributions (*cf.* p. 14) involving μ and ψ (the latter, since the distributions will involve potentials within the solution phase due to net charge on the metal electrode surface).

2. ION DISTRIBUTION

The simplest model of the distribution of ions at interfaces was proposed by Helmholtz, who regarded the behaviour of the "double-layer" of charges on the surface and those in solution as approximating to that of a parallel-plate condenser (Fig. 4a) having an electrical capacity C. A necessary aspect of this and

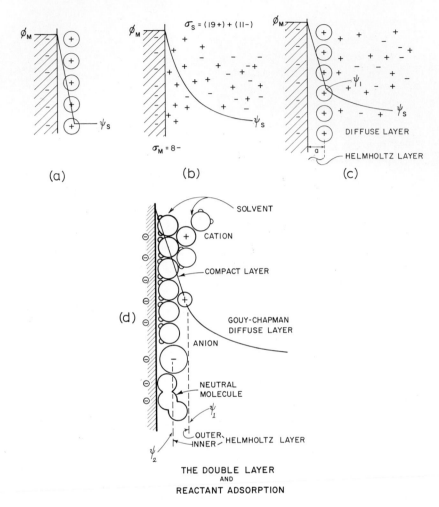

Fig. 4. Models of the double-layer: (a) Helmholtz model; (b) Gouy point-charge model (specific charges σ per unit area as indicated for anions and cations as an example); (c) Stern model for finite ion size with thermal distribution; (d) general representation for reactant adsorption in the double-layer.

other models to be discussed below is that the separated charge is in electrostatic equilibrium and *no charge transfer* in either direction across the double-layer can occur, i.e., with change of p.d. across the metal-solution interface, only the charge in the solution near the metal interface changes. This implies that the electrical behaviour of this double-layer of charges is purely capacitative and has no ohmic leakage resistance component in parallel with it corresponding to discharge of the ions (see Chapter 6). This requirement is an idealisation since, under most practical conditions, any electrode interface which is charged will have at least a very small current passing corresponding to the occurrence of some net electrode process. In practice, the behaviour of the mercury cathode between the reversible hydrogen potential and *ca.* −0.9 v., with respect to it, approaches that of the so-called "ideally polarisable" electrode, since hydrogen ion discharge is very slow within this potential range. Also anodically at platinum, between *ca.* +0.2 and +0.6 v., a limited region of more or less ideal polarisability can be realised in aqueous alkali or oxyanion acid solutions. Another electrochemical system that approaches ideal polarisability over about 1 v. is the platinum anode in trifluoracetic acid solutions of trifluoracetate salts.

Gouy (44) pointed out that the Helmholtz model neglects the thermal distribution of ions which will occur at finite temperature depending on the exponential of their electrostatic energy at various positions in comparison with RT. This distribution is analogous to that considered for counter ions around a given ion in the Debye-Hückel theory of electrolyte solutions which introduced the concept of an ionic atmosphere. However, the theory of an ionic charge distribution normal to the electrode surface was already developed by Chapman (45) some eight years before the development of the Debye-Hückel theory for solutions. In the present problem for the electrode interface, the distributed space charge near the interface can be regarded as the ionic atmosphere of the charged electrode surface (Fig. 4b). The mathematical theory was developed by Chapman (45), following Gouy's treatment (44), and was based on the assumption that the ions were point charges (*cf.* 46). A physically more realistic treatment is that of Stern (47), who took into account the possibility that the ions may have finite sizes and approach the electrode only to within a certain critical distance, and also in some cases may be chemisorbed or suffer so-called specific adsorption, i.e., when other than purely electrostatic "potential-charge" interactions arise.

If ψ_r is the potential at a distance r from the electrode surface, the local concentration of cations and anions, c_+ and c_-, at r will be

$$c_{\pm} = c_{\pm}^0 \exp\left[-\frac{z_{\pm} e\psi_r}{kT}\right] \tag{19}$$

where c^0 terms refer to the bulk average stoichiometric concentrations of cations and anions related by $c_+ z_+ = |c_- z_-|$. The space charge density ρ at r is then

$$\rho_r = z_+ e c_+^0 \exp\left[-\frac{z_+ e\psi_r}{kT}\right] + z_- e c_-^0 \exp\left[-\frac{z_- e\psi_r}{kT}\right] \tag{20}$$

if only electrostatic interactions determine the ion distribution. As in the Debye-Hückel theory, a further relation is available between ψ_r and ρ_r by use of Poisson's equation but expressed for a one-dimensional electrostatic distribution of ions in the form

$$\frac{\partial}{\partial r}\left(\epsilon_r \frac{\partial \psi_r}{\partial r}\right) = -4\pi\rho_r \tag{21}$$

since ϵ_r may be a function of r in the double-layer (see Fig. 5) as first discussed by Conway (48) and Conway, Bockris and Ammar (49) (*cf.* 50). Substitution of ρ_r from Equation 20 in Equation 21 gives

$$\frac{\partial}{\partial r}\left(\epsilon_r \frac{\partial \psi_r}{\partial r}\right) = -4\pi e \sum_+^- c_{\pm}^0 z_{\pm} \exp\left[-\frac{z_{\pm} e\psi_r}{kT}\right] \tag{22}$$

Using the identity

$$2\frac{\partial^2 \psi_r}{\partial r^2} = \frac{\partial}{\partial \psi_r}\left(\frac{\partial \psi_r}{\partial r}\right)^2 \tag{23}$$

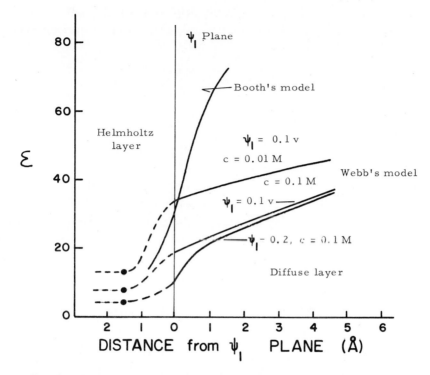

Fig. 5.   Dielectric constant ϵ in the double-layer calculated for field dependence of ϵ due to Webb and to Booth (based on the Debye and Kirkwood-Onsager theories of dielectrics, respectively).   (Based on Conway et al., *Trans. Faraday Soc.* 47, 755 (1951), Fig. 5.)

In Equation 22, and integrating with $c_r - \bar{\epsilon}$, a mean constant value of ϵ in the double-layer (since ϵ_r is not very sensitive to variation of r except very close to the electrode surface), gives

$$\frac{\partial \psi_r}{\partial r} = \pm \left[\frac{8\pi kT}{\bar{\epsilon}} \sum_+ c_\pm^0 \left\{ \exp\left[-\frac{z_\pm e(\psi_r - \psi_S)}{kT} \right] - 1 \right\} \right]^{1/2} \quad (24)$$

for the boundary conditions $\partial\psi_r/\partial r \to 0$, $r \to \infty$; and $\psi_r \to \psi_S$, the potential in the bulk of the solution where $\rho_r = 0$.   The term -1 in the { } bracket in Equation 24 arises from the integration constant, i.e., when $r \to \infty$, $\exp\left[(\psi_r - \psi_S)/kT\right] = 1$ for $\partial\psi_r/\partial r = 0$.

If a is the distance of closest approach of the ions to the electrode and q_M is the charge per unit area, at the metal surface, the field at a is limitingly

$$\left(\frac{\partial \psi_r}{\partial r}\right)_a = -\frac{4\pi q_M}{\epsilon_a} \tag{25}$$

where ϵ_a is the dielectric constant in the region $r \leqslant a$. Usually it has been assumed (30) that the dielectric constant $\epsilon_a \doteqdot \bar{\epsilon}$, although calculations indicate (48, 49) that near the electrode surface this assumption may be rather unsatisfactory. Also, solvent dipole orientation (*cf.* dielectric saturation effects, 50, 51) at the electrode surface (52) leads to a lower value of ϵ in the region $r \sim a$ than farther away from the electrode. From Equations 24 and 25, q_M is obtained with the above assumptions as

$$q_M = \pm \left(\frac{kT\bar{\epsilon}}{2\pi} \sum_+ c_\pm \left\{\exp\left[-\frac{z_\pm e(\psi_a - \psi_S)}{kT}\right] - 1\right\}\right)^{1/2} \tag{26}$$

For a symmetrical electrolyte, when $|z_\pm| = z_+ = |z_-|$ $(= z,$ say) and $c_\pm = c_+ = c_-$ $(= c,$ say),

$$q_M = \left(\frac{2kT\,c\bar{\epsilon}}{\pi}\right)^{1/2} \sinh\left[\frac{ze(\psi_a - \psi_S)}{2kT}\right] \tag{27}$$

noting that q_M will be positive when $\psi_a - \psi_S$ is positive.

3. CAPACITY

If the ions are point charges as considered by Gouy, ψ_a becomes identical with ϕ_M, the potential of the metal with respect to the solution, and the distribution of the ions continues right up to the metal surface. By Equation 27 a quantity $\partial q_M / \partial(\psi_a - \psi_S)$ can be evaluated as

$$\frac{\partial q_M}{\partial(\psi_a - \psi_S)} = \left(\frac{z^2 e^2 c\bar{\epsilon}}{2\pi kT}\right)^{1/2} \cosh\left[\frac{ze(\psi_a - \psi_S)}{2kT}\right] \tag{28}$$

which may be identified with the differential double-layer capacity C that is associated with the ionic atmosphere charge distribution dependent on $\partial \psi_r / \partial r$ and hence on q_M. Comparison of values of the capacity calculated from Equation 28 with those measured experimentally (see Chapter 4 and references 53 and 54) from the dependence of surface charge q_M, at the metal, on measured electrode potential E, indicates a major discrepancy, e.g. with regard to the rate of change of C with $\phi_M - \psi_S$ and the absolute magnitude of C at values of $\phi_M - \psi_S > ca.$ 0.1 v. Only near the potential at which $q_M = 0$ (the so-called potential of zero charge, "p.z.c.") is the experimental behaviour numerically comparable with that predicted by Equation 28.

The principal reason for failure of this relation lies in the assumption that the ions are point charges so that the ionic charge distribution can be continuous up to the electrode surface. This allows a large space charge to arise very near the electrode, and hence an anomalously large capacitance is calculated. If the ions have finite size [e.g., as determined by their crystallographic or more appropriately their primary hydration (8) radii, a], the continuous charge distribution must be cut off at $r = a$, and the potential-distance relation near the electrode is then discontinuous as in Fig. 4c. The importance of a distance of closest approach a for ions of finite size has been discussed by Grahame (54) but was already recognised by Stern (47) and mentioned by Gouy in regard to an effective "thickness" of the double-layer (55). The potential difference $\phi_M - \psi_S$ between the metal and the solution can then be regarded as made up of two parts $\phi_M - \psi_1$ and $\psi_1 - \psi_S$ where ψ_1 is the mean* potential at $r = a$. Both these contributions can be dependent on q_M so that

$$\frac{\partial(\phi_M - \psi_S)}{\partial q_M} = \frac{\partial(\phi_M - \psi_1)}{\partial q_M} + \frac{\partial(\psi_1 - \psi_S)}{\partial q_M} \qquad (29)$$

The first term is the reciprocal of the capacity C mentioned above, and the other terms have a similar nature, so that Equation 29

---

* ψ_1 is referred to as a *mean* potential since the potential in the double-layer will fluctuate laterally across the interfacial region because of discreteness of the ionic charges involved. The symbol ψ_1 is used to maintain conformity with the earlier Russian literature, but ϕ_2 has been used as the symbol for this quantity in some later publications (30).

can be written

$$\frac{1}{C} = \frac{1}{C_1} + \frac{1}{C_2} \tag{30}$$

where C_1 and C_2 are obviously defined by comparison with the two terms on the right-hand side of Equation 29. Equation 30 also implies that C_1 and C_2 are additive in a *series* combination. The C_2 term associated with the ionic atmosphere distribution will be given by Equation 28 with $\psi_a = \psi_1$, so that taking reciprocals of Equation 30 yields

$$C = \frac{C_1(z^2e^2c\bar{\varepsilon}/2\pi kT)^{1/2}\cosh\left[ze(\psi_1 - \psi_S)/2kT\right]}{C_1 + (z^2e^2c\bar{\varepsilon}/2\pi kT)^{1/2}\cosh\left[ze(\psi_1 - \psi_S)/2kT\right]} \tag{31}$$

It is seen that when $C_1 \gg C_2$, $C \doteq C_2$ (from Equation 28 with $\psi_a = \psi_1$), or when $C_2 \gg C_1$, $C \doteq C_1$; the first inequality is valid when $\psi_1 - \psi_S$ is very small, and the second when it is large. The value of the *smaller* capacity contribution hence mainly determines the over-all value of C since the two contributions are in a series relationship, Equation 30. Equation 31 represents the data for capacitance at the mercury-solution interface, e.g. for KCl solutions (56) if $C_1 \doteq 20\,\mu\mathrm{F}$. cm.$^{-2}$ is assumed when cations preferentially populate the interface region ($\phi_M - \psi_S$ negative), and $C_1 \doteq 38\,\mu\mathrm{F}$. cm.$^{-2}$ when anions predominate in the double-layer ($\phi_M - \psi_S$ positive). Typical capacity-potential profiles for the mercury electrode are shown in Fig. 6 (see ref. 54). The capacity contribution C_1 is often referred to as the capacity of the Helmholtz layer and C_2 that of the "diffuse layer" or ionic atmosphere region. Further division of C_1 into contributions from the "inner" or the "outer" Helmholtz layers (54) will be discussed below. In Equation 31, it will not generally be valid to assume that the *same* potential ψ_1 applies to the position of closest approach for anions and for cations. Owing to the more polarisable nature of anions and the existence of specific affinity as adsorbed surface "ligands" for some metal surfaces, anions may approach more closely than hydrated cations at a given potential, so that ψ_1 will not have quite the same significance for anions and cations. It is convenient to call this potential ψ_2 for the region of closer approach and specific adsorption associated with anions. This matter will now be examined in more detail according to the theory developed by Stern (47) and reviewed by Parsons (30).

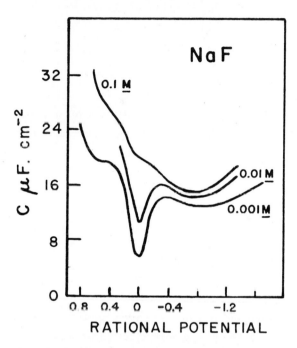

Fig. 6. Double-layer capacity profiles for dependence on potential (aqueous solutions of NaF at the indicated concentrations, 25°C).

4. STERN'S TREATMENT

Stern recognised (47) that a satisfactory theory of the double-layer must take into account both the finite size of the ions adsorbed and any specific "chemisorption" interactions they may suffer with the metal surface. The charge q_S on the solution side of the double-layer may be regarded as made up of two contributions q_2 and q_1 arising, respectively, from space charge associated with the ionic atmosphere and from charge associated with specifically adsorbed ions. Then, since $q_M = -q_S$,

$$-q_M = q_S = q_1 + q_2 \tag{32}$$

The charge q_2 will be given by Equation 26 with ψ_1 as the relevant potential, i.e. $\psi_a = \psi_1$. The charge q_1 was obtained in terms of site-fraction statistics for solution and surface phases by applying a form of the Langmuir isotherm (see Chapter 7) with an electrochemical free energy of adsorption determining the extent of adsorption as a function of solution concentration of the ions. The derivation of Stern for the quantity ψ_1 was unnecessarily involved, and Parsons (30) has given a clarification of the calculation which need not be repeated here. The result of applying the Langmuir isotherm is

$$q_1 = e\,\Omega \left[\frac{z_+}{1 + (1/x_S) \exp\left[\Delta \bar{G}^0_+/kT\right]} + \frac{z_-}{1 + (1/x_S) \exp\left[\Delta \bar{G}^0_-/kT\right]} \right] \tag{33}$$

where $\Delta \bar{G}^0_\pm$ are the standard *electrochemical* free energies of adsorption of the indicated cations or anions, e.g., the $\Delta \bar{G}^0_\pm$ terms normally contain "electrical" and "chemical" free-energy contributions, the latter defined for some standard state concentration or mole fraction x_S of salt in the bulk solution. The term Ω is defined as the number of sites per square centimeter available for adsorption at the electrode interface. It is assumed that this number is the same for cations and anions, and that the adsorbed ion can freely replace solvent molecules which are also necessarily adsorbed at the surface, with a relative coverage near unity. Reference has been made above to the fact that the $\Delta \bar{G}^0_\pm$ terms are electrochemical free energies of adsorption, and in fact, following Stern's assumptions, they may be written for convenience in the form

$$\Delta \bar{G}^0_\pm = \Delta G^0_\pm + z_\pm e(\psi_2 - \psi_S) \tag{34}$$

where $\Delta G^0_\pm$ terms are the "chemical" standard free energies of adsorption of the indicated ions ($\pm$), and ψ_2 is the mean potential in the plane of specifically adsorbed ions. Experimentally, however, it will not usually be possible to separate the $\Delta \bar{G}_{\pm}^0$ terms into their component chemical and electrical contributions. In most cases only one type of ion is adsorbed (the anion, except in cases of organic electrolytes such as tetraalkyl-ammonium salts) so that Equation 33 could be written, for anions, as

$$q_1 \doteq z_- e x_S \Omega \exp \left[-\frac{\Delta \bar{G}_-^0}{kT} \right] \qquad (35)$$

since usually, for dilute solutions, $(1/x_S) \exp \Delta \bar{G}_{\pm}/kT \gg 1$. It is clear that $q_1/z_- e$ is the number n_1 of ions in the adsorbed layer and that n_1/Ω is the relative coverage θ_1 of these ions, i.e.,

$$\theta_1 \doteq x_S \exp \left[-\frac{\Delta \bar{G}_-^0}{kT} \right] \qquad (36)$$

which is a limiting form of the Langmuir isotherm for low coverage $(1 - \theta_1 \doteq 1)$ or a two-dimensional form of Henry's law (concentration in surface phase, θ_1, proportional to mole fraction in bulk phase is analogous to the gas solubility relation where mole fraction of dissolved gas in solution is proportional to partial pressure in the gas phase). It is to be noted that the form of the adsorption Equation 36 also follows rigorously for mobile adsorption of species at a surface, whereas the Langmuir isotherm (see Chapter 7) applies strictly (57) only to fixed site adsorption on a lattice of identical sites with no lateral interactions between adsorbed species. Neither of these assumptions is likely to be physically realistic at the mercury electrode, where the adsorption will certainly be mobile, and, in general, two-dimensional lateral interactions between adsorbed ions and their image charges "in" the metal will not be negligible. Apart from interaction effects, the approximate form of the isotherm written as Equation 36 may in fact therefore be physically the more reasonable.

Stern expressed the integral capacity K_1 of the double-layer as

$$-q_M = K_1(\phi_M - \psi_2) = q_1 + q_2 \qquad (37)$$

and assumed $\psi_2 \doteq \psi_1$ which enables values of ψ_1 to be calculated as a function of ϕ_M, the potential of the metal, for known K_1 and solution concentrations in the absence of specific adsorption. [Usually this evaluation is most conveniently performed (58) numerically by choosing ψ_1 values and obtaining ϕ_M as the dependent variable, since ψ_1 enters the arguments of exponentials in q_2.] The term K_1 is the integral capacity* of the region between the metal surface and the plane of centres of the adsorbed ions. The assumptions $\psi_2 = \psi_1$ and $\Delta \bar{G}_+^0 = 0$ are equivalent to taking $q_1 = 0$, i.e., when specific adsorption is absent. Stern did not distinguish, however, between ψ_2 and ψ_1 for the case of specific adsorption, and this distinction constitutes an important element of Grahame's treatment (54).

5. OTHER MODIFICATIONS

Detailed analysis (30) of the observed shift of potential of zero charge at mercury in the presence of adsorbed anions shows that ψ_2 cannot be identified with ψ_1. The picture of the double-layer is then as shown in Fig. 4d, in which three regions of potential drop are involved: from metal to layer 2 of specifically adsorbed ions (potential ψ_2); from this layer to the inner limit of the diffuse layer (potential ψ_1); and across the diffuse layer itself to the region where the average potential is ψ_S. Such a model has been treated by Grahame (54) who suggested calling the inner layer of ions at potential ψ_2 the "inner Helmholtz plane," and the layer at potential ψ_1, the "outer Helmholtz plane." The models of Stern and Grahame do not, however, take into account the effects of adsorbed solvent dipoles which must contribute an

---

* In general, differential capacities (the C terms used in the earlier equations, e.g. Equation 31) may be defined by $C = (dq/d\phi)_\phi$ while integral capacities K are defined by a relation of the form $K = q/\phi$ or $\Delta q/\Delta \phi$ where Δ is not an infinitesimal change. It is clear that K and C will be related by

$$\phi K = \int_0^\phi C_\phi \, d\phi \quad \text{(where } C_\phi \text{ may be } f(\phi)\text{)} \tag{38}$$

or equivalently, since $dq = K \, d\phi + \phi \, dK = C \, d\phi$,

$$C = K + \phi \frac{dK}{d\phi} . \tag{38a}$$

appreciable surface dipole p.d. across the region from the metal to the ψ_2 plane, and this p.d. will probably vary with electrode potential (particularly near the p.z.c.) on account of a field-dependence of the extent of orientation of solvent dipoles (see below).

In a number of papers (59,60,61,62,63), Grahame gave a quantitatively successful account of the behaviour of the double-layer as a function of concentration of electrolyte particularly for salts, the ions of which are not specifically adsorbed. The most complete experimental study is that for NaF at mercury (60).

In the case of specifically adsorbed ions (usually anions), a quantitative account of the behaviour of the double-layer, e.g. with regard to the dependence of shift of the p.z.c. (see Chapter 4) on adsorbed ion concentration, is more difficult to obtain. Esin and Shikov (64) proposed a model of oriented adsorbed cation-anion ion-pairs in the double-layer, but a better account of the experimental behaviour is obtained in terms of a model proposed by Ershler (65), in which anions are regarded as specifically adsorbed in a disordered hexagonally packed array with a cation ionic atmosphere on the solution side of this layer. Taking into account the image charges (associated with the anions) in the metal surface and in the outer Helmholtz layer region (where the dielectric constant is probably higher), Ershler (65) and Grahame (61) were able to derive a more satisfactory relation for the potential drop $\psi_2 - \psi_S$ and the capacity of the inner region of the double-layer in the presence of specifically adsorbed ions. Other calculations concerning "discreteness of charge" effects have been made by Levine (66). Further details of the above treatments are given in references 30 and 67. While the above remarks have been made with regard to specific adsorption of anions, it must be noted that significant evidence exists for specific adsorption of simple *cations*, e.g. Tl^+ (68) and to some extent Cs^+ (69); such effects are more marked on solid metals, e.g. Pt (70). Large organic cations, e.g. R_4N^+, are, of course, also specifically adsorbed, but here the effect may be due in part to the tendency of the large organic residues to withdraw themselves from the aqueous phase to any interface (e.g. also the air-water interface) rather than because they have specific affinity for the metal surface. However, Van der Waals interaction with the metal surface can be significant. Also, with the larger, less hydrated, inorganic cations, such as Tl^+ and Cs^+, the image interaction may not be entirely negligible, and this effect requires further consideration, particularly for the less hydrated ions (8).

6. DIELECTRIC CONSTANT AND ELECTRO-STRICTION IN THE DOUBLE-LAYER

In early treatments of the double-layer, the dielectric constant was regarded as having its normal value. However, at all but the smallest potential differences at the electrode-solution interface, the field close to the metal surface will be of the order of 10^5–10^7 v. cm.$^{-1}$, which is sufficient to cause appreciable dielectric saturation (71) or equivalent orientation effects in the double-layer analogous to those arising in the primary hydration shells of ions (72, cf. 73). Also, apart from applied field effects, specific orientation of solvent at the electrode interface due to chemical interactions (which may arise most strongly at the transition metals) in the adsorption of solvent, will cause a local depression of the dielectric constant in the double-layer. The first treatment of dielectric saturation effects in the double-layer was given by Conway (48) in 1949 and published in 1951 about the same time (49) as a similar treatment by Grahame (50). The general conclusion is that dielectric saturation effects are significant but not very important in the diffuse part of the double-layer; however, appreciable saturation can arise in the higher field region near the electrode surface. Correspondingly, since the electrostatic pressure due to a field $\mathscr{E}$ is

$$P_{\mathscr{E}} = \frac{\mathscr{E}^2}{8\pi} (\epsilon - 1) \tag{39}$$

local pressures in the double-layer can be of the same order as those near ions, viz. 50,000 atm. Equation 39 must usually be applied with variable ϵ, i.e., ϵ is $f(P, \mathscr{E})$ and the result is then more complex. It has been evaluated, however, for the case of ions in aqueous solutions (74,75). Applications of these considerations to the behaviour of the inner layer capacity at the mercury electrode have been made by MacDonald (76), who takes into account both dielectric saturation and electrostriction effects.

7. SOLVENT ORIENTATION THEORY OF THE DOUBLE-LAYER

The theories of the double-layer discussed above leave a number of experimental results unexplained, which have been discussed by Devanathan, Bockris and Müller (52). Thus, the capacity of the double-layer at mercury at appreciable cathodic potentials is largely independent of size of the cation for the alkali and alkaline earth ions. Since various cations would be expected to have different distances of closest approach to the metal, the above result is one that is difficult to reconcile with the Stern-Grahame model. Secondly, specific adsorption of anions is not readily related to the properties of these ions, e.g. the extent of chemisorption of a halide X^- is inversely related (52) to the bond strength of Hg to the halogen X. However, this effect may be related to the hydration of X^-, which will be more exoenergetic the smaller the ion X^- (e.g. F^-), but the smaller ions are the more electronegative and would tend to form stronger bonds with Hg. The third factor concerns the degree of anion adsorption, which, as a function of electrode surface charge, undergoes an inflexion at moderate positive charges. A fourth fact which has not received any satisfactory final explanation is the existence of a maximum on the positive side of the capacity-charge or potential relationship. This effect depends on the anion adsorbed and appears with most aqueous solutions unless obscured by strong specific adsorption effects at anodic potentials. It has been suggested (67,77,78) that the effect is connected with the properties of adsorbed water in the double-layer, e.g. changing orientation polarisation of the adsorbed solvent at positive potentials. The effect is not confined to aqueous solutions and has recently been confirmed for dimethyl formamide, but the capacity maximum appears at *negative* rather than positive potentials with respect to the p.z.c. in this solvent (79).

A new theory of the distribution of ions and solvent dipoles in the double-layer has been advanced recently by Devanathan, Bockris and Müller (52), in which the adsorbed cations with their primary hydration shells are regarded as remaining *outside* a layer of strongly oriented adsorbed solvent dipoles (Fig. 7). Specifically adsorbed anions are regarded as being able to penetrate the inner solvent layer. This theory has the advantage of taking into account in a realistic way the presence of adsorbed solvent neglected in previous theories of the double-layer. The inner oriented layer is regarded as having a dielectric constant ϵ_l [a low value (*cf.* 49) approaching the limiting Maxwell value, viz. the square of the refractive index], and the outer region, containing the adsorbed cations, a dielectric constant ϵ_h, a higher value estimated as *ca.* 30–40. Water molecules are regarded as being potentially adsorbed with their negative ends pointing either towards or away from the metal surface, depending on electrode charge or potential. Such a theory is first of all able to explain the important fact that the cathodic capacity is largely independent of cation radius.

Using a form of Gauss's equation, the potential difference $\Delta\phi$ across the inner and outer regions of the interfacial region shown in Fig. 7 is written (52) as

$$-4\pi q_M \sum \frac{x_i}{\epsilon_i} = \Delta\phi \qquad (40)$$

for distances x_i from the metal surface where ϵ_i is the local dielectric constant (for a given region, $\Delta\phi/x_i$ is a quantity related to the field). The over-all integral inner layer capacity K is then given by

$$\frac{1}{K} = 4\pi \left[\delta_1 \left(\frac{1}{\epsilon_l} - \frac{1}{\epsilon_h} \right) + \frac{\delta_2}{\epsilon_h} \right] \qquad (41)$$

where δ_1 is the thickness of the inner oriented water layer, and δ_2 the average distance of coulombically adsorbed ions from the

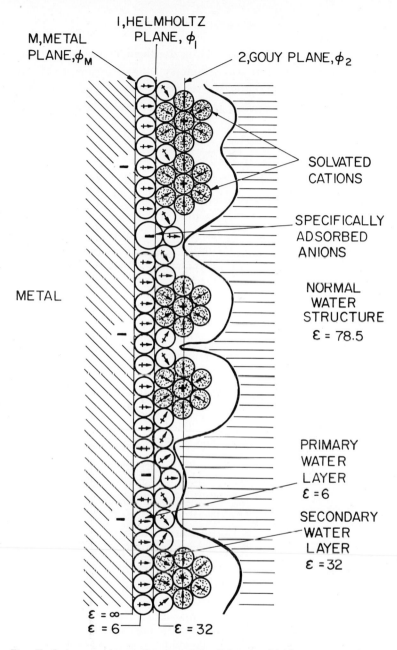

M, METAL PLANE, ϕ_M

1, HELMHOLTZ PLANE, ϕ_1

2, GOUY PLANE, ϕ_2

METAL

SOLVATED CATIONS

SPECIFICALLY ADSORBED ANIONS

NORMAL WATER STRUCTURE $\varepsilon = 78.5$

PRIMARY WATER LAYER $\varepsilon = 6$

SECONDARY WATER LAYER $\varepsilon = 32$

$\varepsilon = \infty$
$\varepsilon = 6$ $\varepsilon = 32$

Fig. 7. Solvent adsorption model of the double-layer according to Devanathan, Bockris and Müller (52). (*Proc. Roy. Soc. London* A274, 55.)

metal interface.*   Equation 41 is deduced by assuming $\Delta\phi/q_M$ gives a reciprocal integral capacity contribution that equals $-4\pi\Sigma x_i/\epsilon_i$, i.e., the capacity contributions from the regions having dielectric constants ϵ_l and ϵ_h are combined in series as

$$\frac{1}{K} = \frac{1}{K_l} + \frac{1}{K_h} = \frac{4\pi\,\delta_1}{\epsilon_l} + \frac{4\pi(\delta_2 - \delta_1)}{\epsilon_h} \tag{42}$$

If $\epsilon_h/\epsilon_l \gg 1$, K becomes independent of δ_2 and hence of the ionic radius, so that the independence of Helmholtz layer capacity on the type of cation can be explained.   The capacity is then determined mainly by the properties of the inner layer of oriented water dipoles.   An explanation of the capacitance hump is also afforded by the treatment of Devanathan et al. (52), who show that the effect can arise from the dependence of rate of change of the specifically adsorbed charge associated with anions, on the electrode charge q_M, taking into account two-dimensional anion repulsion in the double-layer.   The calculated effect depends on the type of adsorption isotherm chosen to represent the behaviour of the adsorbed anions (see Chapter 4).   Since similar effects do not arise at cathodic potentials, the anomalous capacity behaviour must be due to the behaviour of the anions possibly in conjunction with the oriented water layer.   The fact that similar effects arise in dimethylformamide for *cation* adsorption at *negative* electrode charges then makes the interpretation discussed above somewhat less satisfactory, and suggests that the effect arises from a combination of specific hydration and solvent orientation effects.   In the above theory (52), the oriented dipoles at negative electrode charges are in the same orientation as those on the electrode side of the coulombically adsorbed cations.   It is hence a difficulty in this theory to see why the hydrated cations cannot penetrate nearer the electrode as in the Stern-Grahame model, where their

---

* Distances from the metal "interface" are difficult to define exactly. Normally such a distance is referred to a tangential plane covering the metal atoms at their normal metallic radii.   However, the effective radius of a metal at its interface may not be the same as the internuclear metallic radius in bulk, because of different hybridisation of orbitals at the surface.

hydration water molecules could, by sharing between the ion and the electrode, form both part of the oriented solvent layer and the hydration shell of the ions on one side. Similar "cooperative" hydration occurs in ion-pair formation, which is analogous. Since the dielectric constant of the metal is effectively infinite, such a closer approach would not be unfavourable energetically. Also, since protons should be able to penetrate to the inner layer of water by the anomalous conductance transfer mechanism, the Helmholtz double-layer capacity for solutions of the strong mineral acids should be larger than that for corresponding alkali metal salts at the same concentrations. This is not experimentally observed. However, this recent theory gives, in most respects, satisfactory explanations of some of the previous anomalies. Its relevance to the problem of neutral molecule adsorption will be considered in Chapter 5.

4

Determination of Reactant Adsorption at Electrodes: Ionic Species

I. ELECTROCAPILLARY METHOD

(i) **Theory.** The electrocapillary method (80,81,82,83) is based on the measurement of the potential and concentration dependence of surface tension of a liquid metal such as mercury, and provides the thermodynamically soundest and most complete method of studying electrochemical adsorption at electrode interfaces. It can be applied to adsorption of neutral molecules (82,84) as well as to that of electrolytes and their individual ions.

The surface tension may be determined either by means of the so-called capillary electrometer, originally developed by Lippmann (85), in which the excess pressure required to force mercury near to the end of a tapering capillary is measured, or by the measurement of weights of drops falling from a capillary of mercury (81,82,84,86,87). The first method is more satisfactory, particularly for studying adsorption processes which may not reach equilibrium very rapidly. Also the exact theoretical relationship between drop weight and surface tension is not well established, and the method is more tedious and irreproducible. However, Craxford and McKay (87) were able to obtain results for KNO_3 solutions in agreement with those obtained by means

44

of a capillary electrometer, but it is doubtful if the method would be satisfactory with organic solutes.

The electrocapillary method was already applied by Gouy at the turn of the century, and the basic relation between surface tension, potential and electrode charge was formulated by Lippmann and Helmholtz. However, the correct detailed theory of electrocapillarity was not understood until much later. Earlier formulations (80,82,83,88) considered equilibrium between the mercury electrode metal and mercurous ions in solution. Although formally the correct relation between surface tension, potential, surface charge and solution concentration can be obtained by this approach, it is misleading since it is now known that the most satisfactory conditions for electrocapillary measurements are those in which no equilibrium of dischargeable ions is involved and the electrode is completely polarised in the sense that an excess (or deficit of) electron charge is built up on the metal, and a corresponding space and surface charge is built up near the metal in the solution, yet no net charge-transfer process occurs. The interface then behaves like an ideal condenser, and the metal can then be referred to as an "ideal polarised electrode" (54). A satisfactory theory of electrocapillarity was given by Koenig (80; see *J. Phys. Chem.* references) and discussed by Adam (29, p. 311), who recognised the conditions required for ideal or "complete" polarisability. A treatment has been given also by Grahame (54) and with modifications by Parsons (30).

The circuit in Fig. 8 may be considered, involving a potentiometer on which a potential E is measured between metals I and II and ϕ quantities are the inner potentials of the indicated phases. When the potentiometer is balanced (zero current in the circuit),

$$E + (\phi_\alpha - \phi_I) + (\phi_\beta - \phi_\alpha) + (\phi_{II} - \phi_\beta) = 0 \qquad (43)$$

If the phase α is mercury, $\phi_\alpha - \phi_I$ is constant, and for changes in the electrochemical condition of the system

$$d(\phi_\beta - \phi_\alpha) = - dE - d(\phi_{II} - \phi_\beta) \qquad (44)$$

The Gibbs adsorption equation (e.g., see ref. 29) relates changes of surface tension γ to changes of composition or chemical potential of a system through the surface excesses Γ of substances

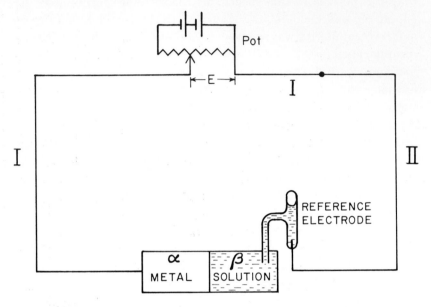

Fig. 8.   Circuit for consideration of electrostatic equilibrium at an ideally polarisable electrode.   (After Grahame, 54.)

adsorbed. For uncharged components, the Gibbs equation has the form

$$d\gamma = -\sum \Gamma_i \, d\mu_i \qquad (45)$$

at constant temperature and pressure. Equation 45 may be applied to an electrochemical adsorption by writing $\bar{\mu}_i$ terms (the electrochemical potentials; see Equation 5) instead of the chemical potentials μ_i. Then

$$d\gamma = -\sum \Gamma_{i,\alpha} \, d\bar{\mu}_{i,\alpha} - \sum \Gamma_{i,\beta} \, d\bar{\mu}_{i,\beta} \qquad (46)$$

for components i in the phases α and β. Since, in general,

$\bar{\mu}_{i,\alpha} = \mu_{i,\alpha} + ze\phi_{\alpha}$, Equation 46 can be written at constant temperature and pressure

$$d\gamma = -\sum \Gamma_{i,\alpha}\, d\mu_{i,\alpha} - \sum \Gamma_{i,\beta}\, d\mu_{i,\beta} - ze\Gamma_{i,\alpha}\, d\phi_{\alpha} - ze\Gamma_{i,\beta}\, d\phi_{\beta}$$

$$(47)$$

The Γ terms are the relative surface excesses of the respective components i in the phases α and β and represent the differences between the amounts of substances i per square centimeter of interface up to some dividing plane parallel to the surface when adsorption is occurring and the amount that would be present if the solution composition were homogeneous up to the metal "surface."* The quantities $ze\Gamma_i$ can be recognised as the charges in the phases α and β, where electrons and "Hg$^+$" ions are formally the charged components i in the metal phase α, and ions of the electrolyte are the charged components in β. Then

$$q_{i,\alpha} = z_i e \Gamma_{i,\alpha}; \quad q_{i,\beta} = z_i e \Gamma_{i,\beta} \qquad (48)$$

For electrical neutrality at the interface, $q_{i,\alpha} = -q_{i,\beta}$, so that

$$d\gamma = -\sum \Gamma_{i,\alpha}\, d\mu_{i,\beta} - \sum \Gamma_{i,\beta}\, d\mu_{i,\beta} - q_{i,\alpha}(d\phi_{\alpha} - d\phi_{\beta}) \quad (49)$$

If the phase α is pure mercury, $d\mu_{i,\alpha} = 0$ for mercury species; also at constant solution composition $\sum \Gamma_{i,\beta}\, d\mu_{i,\beta} = 0$, so that, with Equation 44,

$$-dE = d(\phi_{\beta} - \phi_{\alpha}) \qquad (50)$$

which follows because $d(\phi_{II} - \phi_{\beta})$ will be constant at constant solution composition, since under these conditions the reference electrode (II–β) will provide a constant p.d. Equation 49 then gives†

$$d\gamma = -q_{i,\alpha}\, dE \qquad (51)$$

---

* A more satisfactory treatment of "surface excess" quantities, given by Guggenheim (89), avoids fictitious concepts such as a two-dimensional phase at the interface. A discussion of this matter is given in ref. 29.

† A more general derivation is given in ref. 30, but the treatment given here serves to exemplify the principles in a less complex manner.

or

$$-\left(\frac{\partial \gamma}{\partial E}\right)_{\mu_{i,\beta},T,P} = q_{i,\alpha} = q_M \qquad (52)$$

since the only charged species whose "quantity" can be varied in the mercury metal at constant "chemical" composition are electrons; q_M is then the surface excess charge on the metal electrode. Equation 52 is the Lippmann equation. It may be noted that Equation 46 strictly involves the solvent and any other neutral components involved in $\Sigma \Gamma_{i,\beta} \, d\bar{\mu}_{i,\beta}$, but for the purpose of deriving Equations 51 and 52 it has been assumed that their activities also remain constant. It is seen that the Lippmann equation (Equation 52) gives the surface charge on the metal only if the variation of γ with E occurs under conditions of constant chemical potentials of components in β, constant temperature and pressure. Similarly, for varying composition of phase β,

$$\left(\frac{\partial \gamma}{\partial \mu_{i,\beta}}\right)_{[\phi_\alpha - \phi_\beta],T,P,\mu_{i,\alpha}\mu_{j,\beta}} = -\Gamma_{i,\beta} \qquad (53)$$

which gives the surface excess of particular components i in β at constant metal-solution potential difference, and constant chemical potential of other components j in β. Thus, Equation 53 can be used to obtain surface excesses of *individual* components in the solution if the chemical potentials of other components remain constant. Experimentally, this can be realised only as an approximation since the Gibbs-Duhem equation requires reciprocal changes in chemical potentials of other components, when that of one is changed. However, since dilute solutions are usually studied, the chemical potential of the solvent* can be regarded as almost constant for appreciable changes of chemical potentials of solute components.

Equation 52 can hence be used to evaluate surface excess charge on the metal as a function of potential, and Equation 53 to evaluate the extent of adsorption $\Gamma_{i,\beta}$ as a function of potential and solution concentration. Hence rather complete information

---

* Normally Γ_{solvent} can be taken as zero, which gives a relative $\Gamma_{i,\beta}$ and avoids the problem that $d\mu_{\text{solvent}} \neq 0$.

on electrochemical adsorption at a liquid metal-solution interface can be obtained by the electrocapillary method.

Upon differentiating Equation 52, it is seen that the right-hand side has the form of a differential capacity, $C = q_M/dE$, so that

$$C = -\left(\frac{\partial^2 \gamma}{\partial E^2}\right)_{\mu_i,\beta,T,P} \tag{54}$$

The capacity C will, however, not be obtainable in practice with very great accuracy on account of the double differentiation of γ with respect to E which is required.

Correspondingly, integration of the Lippmann equation (Equation 52) and substitution of $q_M = KE$, gives

$$\gamma = -\tfrac{1}{2}KE^2 + I \tag{55}$$

where K is the integral capacity, and I is an integration constant equal to the surface tension when γ is a maximum and E,* the "coulombic" part of the metal-solution p.d., is zero. Correspondingly, $q_M = 0$ when the curve corresponding to Equation 55 is at its maximum, as is seen from Equation 52. These conditions define the so-called electrocapillary maximum, and the potential (with respect to that of some reference electrode) at which this condition obtains is called the potential of zero charge (p.z.c.). It is important to note that the potential of zero charge is not necessarily the potential of zero metal-solution field since surface dipole potential differences may still remain when $q_M = 0$; they may depend also on surface charge owing to orientation effects caused by the applied coulombic field, and to any preferential chemisorption of one end of the solvent molecule at the metal surface.

(ii) Components of Charge from Electrocapillary Data. Equation 53 has been written in a general form, but it is possible to derive it in a form applicable to one or other of the types of ion in the solution (since there are necessarily at least two types of

---

* That is, when the p.d. E is referred to that for the p.z.c. and the scale for E values is then the so-called rational scale (see p. 68).

ion resulting from solution of any electrolyte). In Equation 47, for a binary electrolyte, the term in Σ for phase β, the solution, may be written $\Gamma_+ \, d\mu_+ + \Gamma_- \, d\mu_-$. For the neutral salt, any change of chemical potential $d\mu$ calculated for the whole salt $M_{\nu_+}^{z+} A_{\nu_-}^{z-}$ can be written

$$d\mu = \nu_+ \, d\mu_+ + \nu_- \, d\mu_- \qquad (56)$$

in terms of ionic components $d\mu_+$ and $d\mu_-$ for the chemical potential term. Also the *single* potential of the reference electrode $\phi_{II} - \phi_\beta$ (if it is reversible to the anion) varies as

$$zF \, d(\phi_{II} - \phi_\beta) = d\mu_- \qquad (57)$$

and the electrical neutrality condition is

$$q_M + z_+ F\Gamma_+ + z_- F\Gamma_- = 0 \qquad (58)$$

By combining these terms and substituting for $\nu_- \, d\mu_-$, the relation

$$d\gamma = -q_M \, dE_- - \Gamma_+ \, d\mu_+ - \Gamma_- \left[\frac{d\mu - \nu_+ \, d\mu_+}{\nu_-} \right] - \frac{q_M \, d\mu_-}{z_- F} \qquad (59)$$

is obtained from Equations 49, 50, 56 and 57. Substituting for Γ_- from Equation 58 leads to

$$d\gamma = -q_M \, dE_- - \Gamma_+ \, d\mu_+ + \frac{z_+ \Gamma_+ \nu_-}{z_- \nu_-} \, d\mu_-, \qquad (60)$$

noting that terms in $(q_M/z_- \nu_- F)\nu_+ \, d\mu_+$ arising in the expansion cancel. At constant E_-, $dE_- = 0$, so that

$$d\gamma = -\Gamma_+ \left(d\mu_+ + \frac{\nu_-}{\nu_+} \, d\mu_- \right) \qquad (61)$$

and since $\nu_+ z_+ = |\nu_- z_-|$ for electroneutrality,

$$d\gamma = -\frac{\Gamma_+}{\nu_+} (\nu_+ \, d\mu_+ + \nu_- \, d\mu_-) = -\frac{\Gamma_+}{\nu_+} \, d\mu \qquad (62)$$

where $d\mu$ refers, as above, to changes of chemical potential of the whole *salt*, and is hence an experimentally variable quantity (the individual ionic $d\mu_\pm$ quantities are not, of course, accessible to variation in a known manner). The derivative giving the *individual* ionic surface excess is then

$$\left(\frac{\partial \gamma}{\partial \mu}\right)_{E_-,T,P} = -\frac{\Gamma_+}{\nu_+} \tag{63a}$$

and correspondingly for anions of the salt

$$\left(\frac{\partial \gamma}{\partial \mu}\right)_{E_+,T,P} = -\frac{\Gamma_-}{\nu_-} \tag{63b}$$

where use of a reference electrode reversible to the *cations* of the electrolyte is implied. Equations 63a and 63b are of great importance since they allow evaluation of individual ionic surface excess quantities* in a rigorous thermodynamic way and allow tests of the theories of the double-layer (see above) to be made. It is to be noted that the $\Gamma_\pm$ quantities so derived represent the *total* surface excess quantities, i.e. the contributions from both the diffuse layer and the specifically adsorbed layer, if present; also the $\Gamma_\pm$ quantities may be negative or positive, e.g., Γ_+ will generally be negative at an anode in the absence of specific adsorption of anions, and similarly Γ_- at the cathode under such conditions.

2. COMPONENTS OF CHARGE FROM THE CAPACITY METHOD

While the data for surface tension and potential can be obtained with inorganic electrolytes with satisfactory precision (see below), the derivation of differential quantities such as are involved in Equations 63a, 63b and the capacity C, is susceptible to inaccuracies. Hence it is preferable to obtain these quantities from direct measurements of the differential capacity by an a.c. impedance method (see below) and obtain derived quantities by integration, a procedure which is usually regarded as being more accurate (but see ref. 90 for comparisons of data). It will be convenient to outline the procedure involved since most of the quantitative

---

* Usually only Γ_+ or Γ_- is required, since, if q_M is known, one or the other $\Gamma_\pm$ term is obtained from the electroneutrality condition.

data on the double-layer in inorganic salt solutions has been derived by Grahame by such a method. Some of the first measurements by this method were made by Proskurnin and Frumkin (91), and for liquid metals the method is capable of giving results of good accuracy and significance owing to the observation that the capacity is largely independent of frequency up to moderate frequencies.

The basic approach in the theoretical treatment of capacity data is the evaluation of an adsorbed charge q_i by integration of the relation $dq_M = C\, dE$. First, Equation 63a or 63b is differentiated with respect to E:

$$\nu_+ \frac{\partial}{\partial E_-}\left(\frac{\partial \gamma}{\partial \mu}\right)_{E_-,T,P} = -\left(\frac{\partial \Gamma_+}{\partial E_-}\right)_\mu \tag{64a}$$

or

$$\nu_- \frac{\partial}{\partial E_+}\left(\frac{\partial \gamma}{\partial \mu}\right)_{E_+,T,P} = -\left(\frac{\partial \Gamma_-}{\partial E_+}\right)_\mu \tag{64b}$$

The quantities on the right-hand side of Equations 64a and 64b are related to capacity contributions from cations and anions, respectively, since

$$z_+F\left(\frac{\partial \Gamma_+}{\partial E_-}\right)_\mu = -C_+ \quad \text{and} \quad z_-F\left(\frac{\partial \Gamma_-}{\partial E_+}\right)_\mu = -C_- \tag{65}*$$

Then, from Equation 64a,

$$z_+F\left(\frac{\partial \Gamma_+}{\partial E_-}\right)_\mu = -\nu_+z_+\frac{\partial}{\partial E_-}\left(\frac{\partial \gamma}{\partial \mu}\right)_{E_-,T,P} = -\nu_+z_+F\left(-\frac{\partial q}{\partial \mu}\right)_E \tag{66}$$

(and analogously from Equation 64b), using the Lippmann equation to express $\partial \gamma/\partial E_-$ or $\partial \gamma/\partial E_+$ in terms of q. Hence the capacity contributions are

$$C_+ = z_+\nu_+F\left(\frac{\partial q}{\partial \mu}\right)_{E_-} \;;\quad C_- = z_-\nu_-F\left(\frac{\partial q}{\partial \mu}\right)_{E_+} \tag{67}$$

* The negative signs appear here because C is normally defined to have positive values in terms of the variation of q_S with E, and the excess charge in the solution side of the double-layer will tend to be more positive with increasing negative electrode potential and vice versa.

Differentiating Equation 58 with respect to E at constant electrolyte concentration gives

$$C = -\left(\frac{\partial q_M}{\partial E}\right)_\mu = z_+F\left(\frac{\partial \Gamma_+}{\partial E}\right)_\mu + z_-F\left(\frac{\partial \Gamma_-}{\partial E}\right)_\mu \qquad (68)$$

and from Equation 67 by differentiation with respect to E,

$$z_+\nu_+F\frac{\partial^2 q}{\partial \mu\, \partial E} = -\left(\frac{\partial C_+}{\partial E}\right)_\mu; \quad z_-\nu_-F\frac{\partial^2 q}{\partial \mu\, \partial E} = \left(\frac{\partial C_-}{\partial E}\right)_\mu \qquad (69)$$

Experimentally dq_M/dE, the over-all capacity given by Equation 68, is measured at various potentials. For values at constant E_- (i.e., using a reference electrode reversible to the anion) determined at various values of μ, the derivative

$$\left(\frac{\partial C}{\partial \mu}\right)_{E_-} = \frac{\partial}{\partial \mu}\left(\frac{\partial q}{\partial E}\right)_\mu \qquad (70)$$

is obtained. The right-hand side of this equation also appears in Equation 69, so that the ionic capacity contributions are

$$z_+\nu_+F\left(\frac{\partial C}{\partial \mu}\right)_{E_-} = -\frac{dC_+}{dE}; \quad z_-\nu_-F\left(\frac{\partial C}{\partial \mu}\right)_{E_+} = \frac{dC_-}{dE} \qquad (71)$$

The evaluation of Γ_+ or Γ_- then requires knowledge of $(\partial C/\partial \mu)_{E_\pm}$ as a function of $E_\pm$. By use of appropriate reference electrodes, the terms of the left-hand side of Equations 71 can be obtained experimentally as a function of E, and integration follows as

$$C_+ = -\int \left(\frac{dC_+}{dE}\right) dE + k_1 \qquad (72)$$

where k_1 is an integration constant and dC_+/dE is given by the terms in Equation 71 as $z_+\nu_+F(\partial C/\partial \mu)_{E_-}$, and similarly for C_-. Also the charge q_+ is given by

$$q_+ = z_+F\Gamma_+ = -\int_{E_{max}}^{\pm E} C_+\, dE + k_2 \qquad (73)$$

where k_2 is another constant resulting after integration and E_{max} is the potential, on the scale of the reference electrode used, at which $q_M = 0$, i.e. the p.z.c. Hence Γ_+ can be obtained from Equation 73 at any potential $\pm E$ by integration of $C_+ \, dE$ up to that potential from the p.z.c. The constant k_2 can be evaluated as follows: Equation 67 can be written

$$-C_+ = z_+ \nu_+ F \left(\frac{\partial q_M}{\partial E}\right)_\mu \left(\frac{\partial E}{\partial \mu}\right)_{q_M} \tag{74}$$

and at the electrocapillary maximum (e.c.m.),

$$-C_+ = z_+ \nu_+ F C_{max} \left(\frac{\partial E_{max}}{\partial \mu}\right)_{q_M} \tag{75}$$

where q_M is zero and C_{max} is the capacity at the e.c.m.; the derivative is a measure of the rate of change of the potential of the e.c.m. with composition, and can be evaluated experimentally, with C_{max}. Hence k_1 can be evaluated. Also, from electrocapillary data, the derivative

$$\left(\frac{\partial \gamma}{\partial \mu}\right)_{E_{max}} = -\Gamma_{salt,\,max} = \frac{-\Gamma_+}{\nu_+} = \frac{\Gamma_-}{\nu_-} \tag{76}$$

can be measured and hence $\Gamma_\pm$ obtained, which then fixes a particular value for the left-hand side of Equation 73, so that k_2 is evaluated. Equation 76 follows, since at the e.c.m., $q_M = 0$, so that $q_S = 0$ and Γ_+ must be equal to Γ_- for electroneutrality on the solution side of the double-layer. In the absence of specific adsorption, Γ_{salt}, Γ_+ and Γ_- are of course zero at the p.z.c.

It will be noted that the capacity method requires electrocapillary data to fix the integration constant k_2. Alternatively, Γ_+ can be calculated *a priori* from the diffuse double-layer theory (it will be the cation contribution in the summation involved in Equation 26) for a sufficiently cathodic potential that no specific adsorption of anions could arise and of course assuming that the cation is not specifically adsorbed. The first procedure is satisfactory with liquid metals, but could not be applied in any direct or unambiguous way for solid metals since their interfacial tensions cannot be directly measured (see below).   Furthermore, at such metals, the measured capacities are usually quite dependent on the frequency used for the measurements, which places severe limitations on the interpretation of the results.   Most solid metal electrodes which exhibit several or many crystal faces will also have several potentials at which different faces attain zero charge, since the p.z.c. depends on electron work function (see below) and the latter depends on the index of the crystal face exposed to an extent of 1–1.5 e.v.   Solid metals will hence exhibit a basic electrochemical heterogeneity, as well as a lattice, surface and catalytic heterogeneity.   This precludes, in principle, the application of the treatment given above, apart from the experimental difficulty of actually measuring $(\partial\gamma/\partial\mu)_{E_{\max}}$.   The electrochemical behaviour of solid metals will be discussed further in Chapter 5.

3.   USE OF DATA ON COMPONENTS OF CHARGE

With data on individual ionic components of charge as a function of electrode charge or potential at liquid metal electrodes, a rather complete quantitative description of the distributions of ions at the interface can be made, and hence theories of the double-layer tested.   Also, for specifically adsorbed ions, the dependence of their surface concentration on solution concentration and electrode potential may be examined, and the adsorption isotherm deduced (see Chapter 6).

For the deduction of information on ion distribution in the double-layer, the following procedure is used.   The experimental quantities which can usually be obtained are q_S ($= -q_M$), Γ_+ and Γ_- from either of the methods discussed above. Γ_+ and Γ_- are, of course, the *total* relative ionic excess quantities, i.e. in the diffuse layer and (if specifically adsorbed) also in the inner layer region.   Generally then the following representation will hold:

$$-q_M = q_S = \underbrace{q_{+,\,\text{diffuse}}}_{z_+\Gamma_+F} + \underbrace{q_{-,\,\text{inner}} + q_{-,\,\text{diffuse}}}_{z_-\Gamma_-F} \qquad (77)$$

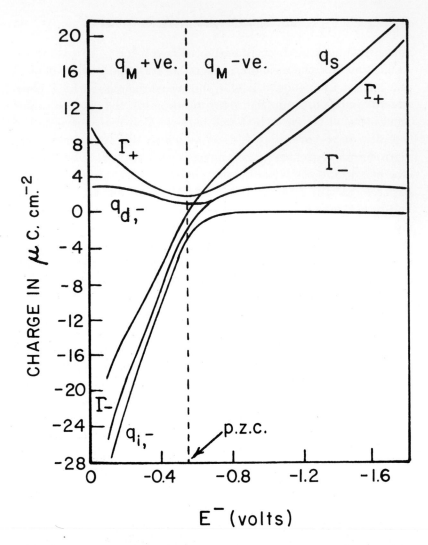

Fig. 9. Components of charge for adsorption of ions from 0.3 M NaCl in the double-layer at a mercury electrode at 25°C (q_S = total net charge on the solution side of the double layer; Γ_+, Γ_- = total surface excesses of cations and anions; q_{i-} = the specifically adsorbed charge due to anions; $q_{d,-}$ = anion charge repelled in the diffuse layer when the charge due to specific adsorption is super-equivalent; Γ_+ is also the cation charge in the diffuse layer in the absence of specific adsorption of the cation). (After Grahame, 54.)

if the cations are not specifically adsorbed. The case of 0.3 m NaCl may be discussed as an example (54) (see Fig. 9). At potentials more anodic than -0.8 v. on the saturated calomel electrode scale, Γ_- exceeds the numerical value of q_M, and electroneutrality is maintained by a positive value of Γ_+; normally at potentials positive to the p.z.c., Γ_+ would be negative, representing a deficiency of cations in the diffuse-layer ionic atmosphere when the electrode carries a positive charge. The positive value of Γ_+ reflects specific adsorption of the *anion* (Cl$^-$ in this case) beyond the extent expected from the purely coulombic interactions with the excess surface charge on the metal [recently (52), this kind of specific adsorption behaviour has been appropriately referred to as *super-equivalent adsorption* in the sense that the extent of adsorption is more than that expected on the basis of equivalence to the net opposite charge residing at the metal surface].

Using the experimental data for Γ_+ [e.g. from $(\partial\gamma/\partial\mu)_{E_-}$], the charge associated with anions in the *diffuse* layer can be calculated from the diffuse double-layer theory through evaluation, for example, of ψ_1 from the known $q_+ (= z_+ F\Gamma_+)$ data. Since the total Γ is known, either by evaluation of $(\partial\gamma/\partial\mu)_{E_+}$ or from $q_S - z_+ F\Gamma_+$, the specific adsorption contribution (if any) in Γ_- can be evaluated and is the term $q_{-,\text{inner}}$ referred to in Equation 77. Hence complete information on the ion distribution in terms of components of charge is known.

Such information has been used by Grahame (60) to test the theory of the double-layer for NaF solutions where no specific adsorption occurs. The latter fact is indicated by the lack of dependence of the coordinates of the e.c.m. on NaF concentration. Under these conditions, the inner layer capacity (C_1 in Equation 30) should be independent of salt concentration. Then from one measurement of the over-all capacity C at a given concentration, the Helmholtz layer capacity C_1 can be deduced by calculation of C_2, the diffuse layer capacity from the electrostatic distribution theory, noting that $1/C = 1/C_1 + 1/C_2$ (series relationship). With this single C_1 value and values of C_2 calculated at other concentrations, it is possible to calculate values of C at all other concentrations and compare them with the measured values. Satisfactory agreement is obtained. However, recent comparisons between surface excess data measured by the electrocapillary method and deduced by integration of capacity data show significant discrepancies which were attributed by Parsons (90) to the fact that the distance of closest approach involved in the interpretation of capacity data (the plane of potential ψ_1) was not identical with the plane of reference for the definition of ionic

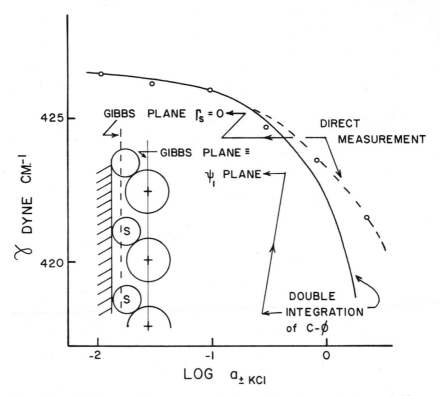

Fig. 10. Difference between variation of surface tension of Hg measured and derived by double integration of capacity-potential dependence; interpreted in terms of difference of Gibbs reference planes as shown. (After Grahame and Parsons, 90.)

surface excess quantities, i.e. the plane where $\Gamma_{\text{solvent}} = 0$. These two matters are illustrated in Fig. 10.

4. COMPONENTS OF CHARGE WHEN IONIC EQUILIBRIA ARE INVOLVED—ADSORPTION OF ORGANIC BASES AND THEIR IONS

A number of organic substances have specific effects on the electrochemical kinetics of, for example, hydrogen evolution, and metal deposition and dissolution. Study of adsorption of such materials is therefore of importance in elucidation of kinetic effects, but is complicated in some cases by acid-base equilibria involving these molecules. Thus, with organic bases in aqueous media, the protonation equilibrium

$$RNH_2 + H_3O^+ \rightleftarrows RNH_3^+ + H_2O \tag{78}$$

makes it impossible to vary the chemical potential of one species alone. The system will normally be composed, for example, of RNH_2 in an acid $H_3O^+X^-$ solution. The components, apart from solvent, will then be RNH_2, RNH_3^+, X^- and H_3O^+. The Gibbs equation for this system is then, at constant T and P,

$$d\gamma = q_S \, dE - \Gamma_{H^+} \, d\mu_{H^+} - \Gamma_{X^-} \, d\mu_{X^-} \\ - \Gamma_{RNH_3^+} \, d\mu_{RNH_3^+} - \Gamma_{RNH_2} \, d\mu_{RNH_2} \tag{79}$$

where the Γ quantities are the surface excesses of the indicated species at the mercury interface. The following conditions for equilibria in the solution are self-evident:

$$d\mu_{H^+} + d\mu_{X^-} = d\mu_{HX} \tag{80a}$$

$$d\mu_{H^+} + d\mu_{RNH_2} = d\mu_{RNH_3^+} \tag{80b}$$

and the condition

$$dE = dE_H + \frac{1}{F} \, d\mu_{H^+} \tag{81}$$

applies to the potential of the mercury electrode, E_H, measured with respect to the hydrogen reference electrode in the solution.

Also the charge q_S in the solution side of the double-layer is

$$q_S = z_i F(\Gamma_{H^+} + \Gamma_{RNH_3^+} + \Gamma_{X^-}) \tag{82}$$

Then from Equations 79 to 82,

$$d\gamma = q_S \, dE_H - (\Gamma_{RNH_3^+} + \Gamma_{RNH_2}) \, d\mu_{RNH_2} - \Gamma_{X^-} \, d\mu_{X^-} \tag{83}$$

from which the Lippmann equation in the form

$$\left(\frac{\partial \gamma}{\partial E_H}\right)_{\mu_{HX}\mu_{RNH_2}} = q_S \tag{84}$$

follows. Also, for the surface excess quantities, it is apparent that only combined terms such as

$$-(\Gamma_{RNH_3^+} + \Gamma_{RNH_2}) = \left(\frac{\partial \gamma}{\partial \mu_{RNH_2}}\right)_{E_H, \mu_{HCl}} \tag{85}$$

can be determined, and

$$-\Gamma_{X^-} = \left(\frac{\partial \gamma}{\partial \mu_{HX}}\right)_{E_H, \mu_{RNH_2}} \tag{86}$$

With regard to the *total* component of positive charge, q_+,

$$q_+ = F(\Gamma_{H^+} + \Gamma_{RNH_3^+}) = -z_{X^-} F \Gamma_{X^-} + q_S \tag{87}$$

From Equation 85, it will be noted that only the *sum* and not the individual values of $\Gamma_{RNH_3^+}$ and Γ_{RNH_2} can be determined. Similarly, only the difference $\Gamma_{H^+} - \Gamma_{RNH_2}$ can be evaluated. Also Γ_+ can be evaluated from q_S (Equation 84) and Γ_{X^-} (Equation 86), or directly from

$$\left(\frac{\partial \gamma}{\partial \mu_{HX}}\right)_{E_{X^-}, \mu_{RNH_2}} = -\Gamma_+ \tag{88}$$

where μ_{RNH_2} refers to constant amine concentration. The latter condition is achieved only if the activity ratio $a_{RNH_3^+}/a_{H^+}$ is constant, since

$$\frac{a_{RNH_3^+}}{a_{H^+}} = \frac{a_{RNH_2}}{K_a}$$

where K_a is the acid dissociation constant of RNH_3^+. The analysis of experimental electrocapillary curves for adsorption of alkaloid bases at mercury has been carried out by Conway et al. (92), and by Blomgren and Bockris (93), for a number of simple bases and by Conway and Barrades (94) with regard to comparison with adsorption of the un-ionised bases in neutral solution, and with the adsorption of corresponding N–Me quaternary salts where the protonation equilibrium such as that in Equation 78 cannot arise; the interpretation of the electro-capillary data for such salts is hence less ambiguous. In most of the cases examined, the organic cation is specifically adsorbed, an effect which is associated with the influence such compounds have on the kinetics of cathodic processes.

5. OTHER METHODS

No other methods for the study of adsorption of molecules and ions give as much information as the determination of electro-capillary and capacity data at mercury; in practice, these approaches are therefore limited to the liquid metals, although capacity measurements have been applied to a number of solid electrodes (95, 96) but the results cannot be treated with the same rigour as is possible at mercury on account of limitations already discussed (see p. 55). A number of other methods lead to information on adsorption but of a less detailed nature. Probably the most useful and generally applicable is that involving radio-isotope labelled ions or molecules. This technique has been developed extensively by Balashova (97) and by Hackerman and Stephens (98), and Wroblowa and Green (99) have applied the technique to the direct measurement of the amount of labelled substance adsorbed at the metal electrode surface (in some of the previous methods, the adsorption was measured by difference of concentrations in solution). A novel development of the latter technique has been reported by Bockris and Swinkells (100), who

TABLE 4-I

Methods for Study of Reactant or Additive Adsorption at Electrodes

Method	System Where Applicable	Principal Limitations	Principal Types of Information or Quantities Obtained
Electrocapillary	Liquid metals, amalgams and molten metals	None, except restriction to liquid metal phase	$\Gamma_A, \Gamma_+, \Gamma_-, q_M, q_S, \Delta\bar{G}^0, \theta$ (Γ_A for a neutral species A)
Capacity (Grahame)	Solid and liquid metals	(a) Requires at least one electrocapillary or equivalent determination (b) Frequency dependence of capacity	$\theta, \Gamma_A, \Gamma_+, \Gamma_-, q_S, q_M, \Delta\bar{G}^0, C$
Capacity (Hansen)	Solid and liquid metals	(a) Frequency dependence of capacity (b) Thermodynamic interpretation not rigorous	Essentially similar to method of Grahame (above) but based on non-thermodynamic deduction of θ
Radio-isotopes	Solid electrodes with radioactively labelled ions or molecules	(a) Irreversible adsorption or (b) Cases where back count (C^{14}) can be done; significance of count may be in doubt	θ; non-equilibrium values of θ in case (a) or equilibrium in case (b) if electrode maintained in solution

D.C. charging determination of H accommodation	Solid transition metals	Requires noble metals where θ_H can be obtained	Coverage by chemisorbed species deduced by change of H accommodation. Used in electrocatalytic oxidation studies
Spectrophotometric	Solid electrodes	(a) Conjugated organic molecules (b) Restricted application to certain organic ions and adsorbents	θ, Γ, $\Delta \bar{G}^0$
Conductance	Solid and liquid electrodes	(a) Ionic species but not neutral molecules	Speculative and not fully explored; based on changes of ionic concentration
Refractometric	Solid and liquid electrodes	(a) Ionic and neutral molecules where changes in refractive index of adsorbate solutions are significant	Speculative and unexplored; based on changes of concentration
A.C. resistance	Solid electrodes	(a) Frequency dependence of impedance measurements (b) Uncertainty of equilibrium thermodynamic significance	Quantitative adsorption parameters not published
Ellipsometric	Smooth solid or liquid electrodes	Requires significant film thickness	Film thickness, based on polarisation of reflected radiation

used a continuously moving metal tape electrode directly scanned by a Geiger counter just outside the electrolyte solution. For organic substances, equilibrium isotherms can be deduced from results obtained from those methods [e.g. (99, 101)] in which potential control and equilibrium with the solution is maintained during the measurement. Another method which satisfies the latter conditions was developed by Conway and Barradas (101) who measured changes of ultra-violet absorbance in solutions containing conjugated organic bases when these substances were adsorbed at equilibrium at large copper, silver and nickel wire gauze electrodes. Equilibrium isotherms were derived. With a number of organic and inorganic adsorbates, the range of potentials over which the adsorption can be followed is limited by the occurrence of net electrochemical reactions which may involve the co-oxidation or reduction of the adsorbate studied. In the ultra-violet absorption method (101), such effects can fortunately be detected by changes of the spectrum of the adsorbate in solution. The difficulty arises since most solid metal-electrolyte interfaces are much less "ideally polarisable" than the mercury-acid or mercury-alkali-metal salt solution interfaces, and studies over an appreciable range of potentials will hence involve significant passage of current in an anodic or cathodic direction with possible disturbance of the adsorption equilibrium. Similar disturbance of the ionic double-layer charge distribution can arise in fast electrode reactions, and corrections are then required in interpretations of the kinetics.

With inorganic electrolytes, individual types of ions can be radio-labelled, e.g. I^{*-}, $S^{*}O_4^{--}$, $P^{*}O_4^{3-}$ so that components of adsorbed charge can be obtained. However, it is not generally possible to distinguish inner and diffuse-layer contributions in the case of specific adsorption, except perhaps by detection of the radio-labelled adsorbate actually on the surface, using a method such as that of Wroblowa and Green (99), which presumably gives principally the surface concentration of the specifically adsorbed ions. A summary of methods for the study of electro-chemical adsorption is given in Table 4–1.

6. SIGNIFICANCE OF POTENTIAL OF ZERO CHARGE

The existence of a characteristic potential at which the excess charge at the electrode metal surface is zero follows from Lippmann's relation deduced above; in terms of surface tension it is the potential of maximum surface tension where $\partial\gamma/\partial E$ is zero; in terms of capacity it is the potential of minimum capacity in dilute solutions of non-chemisorbed ions, where the charge in the diffuse layer is zero at the p.z.c. In the presence of specifically adsorbed ions, the diffuse-layer charge is equal and opposite to the inner-layer charge at the p.z.c. The general importance of the p.z.c. as a characteristic electrochemical property of the metal was early recognised by Frumkin (103) and has more recently been discussed with regard to a number of electrochemical phenomena by Antropov (104), Ruetschi (105) and Ershler (106). The difference of p.z.c. values for different metals was first demonstrated for a cell of Hg and Tl electrodes both at their potentials of zero charge ($\partial\gamma/\partial E = 0 = -q_M$), where the cell e.m.f. was about 0.45 v. (103). The requirement of $q_M = 0$ does not of course imply that at the p.z.c. the metal-solution p.d. is zero. In most cases, this is probably finite on account of the surface potential at the metal [$ca.$ 0.5–1 v. (106)] and orientation of solvent dipoles [several decivolts, negative outwards (106)] and the mutual effects associated with the influence of solvent dipoles on electron distribution at the metal interface and vice versa. The p.z.c. will also change, for a given metal, upon specific adsorption of ions from the solution (107).

The p.z.c. is directly related to the electronic work function, and, as far as existing data are available (105, $cf.$ 30), the relation is a linear one. At solid polycrystalline metals, the values measured are probably average ones characteristic of a distribution of crystal faces exposed. Since the variation of work function from one crystal face to another of single crystal metals can be as large as 1–1.5 v., corresponding variations of p.z.c. can arise. It will be seen subsequently that these variations can be an important source of heterogeneity of rate constants for

TABLE 4-2

Methods for Estimation of the Potential of Zero Charge of Metals

Method	Comments	Reference
Electrocapillary, based on direct surface tension measurements	Applicable only to liquid metals; p.z.c. can be unambiguously evaluated; also determined as a function of solute additions	General; see (30,45)
Capacity minimum (in differential capacity-potential plot)	Applicable in dilute solutions of surface-inactive agents; less applicable to solid metals where sharp minimum is obscured by heterogeneity of p.z.c. and greater specific adsorption; frequency-dependence of capacity leads to some ambiguities; surface active neutral molecules and some ions give wide capacity minimum	General; see (30,54); Frumkin (95,96)
Decrement of swings of pendulum from pivot of the metal	Based on potential dependence of interfacial frictions or hardness and, indirectly, on surface tension at pivot; possible applications to solid metals	Rehbinder and Wenström (111); Bockris and Parry-Jones (112)
Angle of contact of bubbles	Applicable to solid and liquid metal interfaces; little developed; experimentally difficult	Gorodetzkaya and Frumkin (113)
Withdrawal of metal wire at surface of solution	Applicable to solid metals; involves three-phase contact; in course of exploration	Kozlowski (114); Parry and Conway
Inflection in overpotential log [current density] curve	Generally applicable in absence of strong specific adsorption; large effects in anion reduction reactions; first suggested for hydrogen evolution reaction at Ni	Legran and Levina (115); Parsons (67)

Method	Comments	Reference
Maximum adsorption of neutral adsorbate	Based on theory of adsorption of neutral molecules; ideally applicable for non-polar adsorbates, where adsorption is determined as a function of electrode potential; maximum adsorption not necessarily exactly at p.z.c. because of H_2O reorientation effects	Butler (84)
Repulsion of closely spaced parallel wires	Based on repulsion of interacting double-layers, as in theory of colloid stability; repulsion will be minimal at p.z.c. as diffuse-layer is eliminated	Frumkin, Voropajova (116)
Electrophoretic migration of metal particles	Effect of adsorbates on sign of net charge can be examined, but no potential control available	E.g. (117)
Interpolation for unknown cases from semiempirical work-function–p.z.c. relation based on known average values and recorded work functions	Limited by inadequate knowledge of dependence of p.z.c. on crystal faces and distribution of such faces on various electrode metal samples; also limited by spread of recorded work-function data	Parsons (30)
Adsorption of radioactively labelled anions (Pt)	Applicable to solid metals; depends on extent of specific adsorption of ions	Balashova and Merkuleva (118)
Non-faradaic charging current as function of potential	Applicable to dropping Hg electrode (or electrodes of changing area) or when disturbance of surface occurs at electrode	Bennewitz and Schultz (131)

electrochemical kinetic processes at solid metals. Similarly, adsorption of ions and molecules at a polycrystalline metal will be determined at a given "equipotential" electrode potential by the signs and magnitudes of the local metal-solution potentials, which will vary if the p.z.c. values depend on crystal faces exposed. Hence the extent of adsorption of species from solution will be heterogeneous across the surface of a polycrystalline metal.

In discussions of the theory of the double-layer, it is usually convenient to refer potentials of the metal to that of zero charge in the absence of specific adsorption, and they are then referred to as *rational* potentials (54). Since the p.z.c. for a given metal can be expressed on some practical experimental scale, e.g. with respect to the normal hydrogen or calomel electrodes, and other potentials can be measured on the same scale, it is experimentally possible to express electrode potentials on the rational scale.

Usually the p.z.c. depends on adsorption of specifically adsorbed ions (107,108,109) and/or oriented adsorbed dipoles and is therefore characteristic not only of the metal but of the adsorption of species from solution and hence of the temperature and composition of the solution.

Various methods have been suggested for the determination of values of the p.z.c., but usually these methods are rigorous only for the liquid metals. Capacity minima in dilute solutions at solid metals could be determined, but the efficacy of this method is limited by the distribution of p.z.c. values at a polycrystalline surface and the usually observed frequency dependence of capacity at solid metals (95,110). Various more recent methods have been discussed by Frumkin (see ref. 96), and a summary is given in Table 4–2.

5

Adsorption Behaviour of Neutral Molecules and Ions

I. INTRODUCTION

Most quantitative studies of the double-layer have been concerned with the electrochemical adsorption of ionic species, as discussed above. However, several treatments for adsorption of neutral molecules have been given which are important since neutral species (apart from the solvent) often have marked and specific effects on the kinetics of electrochemical reactions. Also, until recently, rather little attention has been given to the role of the *solvent* at the electrode interface. Qualitatively, most neutral molecules cause a diminution of surface tension across the top of the electrocapillary curve to a relatively greater extent at potentials at or near the p.z.c. (102,103). Some aromatic polar molecules give a depression of surface tension over a wider range of potentials, resulting in a general lowering of γ values throughout the curve. Usually the adsorption effect is asymmetric, being more on one branch of the electrocapillary curve than on the other, e.g. with pyridine (94) or thiourea (119). The latter effect is probably associated with different interaction with the surface [and with the solvent, e.g. through H-bonding (120)] when the adsorbate molecules are oriented one way or the other by the cathodic or anodic field at potentials appreciably displaced from that of zero charge. Alternatively, specific adsorption of anions

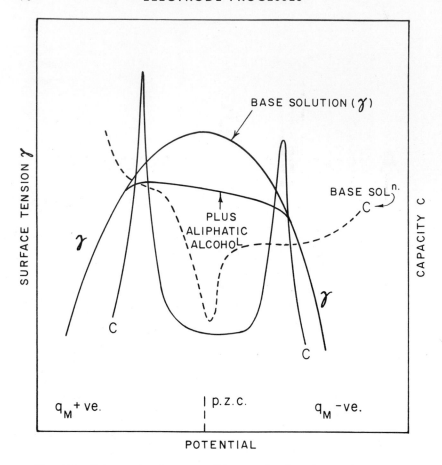

BASE SOLUTION (γ)

BASE SOL.n.

PLUS
ALIPHATIC
ALCOHOL

q_M +ve.

p.z.c.

q_M -ve.

SURFACE TENSION γ

CAPACITY C

POTENTIAL

Fig. 11. Schematic electrocapillary and related capacity curves as a function of potential for adsorption of a neutral organic molecule, e.g. *n*-amyl alcohol.

on the anodic branch inhibits molecule adsorption. The onset of adsorption or desorption is indicated more clearly by differential capacity measurements which show sharp peaks in the regions of potential on each side of the e.c.m. where neutral solute molecules are adsorbed (Fig. 11). Physically, the sharp capacity maxima reflect a relatively rapid change of charge held in the double-layer, with change of potential, as the organic molecules are displaced from the interface with increasing cathodic or anodic field.

2. THEORIES OF ADSORPTION

The first theory of neutral molecule adsorption, applied to amyl alcohol, was proposed by Frumkin (121), who considered the change of energy of the double-layer in terms of its change of capacity ΔC when neutral molecule adsorption occurred. In Frumkin's theory, the energy change associated with completion of a monolayer of adsorbed substance A can be written (123)

$$\Delta \bar{G}^0 = \Delta G^0 + \tfrac{1}{2}(C_s - C_A)E^2 + E\left(\frac{m_s}{l_s} - \frac{m_A}{l_A}\right) \qquad (89)$$

where $\Delta C = C_s - C_A$ is the difference of capacity in the absence (C_s) and in the presence (C_A) of a monolayer of the adsorbate; here E is the p.d. across the inner region of the double-layer of thickness l_s in the absence of A and l_A is the thickness in the presence of the layer A; m_s and m_A are the corresponding components of dipole moments of the species in the double-layer normal to the surface. The electrochemical standard free energy $\Delta \bar{G}^0$ has a maximum value when the rational potential E has a value

$$E_{max} = \frac{m_s/l_s - m_A/l_A}{C_s - C_A} \qquad (90)$$

so that $\Delta \bar{G}^0$ can be expressed in terms of a quantity $E - E_{max}$:

$$\Delta \bar{G}^0 = \Delta \bar{G}^0_{max} + \tfrac{1}{2}(C_s - C_A)(E - E_{max})^2 \qquad (91)$$

where $\Delta \bar{G}^0_{max}$ is defined as

$$\Delta G^0 - \frac{(m_s/l_s - m_A/l_A)^2}{2(C_s - C_A)} \qquad (92)$$

It will be seen below that this relation is similar to that deduced by Butler (84) by another method. The extent of adsorption, expressed as a Γ value for A, can be obtained from a distribution function involving the standard electrochemical free energy of adsorption $\Delta \bar{G}^0$ as in Butler's theory (see below).

A more explicit theory in terms of molecular properties was proposed by Butler (84) and is similar to his theory of salting-out of non-electrolytes by the fields of ions in solution; in fact, the change of adsorption with electrode potential can be regarded as a "salting-out" or "salting-in" of the neutral adsorbate in the interfacial region of the electrode by the electrode double-layer field. Taking into account polarisation energy, including interaction of any permanent dipoles with the electrode field, Butler wrote the work of adsorption at the interface, when the *field* was $\mathscr{E}$, as

$$W = [\tfrac{1}{2}(\alpha_s - \alpha_A)\mathscr{E}^2 + (P_s - P_A)\mathscr{E}]v_A \qquad (93)$$

where v_A is the volume of the molecule of adsorbate A, the P terms the permanent polarisations of solvent s and solute A, and α terms the corresponding polarisabilities. It was supposed that the surface excess at field $\mathscr{E}$ was related to that (Γ_0) at zero applied field (i.e. at the e.c.m.; but the actual field is not necessarily zero at the p.z.c.) by

$$\Gamma_\mathscr{E} = \Gamma_0 \exp\left[-\frac{W}{kT}\right] \qquad (94)$$

In Equation 93 the differential nature of adsorption from aqueous solutions is taken into account by writing the difference of α_s and α_A, and P_s and P_A terms. However, in the relatively high field of the double-layer, the polarisation of the interfacial region will vary with field. In solutions in which no dipole association effects arise, the polarisation will be given approximately by the high-field case of the Debye-Langevin theory, which will begin to be applicable ($\mathscr{E}m \geqslant kT$) when the field $\mathscr{E}$ is *ca.* 4×10^4 e.s.u. cm.$^{-1}$ (12×10^6 v. cm.$^{-1}$) for a dipole of moment $m = 1$ Debye, and $T = 300°$K. This condition will arise when the p.d. across the inner region of the double-layer is about ± 0.3 v. At potentials numerically greater than this value, dipole orientation will tend to be complete in the double-layer. At low fields the total polarisability will be $\alpha + m^2/3kT$, where $m^2/3kT$ is the orientation polarisability contribution. Normally, in aqueous solutions, the term in P's in Equation 93 will be larger than that in α's unless a large polarisable organic solute is involved. Furthermore $P_s \gg P_A$ for many organic solutes in water, so that W will be a *positive* term and increase with increasing $\mathscr{E}$. Hence $\Gamma_{\mathscr{E}} < \Gamma_0$ with increasing numerical value of $\mathscr{E}$ or E, so that the extent of adsorption will tend to *decrease* away from the e.c.m., as is usually found experimentally. The sharp desorption peaks usually observed in capacity studies of adsorption of aliphatic neutral molecules are probably related to the relatively sudden onset of cooperative orientation amongst the solvent molecules as dielectric saturation $(m\mathscr{E} \gg kT)$ of the solvent in the inner region of the double-layer (48,49,73) becomes appreciable.

For neutral molecules adsorbed in the double-layer which are not associated with the solvent by strong hydrogen bonds, it will be legitimate to apply the Debye-Langevin theory to examine the extent of orientation with field in the inner region of the double-layer. This approach will be limited to relatively low coverages, where interaction effects between adsorbate molecules will be small. For dipoles of moment m, the electrical energy W in the double-layer field $\mathscr{E}$ will be

$$W_{\theta=0} = -m\mathscr{E}\,;\quad W_{\theta} = -m\mathscr{E}\cos\theta \tag{95}$$

for angles of orientation θ to the normal to the surface. The distribution of orientations dN/N will be given by

$$\frac{dN}{N} = \frac{\exp\left[(m\mathscr{E}\cos\theta)/kT\right]d(\cos\theta)}{\displaystyle\int_{-1}^{1}\exp\left[(m\mathscr{E}\cos\theta)/kT\right]d(\cos\theta)} \tag{96}$$

or

$$\frac{1}{N}\frac{dN}{d(\cos\theta)} = \frac{\exp\left[(m\mathscr{E}\cos\theta)/kT\right]}{(2kT/m\mathscr{E})\sinh\left[m\mathscr{E}/kT\right]} \tag{97}$$

Evaluation of the distribution function $(1/N)\,dN/d(\cos\theta)$ gives the relation shown in Fig. 12 for various fields and for a solute dipole of moment $m_A = 3.3$ Debyes [e.g. calculated for 2-chloropyridine studied by Conway and Barradas (94)]. The plot of the function $(1/N)\,dN/d(\cos\theta)$ is made for convenience with respect to θ rather than $\cos\theta$. It is clear that even for fields as high as

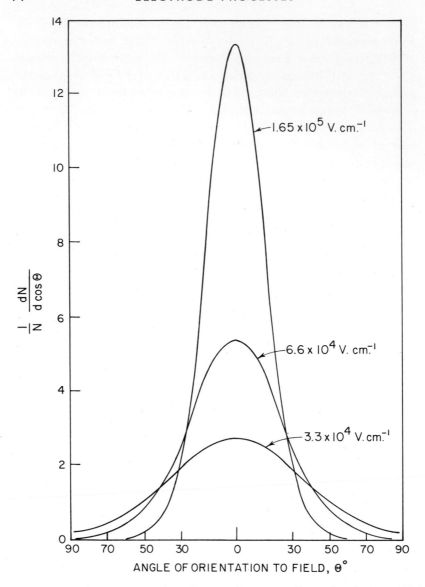

Fig. 12. Orientation distribution functions for a dipolar organic molecule (2-chloropyridine) at the Hg electrode (not normalised).

1.7×10^5 v. cm.$^{-1}$, appreciable disorientation is still apparent. For a dipole of moment 3.3 Debyes, $m\mathscr{E} > kT$ when $\mathscr{E} > 4 \times 10^6$ v. cm.$^{-1}$, and orientation saturation will begin to set in at fields of this magnitude. This would correspond to a p.d. in the inner region of the double-layer of only about 0.1 v. Strong orientation of most dipolar solutes will hence arise over most of the potential range normally studied at Hg except quite near the e.c.m. These calculations will not apply to the water solvent molecules, since free orientation will not arise because of association effects (*cf.* the theories of the dielectric constant for water).

A related approach has been made by Devanathan *et al.* (52), who considered dependence of solvent adsorption on the electrode field in terms of a distribution of solvent molecules with dipole orientation "up" or "down" with respect to the metal surface. The population of dipoles in "up" or "down" states is dependent on the field and the mutual lateral interaction between the oriented dipoles. The dipole orientation corresponds to a capacity (122) (see p. 76) which is dependent on the applied coulombic field $4\pi q_M/\epsilon_i$, and is hence dependent on the electrode charge q_M. When interaction effects are considered, the dipole double-layer capacity contributes about 120 μF. cm.$^{-2}$ at the e.c.m. This kind of calculation may be applied to the case where competitive adsorption between an organic neutral solute and the solvent water arises, so that the organic solute displaces an equivalent volume of water adsorbed in "up" or "down" configurations. Qualitative agreement with experiment for the relation between surface coverage and the surface charge is obtained, which is improved when allowance for lateral interactions between oriented solvent molecules is made in the calculations. However, the extent of agreement between experiment and theory is rather less satisfactory than that obtained in Butler's original calculations (84), but the model and assumptions in the recent treatment (52) are, nevertheless, physically rather more realistic.

The consequences of assuming various kinds of isotherms and potential or field dependence in the electrochemical free energy of adsorption (*cf.* Equations 89 and 93), have been explored by Parsons (123) with regard to the theoretical capacity behaviour to which these assumptions lead.* In most cases, the capacity profile as a function of the potential parameter $E - E_{\max}$ is characteristic of the isotherm and type of potential dependence of $\Delta \bar{G}^0$.

3. GENERAL ELECTROSTATIC THEORY OF NEUTRAL MOLECULE ADSORPTION

In the absence of specific adsorption, the integral capacity K_1 of the Helmholtz region of the double-layer may be written (47) (see p. 33)

$$K_1 = \frac{q_2}{\phi_M - \psi_1} \tag{98}$$

In the presence of specifically adsorbed ions and oriented neutral molecules A, the p.d. $\phi_M - \psi_1$ will be modified to $\phi_M + \Delta\phi_{\mathrm{ion}} + \Delta\phi_A - \psi_1$, where the $\Delta\phi$ quantities refer to *changes* of the measured potential of the metal by adsorbed ions or dipoles. The term $\Delta\phi_{\mathrm{ion}}$ can be written as q_1/K_2, and $\Delta\phi_A$ as $2\pi\Gamma_A m/\epsilon_1$, where Γ_A is the surface excess of A having a dipole moment m, and ϵ_1 is the dielectric constant between the metal and the inner limit of the diffuse layer. The term for $\Delta\phi_A$ can be written equivalently as $e\Gamma/K_A$ where e is the electronic charge in the dipole of A, and K_A is a dipole layer capacity associated with oriented A.   Combining these terms gives

$$\phi_M = \frac{q_2}{K_1} + \frac{q_1}{K_2} + \frac{e\Gamma}{K_A} + \psi_1 \tag{99}$$

or since

$$q_S = q_2 + q_1, \tag{100}$$

$$\phi_M = \frac{q_S}{K_1} - \frac{q_1}{K_1} + \frac{q_1}{K_2} + \frac{e\Gamma}{K_A} + \psi_1 \tag{101}$$

---

* An analogous treatment was first given (124) for adsorbed intermediates and is discussed in Chapter 7.

The experimentally measured differential capacity is $dq_S/d\phi_M$, which may be obtained by differentiating Equation 101 with respect to q_S:

$$\frac{1}{C} = \frac{d\phi_M}{dq_S} = \frac{1}{K_1} - \left(\frac{1}{K_1} - \frac{1}{K_2}\right)\frac{dq_1}{dq_S} + \frac{e}{K_A}\frac{d\Gamma}{dq_S} + \frac{d\psi_1}{dq_S} \quad (102)$$

Since $q_S = q_1 + q_2$ and $1/K_1 = 1/K_2 + 1/K_3$, where K_3 is the capacity of the region *between* the planes of potential ψ_1 and ψ_2 (see Fig. 4d), C is obtained as

$$\frac{1}{C} = \frac{1}{K_2} + \left(\frac{1}{K_3} + \frac{1}{C_2}\right)\left(1 - \frac{dq_1}{dq_S}\right) + \frac{e}{K_A}\frac{d\Gamma}{dq_S} \quad (103)$$

In the absence of adsorbate A, let the capacity be C_0, i.e., when the term $(e/K_A)\, d\Gamma/dq_s$ (which arises from $\Delta\phi_A$) is zero, then

$$\frac{1}{C} = \frac{1}{C_0} + \frac{e}{K_A}\frac{d\Gamma_A}{dq_S} \quad (104)$$

so that the Γ_A can be related to surface charge on the metal by

$$-\frac{d\Gamma_A}{dq_M} = \frac{K_A}{e}\left(\frac{1}{C} - \frac{1}{C_0}\right) \quad (105)$$

This type of equation has the advantage of giving Γ directly in terms of (a) capacities in the presence and absence of adsorbate A (*cf.* Frumkin's theory) and (b) the charge q_M: Γ values can then be obtained by integration of the appropriate experimental data for C as $f(q_M)$. Γ as $f(q_M)$ can also be obtained from electrocapillary data.

It is also of interest to note that differentiation of Equation 101 at constant charge gives

$$\frac{\partial\phi_M}{\partial\Gamma} = \frac{e}{K_A} - \frac{2\pi m}{\epsilon_1} \quad (106)$$

At the e.c.m., $q_M = 0$, so that this equation should give the shift of e.c.m. potential with surface excess of adsorbed A. Previously, this has usually been assumed to be given in terms of the Helmholtz formula $\chi = 4\pi m\Gamma/\epsilon_1$, involving the factor 4π instead of

2π. Comparison of calculated (122) and experimental data (119) for Γ for thiourea at the e.c.m. gives good agreement by using Equation 106 with $\epsilon_1 = 7.2$. However, it is doubtful if the dielectric constant ϵ_1 can be known (122) within the required factor of 2 at these degrees of saturation.* A discrete molecular model will be preferable for regions close to the electrode. A further deduction from the work on thiourea adsorption (119,122) is that the *chemical* part of the free energy of adsorption (exclusive of lateral interaction effects) depends on surface charge of the metal, becoming less negative at more positive q_M, where the number of electrons per atom of mercury is somewhat diminished from the normal value at the surface.

4. ISOTHERMS FOR REACTANT IONS AND MOLECULES AT ELECTRODES

The isotherm defining the equilibrium between particles in the bulk phase and at an electrode surface (interphase) is important in electrode processes in two ways: (a) in determining the local reactant concentrations at the electrode and (b) in hence determining indirectly the kinetics of electrochemical reactions proceeding at the surface, e.g. with regard to reaction order. When adsorbed intermediates are involved in consecutive electrochemical reactions, a more direct and specific influence on the electrode kinetics may arise and will be discussed in a following chapter. Here, the treatment will be confined to discussion of the two principal types of isotherms which have been used in the examination of electrode processes as applied to reactant ion and molecule adsorption.

(i) Langmuir Isotherm. Despite the fact that the Langmuir isotherm is often deduced by reference to the kinetics of adsorption and desorption of adsorbate molecules, such a deduction indicates

---

* Also with some molecules, e.g. aromatic structures with π-orbitals, complete orientation of the dipole may not occur until rather higher fields than indicated by the calculations above. Evidence for this type of behaviour has been given by Conway and Barradas (94), so that the relevant moment m may be in doubt.

little concerning the conditions under which Langmuir adsorption strictly applies.   These are (a) fixed-site adsorption (immobility of adsorbate); (b) no lateral interaction or heterogeneity in the surface, i.e. an energy of adsorption which is independent of coverage θ; and of course (c) equilibrium between the interphase (surface) and the bulk phase for adsorption up to a monolayer ($\theta = 1$).   If U is the energy barrier height for surface diffusion or mobility, fixed-site adsorption occurs when $kT \ll U$.   The adsorption equilibrium will be defined by equality of chemical potentials of adsorbate in the interphase and the bulk phase, p. The chemical potential in the latter is simply

$$\mu_\mathrm{p} = \mu_\mathrm{p}^0 + RT \ln a_\mathrm{p} \tag{107}$$

for activity a_p in the bulk phase p.   The chemical potential in the interphase is obtained from the partition function for the adlayer.   In the absence of any effects of the surface on the internal partition functions of the molecules adsorbed (i.e. for some cases of physical adsorption), the partition function for the particles on a surface of identical sites is a configurational one determined by the number of ways of placing N particles on n sites ($N/n = \theta$). There are obviously n ways of placing the first of the N particles, and $n - 1$ for the second, $n - 2$ for the third, and so on.   For the N molecules there are

$$n(n - 1)(n - 2) \cdots [n - (N - 1)] \text{ ways}$$

i.e.,

$$\frac{n!}{(n - N)!} \text{ configurations}$$

Of these, $N!$ are indistinguishable, since molecules A and B on sites 1 and 2, for example, are obviously configurationally identical with molecules B and A on 1 and 2 respectively, if A and B are identical species.   Hence the partition function is

$$Q_n = \frac{n!}{(n - N)! \, N!} \tag{108}$$

and the total partition function for the N particles with energies referred to that of the particles in the bulk phase will be

$$Q_{n,\,\text{total}} = \frac{n!}{(n-N)!\,N!}\,Q_i{}^N \exp\left[-\frac{NU}{kT}\right] \qquad (109)$$

where NU is the total energy of adsorption and will normally be a negative quantity, and Q_i is the internal partition function. The Helmholtz free energy A_s for the surface layer will then be obtained as

$$A_s = -kT \ln Q_{n,\text{total}} \qquad (110)$$

which can be obtained from Stirling's approximation [$\ln x! = (x+\frac{1}{2})\ln x - x$, or with $x \gg 1$, $\ln x! = x \ln x - x$] as

$$A_s = -kT\left[n \ln \frac{n}{n-N} - N \ln \frac{N}{n-N} + N \ln Q_i - \frac{NU}{kT}\right] \qquad (111)$$

Taking the chemical potential μ_s as $(\partial A_s / \partial N)_{T,n}$, then

$$\mu_s = -kT \ln \frac{n-N}{N} - kT \ln Q_i + U \qquad (112)$$

By dividing $n - N$ and N in the ln by n to obtain θ and equating to μ_p, the isotherm, say

$$\mathscr{K} = kT \ln\left(\frac{\theta}{1-\theta}\frac{1}{a_p}\right) = \mu_p^0 - U + kT \ln Q_i \qquad (113)$$

is obtained, i.e.,

$$\frac{\theta}{1-\theta} = \left(\exp\left[\frac{-\mathscr{K}}{kT}\right]\right)a_p = l a_p \qquad (114)$$

where $l = \exp[\,\mathscr{K}/kT\,]$ and $-\mathscr{K}$ has the significance of a standard free energy of adsorption. Equation 114 is a form of the Langmuir isotherm. If the species were mobile on the surface, the configurational partition function will be replaced by a two-dimensional translational partition function and the relation

$$\ln \frac{\theta}{a_p} = \text{constant} \qquad (115)$$

results, which is a form of Henry's law for a surface-bulk phase equilibrium. In practice, this will not hold for coverages approaching unity if the particles have finite size.

(ii) Temkin Isotherm and Heterogeneity or Interaction Effects. Usually interactions and/or heterogeneity arise at real surfaces. The former can be taken into account by introducing a coverage-dependent interaction energy in the configurational partition function, and the latter can be taken into account in several ways, the best-known of which is that described by Temkin (see below). For *immobile* adsorption, heterogeneity will not be detectable by observation of coverage-dependent heat of adsorption, since sites of varying energy will be filled at random and the measured heat of adsorption will be an average value. However, interaction effects, if significant, would lead to coverage-dependent adsorption energy since the probability of near neighbor configurations increases with θ. When surface diffusion is possible, the particles will distribute themselves at optimum distances on a homogeneous surface, and the interaction energy at a given coverage will be an average value determined by θ; at a heterogeneous surface the particles will, however, preferentially tend to populate regions of highest adsorption energy and local lateral interactions may then also be significant, and depend themselves on the heterogeneity effects.

The basic assumption in the Temkin isotherm (125) is that varying energies of adsorption can arise on account of heterogeneity so that the surface is regarded as made up of a distribution of patches, at each of which the Langmuir isotherm holds independently with a characteristic local standard free energy or heat of adsorption, depending on the patch distribution, and decreasing linearly with coverage. Other types of distribution of affinities of sites could arise [e.g. the exponential distribution of Zeldowitch (126)], but that assumed by Temkin corresponds to variation of heats of chemisorption of a number of adsorbates at the gas-solid interface for $0.1 < \theta < 0.9$, approximately. The isotherm was also derived to provide a basis for the observation of constant electrode·capacitance which is observed over an appreciable potential range in the electrochemical desorption of hydrogen at platinum electrodes. This will be discussed further in Chapter 7.

The full treatment of Temkin cannot be given here, but the essential results will be recorded. The standard free energy of adsorption (for each patch) was assumed to decrease by equal small decrements over successively covered patches, as coverage increased. The variation of standard free energy of adsorption* with coverage could thus be expressed by the equation

$$\Delta G_\theta^0 = \Delta G_0^0 - fRT\theta \tag{116}$$

where ΔG_0^0 and ΔG_θ^0 are the standard free energies of adsorption corresponding to $\theta = 0$ and to a finite θ, respectively, and the standard state has been chosen corresponding to $\theta = 0$, the pure bare metal surface. With these and other assumptions, Temkin derived the following isotherm for θ as a function of pressure P:

$$\theta = \frac{1}{f} \ln \frac{1 + l_0 P}{1 + l_0 P \exp[-f]} \tag{117}$$

where l_0 is the value of the Langmuir constant (Equation 114) for the first micro-adsorption patch covered ($\theta = 0$), and f is defined by Equation 116, or differentially by

$$f = \frac{1}{RT} \frac{d(\Delta G_\theta^0)}{d\theta} \tag{118}$$

* A difficulty arises here with the definition of the standard free energy. Normally the standard free energy of adsorption will be a unique quantity for a given system defined for a particular standard state in the bulk phase and a particular coverage (usually $\theta = 0.5$) of the surface. For heterogeneity of a surface in terms of patches it is, however, legitimate to regard the standard free energy of adsorption as being dependent on the patch being filled so that this quantity can vary with coverage. When there are interaction effects and the standard free energy of adsorption is estimated experimentally from adsorption data at various θ values and found to vary with θ, it is best to regard this quantity as an "apparent standard free energy of adsorption" analogous to a standard free energy of a chemical equilibrium calculated from concentration data rather than from equilibrium activities. In the original treatment (125), it was assumed that the standard free energy of adsorption varied with θ in the same way as the heat of the adsorption process.

The factor f is thus strictly a free-energy parameter although it is usually the *heat* of adsorption which is regarded as falling linearly with coverage, as $0.1 < \theta < 0.9$.   In some cases ΔG_θ^0 may appear constant with θ, yet its component enthalpy and entropy terms ΔH_θ^0 and ΔS_θ^0 may vary with θ in a compensating way.   Under such conditions, the Langmuir isotherm would apparently hold, but the conditions (varying ΔH_θ) would not strictly correspond to the Langmuir assumptions.   Temkin argued that if the parameter f were large enough, an *intermediate* range of values of P would exist where $l_0 P \gg 1$ and yet $l_0 P \exp(-f) \ll 1$ so that Equation 117 could limitingly have the simplified form

$$\theta = \frac{1}{f} \ln l_0 P \qquad (119)$$

i.e., θ is *logarithmic* in P at intermediate coverages.   The Langmuir isotherm, written logarithmically in P for comparison, would read (*cf.* Equation 114)

$$\ln \theta - \ln (1 - \theta) = \ln l_0 P$$

Hence θ varies more slowly with increasing P in the Temkin isotherm than in the Langmuir, the more so the larger the f value. Physically, this situation arises since, with increasing coverage, further adsorption beyond a given coverage becomes energetically relatively more difficult because $|\Delta G_\theta^0|$ is decreasing.   A comparative illustration is given in Fig. 13.   Generally at quite low $(\theta < 0.1)$ and high $(\theta > 0.9)$ coverage, Langmuir isotherm behaviour will always tend to be approached limitingly.

The model used by Temkin may not appear too realistic. However, there are several other models physically more realistic which can lead to the same linear dependence of ΔG_θ^0 on θ, and to an isotherm that is rather similar to that of Temkin.   The model of "induced heterogeneity" proposed by Boudart (127) has been applied by Conway and Gileadi (124,128) to electrochemical adsorption and leads to an isotherm similar to Temkin's, since the energy of adsorption varies as the surface potential change $\chi_\theta = 4\pi nm/\epsilon_s$, and n, the number of particles per square centimeter, is proportional to θ; m is the moment per particle arising in the chemisorption, and ϵ_s the dielectric constant of the surface layer. The surface potential is associated with a change of work function of the metal, and for electron transfer or electron withdrawal chemisorption, this effect will change the energy of adsorption by a

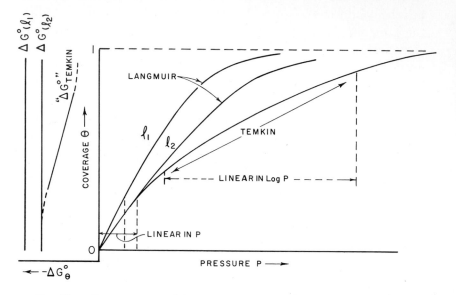

Fig. 13. Comparison of Langmuir and Temkin isotherms for relative coverage θ as a function of pressure P of adsorbate.

factor of about $0.5\chi_\theta$ (127). A related model of electronic interactions in the surface has been discussed by Temkin (129), who supposes that a two-dimensional surface "electron gas" takes part in the chemisorption process (cf. the magnetic and conductivity changes which occur at surfaces upon adsorption). The coverage-dependent heat of adsorption is related to changes of kinetic energy of electrons, viz.

$$- \Delta H_\theta = \frac{h^2 \sigma_m \theta}{4\pi M_e} \qquad (120)$$

where h is Planck's constant, M_e the mass of the electron and $\sigma_m\theta$ is the number of adsorbed atoms per square centimeter (σ_m being that for full coverage). Such effects would be communal, since the effect of any given adsorbed atom on the properties of the electron gas will be relayed reciprocally to all others and determine the variation of over-all energy of adsorption with θ.

5. ELECTROCHEMICAL ISOTHERMS FOR ION ADSORPTION

Empirical examination of electrochemical adsorption behaviour is possible by obtaining Γ_i data for adsorbed ions at electrodes from capacity or electrocapillary measurements, and evaluating corresponding θ quantities. Calculation of an apparent standard electrochemical free energy of adsorption $\Delta\bar{G}_\theta^0$ for various θ values (and corresponding solute activities) is then possible. If the $\Delta\bar{G}_\theta^0$ values are constant, then Langmuir behaviour is indicated (unless independent $\Delta\bar{H}_\theta^0$ and $\Delta\bar{S}_\theta^0$ terms compensate with changing θ—see p. 83); if they are not, it is possible to examine what kind of model would lead to the observed variation of $\Delta\bar{G}_\theta^0$ with θ. This approach has been made, for example, for electrochemical adsorption of organic ions (93,94). The electrostatic interaction potential is written for nearest-neighbour adsorbed univalent ions at an average distance apart r, as

$$u_{11} = \frac{e^2}{\epsilon_s r} - \frac{B}{\epsilon_0 r^6} \tag{121}$$

where B is the Van der Waals–London coefficient related to characteristic frequencies in the molecules (130), ϵ_0 is the electronic dielectric constant of the layer and ϵ_s is the static dielectric constant of the solvent at the electrode interface. The total energy U_{11} for a two-dimensional array of coordination number C.N. is $\frac{1}{2}(C.N.)u_{11}$. Up to moderate coverages, with $1/r = (\theta/A)^{1/2}$ and A the projected area of the adsorbed ions,

$$U_{11} = \tfrac{1}{2}(C.N.)u_{11}N_A = \frac{\tfrac{1}{2}N_A(C.N.)e^2\theta^{1/2}}{A^{1/2}\epsilon_s} \tag{122}$$

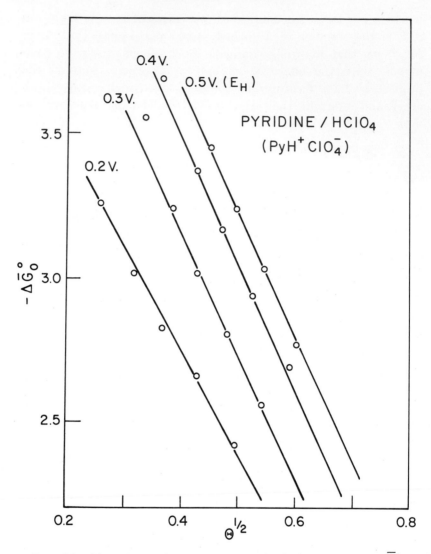

Fig. 14. Variation of apparent standard free energy $\Delta \bar{G}_\theta^0$ of adsorption of pyridinium perchlorate at mercury as a function of square root of coverage (ion-repulsion isotherm, Conway and Parry, in course of publication).

neglecting terms in θ^3, when θ does not exceed *ca.* 0.5. Relation 122 is observed experimentally with a number of specifically adsorbed organic cations (93,94). A typical plot for pyridinium perchlorate is shown in Fig. 14 for various electrode potentials. It may be argued (52) that image interactions should be taken into account in the latter interaction between adsorbed ions, as considered for oriented dipolar molecules by Conway and Barradas (94). In such a case, the potential energy U_{11} would then be given, to a first approximation, by (*cf.* Langmuir, 131)

$$U_{11} = (\text{C.N.})N_A \frac{2e^2}{\epsilon_s r_i} \theta^{3/2}[1 - 3\theta^2] \text{ per mole} \qquad (123)$$

which accounts for nearest-neighbour ion-ion repulsion and ion–ion-image attraction, for ions of radius r_i. However, it has been argued (52) that direct image interactions are negligible in specific adsorption, so it may be supposed that they are correspondingly of little importance for lateral interactions where the interionic distances are usually greater than the ion-image distance except near $\theta = 1$. This is supported by the $\theta^{1/2}$ relation in Fig. 14 (*cf.* 93). The image relation (Equation 123) would give a leading term in $\theta^{3/2}$, as for dipole-dipole interaction (94) (see p. 89), which does not seem to be observed for ion adsorption. For dipolar molecule adsorption, the dipole-image interaction energy is only some ten per cent of the total adsorption energy (94).

The procedures described above involve differentiation of electrocapillary data to obtain derivatives of the form $(\partial \gamma / \partial \mu_S)_{E_\pm, T}$ for a salt S giving $\Gamma_\pm$; the latter quantity can also be derived from analogous operations on capacity data. An alternative procedure (132) is to define a parameter

$$\xi = \gamma + q_M E \qquad (124)$$

in terms of surface tension γ and charge q_M, and relate ξ at constant q_M (rather than Γ determined at constant E) to μ_S by means of isotherms of various assumed forms expressed in terms of surface pressures Φ as a function of ionic concentration. For electrocapillary data obtained with an electrode reversible to the cation,

$$d\xi^+ = d(\gamma + q_M E_+) = -\Gamma_{A^-} d\mu_S \quad (q_M = \text{constant}) \quad (125)$$

where Γ_{A^-} is the surface excess of A^- which will be made up of a specific adsorption contribution Γ_{1,A^-} and a diffuse-layer contribution Γ_{2,A^-}, which can be calculated as discussed in Chapter 4. Integration of a plot of Γ_{2,A^-} *vs.* μ_S for given q_M may be carried out graphically, to give a quantity

$$\xi_2^+ = \int_{-\infty}^{\mu} \Gamma_{2,A^-} d\mu_S \qquad (126)$$

and this can be combined with ξ^+ to give

$$\xi^+ + \xi_2^+ - \xi_0^+ = -\int_{-\infty}^{\mu} \Gamma_{1,A^-} d\mu_S \quad (= -\Phi) \qquad (127)$$

where ξ_0^+ is the value of ξ^+ when $\mu_S \rightarrow -\infty$ (i.e. at infinite dilution) and can be evaluated for a given value of q_M (132). The integral in Equation 127 has the form of a surface pressure Φ. Values of ξ^+ can be obtained experimentally as $\gamma + q_M E_+$ for given q_M data, and hence Φ values can be obtained numerically. Test of fit to various possible isotherms is then made as follows. First, as a simple case, the Henry's law isotherm $\Phi = \Gamma_{1,A}-kT$ gives $\Gamma_{1,A^-} = \Phi/kT$, and from Equation 127, $d\Phi/d\mu_S = \Gamma_{1,A^-}$; therefore

$$\frac{d\Phi}{d\mu_S} = \frac{\Phi}{kT} \qquad (128)$$

or

$$d \ln \Phi = d \ln a_{\pm}^2 \qquad (129)$$

from the definition of μ_S for a symmetrical electrolyte S. Hence applicability of the isotherm can be tested by plotting $\ln \Phi$ *vs.* $\ln a_{\pm}^2$. For the case of adsorption of I^- ions at mercury, a square-root isotherm of the form

$$\frac{1}{\Gamma_{1,A^-}} = \frac{kT}{\Phi} \left[1 + \frac{B\Phi^{1/2}}{2} \right] \qquad (130)$$

fits the results satisfactorily. In this case, from the above isotherm,*

$$\frac{d\mu_S}{d\Phi} = \frac{1}{\Gamma_{1,A^-}} = \frac{kT}{\Phi}\left[1 + \frac{B\Phi^{1/2}}{2}\right] \qquad (131)$$

which upon integration gives

$$\ln a_{\pm}^2 = \ln \Phi + B\Phi^{1/2} \qquad (132)$$

This can be tested by plotting $\Phi^{1/2}$ vs. $\ln(a_{\pm}^2/\Phi)$; the relation is linear, indicating that the $\Phi^{1/2}$ isotherm is applicable. The $\Phi^{1/2}$ term originates from long-range ionic interactions as in Equation 122, where such forces are taken into account more explicitly. These results also indicate that the Langmuir isotherm is not obeyed for I^- adsorption, and hence that the specific adsorption terms in the Stern theory discussed above are inapplicable as written when chemisorption effects arise.

6. ELECTROCHEMICAL ISOTHERMS FOR NEUTRAL MOLECULES AT ELECTRODES

Following the procedure discussed in Section 3 (Equation 121), the dipole repulsion energy for molecules of moment m can be obtained for nearest-neighbour interactions as

$$u_{11} = \frac{m^2}{\epsilon_s r^3} - \frac{B}{\epsilon_0 r^6} \qquad (133)$$

or (cf. Equation 122)

$$U_{11} = \tfrac{1}{2}(\text{C.N.})N_A\left[\frac{m^2}{\epsilon_s}\frac{\theta^{3/2}}{A^{3/2}} - \frac{B}{\epsilon_0}\frac{\theta^3}{A^3}\right] \qquad (134)$$

Up to moderate coverages, the $\theta^{3/2}$ term is the leading one, and $\Delta\bar{G}_\theta^0$ for molecule adsorption should be a function of $\theta^{3/2}$. This was found by Conway and Barradas (94) for adsorption of pyridine derivatives at Hg, who also observed a sharp inflection of the relation between $\Delta\bar{G}_\theta^0$ vs. $\theta^{3/2}$ in two linear parts, the inflection depending on electrode potential (see Fig. 15). The break in the

---

* From Equation 127, which defines Φ.

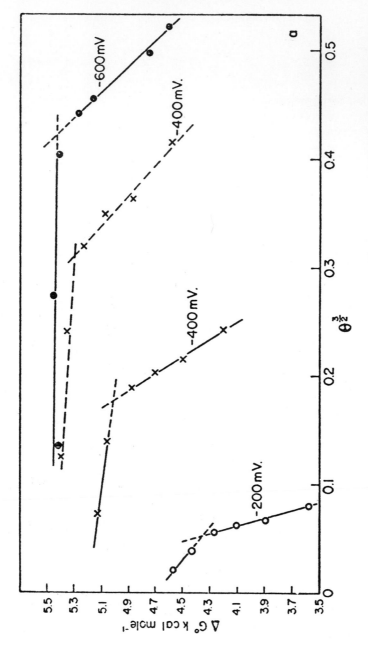

Fig. 15. Variation of apparent standard free energy $\Delta \bar{G}_\theta^0$ of adsorption of 2-chloropyridine in N KCl with the $\frac{3}{2}$ power of coverage θ (dipole-repulsion isotherm) for various electrode potentials (based on coverages calculated assuming two possible values of the maximum surface excess Γ_{max} ($\theta = 1$) for $\Gamma_{max} = 5.2 \times 10^{-10}$ or $\Gamma_{max} = 7.4 \times 10^{-10}$ mole cm.$^{-2}$ depending on orientation). (Conway and Barradas, 94.)

plots was attributed to onset of extensive orientation (see p. 73) in the electrode field (*cf.* 120). The slopes of the steep part of the $\Delta \bar{G}_\theta^0$ *vs.* $\theta^{3/2}$ relations for various molecules were proportional to m^2 as required by Equation 133 up to moderate coverages. The shifts of the p.z.c. plotted against Γ_A or $\ln C_A$ for substances A also showed corresponding inflections indicating a more rapid change of surface potential (onset of cooperative orientation at a critical coverage). At high coverages, the θ^3 term becomes significant and dipole depolarisation may become appreciable (see p. 19).

Tests of isotherms may also be made by reference to capacity data, and a double integration procedure similar to that described in Chapter 4 can be used (133). In investigating the adsorption behaviour, the electrical parameter to be held constant is preferably the surface charge rather than the potential, as was the case in the analysis for ion adsorption. Various capacity-potential relationships have been deduced by Parsons (123) for different isotherms, assuming that the free energy of adsorption depends on the *square* of the potential, i.e. when an electrostatic polarisation term such as that considered by Frumkin (121) and Butler (84) holds. When adsorption of strongly oriented dipoles of appreciable moments occurs, the principal field dependence of the free energy of adsorption will, however, tend to be a linear one (see p. 73) arising from the dipole-field interaction (Equation 93). The adsorption of aliphatic organic amines has been carefully studied by Lorenz and Möckel (134) by the capacity method. With aromatic amines and heterocyclic bases, specific effects associated with interaction of the π-orbitals with the anodic mercury surface arise (94,135,136) and compete with the orienting influence of the electrode field.

6
Electrochemical Kinetic Principles

1. BASIC FACTORS IN ION DISCHARGE

(i) Introduction and Definitions. Electrode reactions are heterogeneous processes in which charge transfer occurs. In so far as they are heterogeneous, their rates will be influenced by (a) the adsorption and hence the surface concentration of reactant ions at the interface; (b) the activation energy for the heterogeneous reaction at the surface, which will depend on the electrochemical nature of the reactants and the catalytic and adsorptive properties of the surface; (c) the presence of adsorbed intermediates and/or reaction products on the surface; and finally (d) the potential difference at the interface, which, amongst other factors, controls the rate of the charge-transfer reaction. The factor (d) is the principal one that will distinguish electrochemical reactions from other heterogeneously catalysed reactions at the solid-solution interface.

The rates of electrochemical reactions may be expressed in conventional terms such as *product moles cm.$^{-2}$ sec.$^{-1}$*, but usually it is more convenient to express the latter units in terms of the equivalent current passing. If the over-all reaction involves the passage of zF coulombs mole^{-1} of products cm.$^{-2}$, the electrochemical rate v in terms of current is simply zFv a. cm.$^{-2}$ For most simple electrode reactions, the number of electrons involved per molecule of product is unambiguous, but for more complex reactions the determination of coulombic yields may be necessary to give a satisfactory chemical account of the total current and charge passed. In organic electrode reactions, this is particularly important as a number of parallel electrochemical pathways are often involved. Even in the deposition of the base metals, e.g. Ni and Zn, apparent deviations from Faraday's laws (with respect to the metal deposition) are encountered which arise because of co-deposition of hydrogen at, and sometimes into, the metal electrode.

In terms of the usual general way of representing a reaction velocity, that of an electrochemical process will be given as

$$i = zFv = \left\{ \tau \frac{kT}{h} \exp\left[-\frac{\Delta \bar{G}^{0^{+}}}{RT} \right] \right\} zF(c_{\text{R}})_{s}(1 - \theta) \quad (135)$$

where the *rate constant* in terms of absolute rate theory (137) is given by the term in curly brackets; τ is the transmission co-efficient (taken as approximately unity, 137), k, T and h have their usual significance and $\Delta \bar{G}^{0^{+}}$ is an *electrochemical* standard free energy of activation analogous to a chemical free energy of activation $\Delta G^{0^{+}}$ for an ordinary chemical reaction; the terms at the end of Equation 135 may be regarded as stoichiometric quantities characteristic of the particular reaction and coverage conditions: zF is the number of coulombs involved (expressed in terms of Faradays) in the charge-transfer step of rate v, $(c_{\text{R}})_{s}$ the surface concentration of the reactant molecule or ion and $1 - \theta$ is a geometrical factor giving the specific fractional area available for discharge of further species on the surface, θ referring to the steady-state coverage of intermediates or products adsorbed on the surface when the rate is v. Usually θ will depend on v but will not generally include coverage by solvent molecules which normally cover initially more or less the whole surface of the electrode but are easily displaced by reaction products or intermediates. The quantity $(c_{\text{R}})_{s}$ must normally be expressed in terms of bulk concentrations $(c_R)_b$ by an isotherm which can be written

$$(c_R)_s = (c_R)_b \exp\left[-\frac{\Delta\bar{G}_R^0}{RT}\right] \qquad (136)$$

where $\Delta\bar{G}_R^0$ is the standard *electrochemical* free energy of adsorption of R and will be defined for appropriate standard states for R in the bulk and in the surface layer. Correspondingly $\Delta\bar{G}^{0\ddagger}$ must be defined for some similar standard state of activated complexes at the electrode surface.

(ii) The Quantities $\Delta\bar{G}_R^0$ and $\Delta\bar{G}^{0\ddagger}$. The $\Delta\bar{G}_R^0$ is relatively easily defined in terms of the treatment of the double-layer and adsorption given in Chapters 3, 4 and 5. If the reactant R is an ion, $\Delta\bar{G}_R^0$ will be of the form

(a) $\quad \Delta\bar{G}_R^0 = \Delta G_R^0 - zF\psi_1$, $\qquad$ or (b) $\quad \Delta\bar{G}_R^0 = \Delta G_R^0 - zF\psi_2$

$$(137)$$

depending on the plane at which the ions are electrochemically adsorbed. Usually if the ions are not specifically adsorbed, $\Delta G_R^0 = 0$ and $\Delta\bar{G}_R^0 = -zF\psi_1$ and ψ_1 can be evaluated from the theory of the diffuse double-layer given in Chapter 3 (Equations 26, 27 and 37). From the Stern equation, up to moderately low concentrations (0.1 M), it is possible to show that ψ_1 varies with ion concentration c_i as*

$$\psi_1 = \psi_1^0 + \frac{RT}{zF}\ln c_i \qquad (138)$$

where ψ_1^0 is a constant. This variation is important in discussions of the concentration dependence of electrochemical rates (138). The potential ψ_1 at the inner limit of the diffuse layer will depend on the rational electrode potential of the metal, ϕ_M, as well as the concentration c_i of the electrolyte ions. Numerical evaluation of ψ_1 may be made from the Stern equation (Equation 37) if the Helmholtz layer capacity is deduced from experimental data;

* For example, this is discussed by Frumkin (19).

values of ψ_1 have been tabulated by Conway and Bockris (57) as a function of ϕ_M and concentration (for HCl) and also by Russell (139). The potential ψ_1 increases, with the same sign, as ϕ_M increases and numerically decreases as c_i increases (Equation 138). If super-equivalent adsorption of one ion occurs by specific adsorption, then the diffuse double-layer charge will not necessarily be opposite in sign to that of the metal surface and ψ_1 cannot be calculated in a simple way except from knowledge of the components of charge in the diffuse layer. When specific adsorption occurs, not only is ψ_2 different from ψ_1 corresponding to a difference of planes at which the ions are adsorbed, but a true chemical interaction with the surface may arise which depends on ϕ_M, e.g. through changes of electron availability at the surface (e.g., see refs. 122 and 54).

If the reactant is a neutral molecule, $\Delta \bar{G}_R^0$ may be more difficult to express in an explicit manner, but the principles given in Chapter 5 will apply.

The quantity $\Delta \bar{G}^{0\ddagger}$, which is involved in the electrochemical rate constant will include (a) any *chemical* effects associated with "activation" of the reacting particle, e.g. stretching of bonds and changes of the configuration of the solvation envelope of the reacting ion, together with (b) changes of electrical energy experienced by the particle in its progress along the reaction coordinate which is usually regarded as normal to the electrode surface. Formally, the electrochemical free energy of activation may be derived by equating the electrochemical potentials (*cf.* Equation 3) of initial reactants and activated complexes since these species are normally regarded (137) as in quasi-equilibrium.* Thus, if

---

* For an irreversible process with $\tau = 1$, the assumption of equilibrium (137) here is actually fictitious. However, this device allows the calculation of the rates of formation and decomposition of activated complexes from the reactants as though equilibrium were involved. Actually, even in an over-all equilibrium between an initial and a final state, the activated complexes which are formed from products and those formed from the reactants are different in the sense that they are vibrationally "polarised" and hence are predisposed to decompose in a particular direction to the respective entities on each side of the equilibrium, if τ is taken as unity.

the reactants are an ion i and z electrons,

$$\bar{\mu}_i + z\bar{\mu}_e = \bar{\mu}^{\ddagger} + z\bar{\mu}_e \tag{139}$$

or

$$\mu_i + zF\psi_1 = \mu_i^{\ddagger} + zF\phi^{\ddagger} \tag{140}$$

if the electrons are not regarded as participating in a classical way in the activated complex, i.e., the activated complex is formed by some bond stretching as in discharge of H^+ from H_3O^+ ions, or by some change of solvation shell configuration as in ionic redox reactions (140,141), or possibly in metal deposition (140), and the electron transfer occurs by tunneling to the activated complex when the latter is in a favourable molecular configuration.

From Equation 140, we may write

$$\mu_i^{\ddagger} - \mu_i = -zF(\phi^{\ddagger} - \psi_1) \tag{141}$$

or, approximately,

$$\mu_i^{0\ddagger} - \mu_i^0 + RT \ln \frac{c^{\ddagger}}{c_i} = -zF(\phi^{\ddagger} - \psi_1) \tag{142}$$

where the c terms are the concentrations of activated complex ($\ddagger$) and initial reactant (i), respectively.

By defining a standard $\Delta G^{0\ddagger}$ quantity as

$$\Delta G^{0\ddagger} \equiv \Delta\mu^{0\ddagger} = \mu_i^{0\ddagger} - \mu_i^0$$

Equation 142 leads to

$$\frac{c^{\ddagger}}{c_i} = \exp\left[\frac{-\Delta\mu^{0\ddagger}}{RT}\right] \exp\left[\frac{-zF(\phi^{\ddagger} - \psi_1)}{RT}\right] \tag{143}$$

Then with $\phi^{\ddagger} - \psi_1$ written as some fraction β of $\phi_M - \psi_1$, where β is a symmetry factor,

$$c^{\ddagger} = c_i \exp\left[\frac{-\Delta\mu^{0\ddagger}}{RT}\right] \exp\left[\frac{-zF\beta(\phi_M - \psi_1)}{RT}\right] \tag{144}$$

As in absolute rate theory for homogeneous reactions, the rate will be proportional to $c^{\ddagger}$ and $\Delta\mu^{0\ddagger} + zF\beta(\phi_M - \psi_1)$ will be a quantity having the significance of a standard electrochemical free energy of activation.

An alternative representation of electrical effects on charge transfer rates is usually given by workers concerned with ion-transfer controlled oxide film growth processes (142). Here the *field* is regarded as the significant electrical quantity, and the charged particle is regarded as passing down the field $\mathscr{E}$ by a length $\delta^{\ddagger}$ from the initial to the activated state with a gain of energy $\mathscr{E}\delta^{\ddagger}zF$ where $\delta^{\ddagger}$ is some fraction γ of the total transfer distance δ between the initial and final stages in the process. Since γ is usually about 0.5, $\delta^{\ddagger}$ is sometimes called the "half-jump distance." In terms of Equation 143, if the potential falls uniformly from M to the plane 1, the field is given by

$$\mathscr{E} = \frac{\phi^{\ddagger} - \psi_1}{\delta^{\ddagger}} = \frac{\phi_M - \psi_1}{\delta}$$

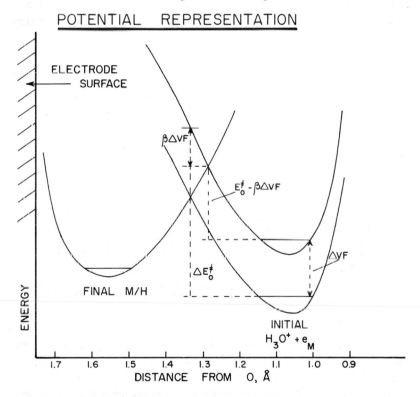

POTENTIAL   REPRESENTATION

Fig. 16. "Potential representation" of effects of applied potential on energy of activation of a charge-transfer process.

or

$$\phi^{\ddagger} - \psi_1 = \frac{\delta^{\ddagger}}{\delta} (\phi_M - \psi_1) = \gamma(\phi_M - \psi_1) \qquad (145)$$

Comparison of Equations 144 and 145 indicates that β and γ have the same significance; however, comparison of potential energy diagram representations indicates that this is not exactly the case. In Fig. 16, the effect of applied potential is shown according to the representation of Horiuti and Polanyi (20) and Butler (21), in which the effect of potential is to shift up the whole initial-state curve ($H_3O^+ + e_M$) by an amount $\Delta\phi_M zF$ without change of its shape, with a consequent change of activation energy by $\beta\Delta\phi_M zF$, where β is determined by the relative slopes m_1 and m_2 of the curves at the point of intersection, as shown in Fig. 17. It may

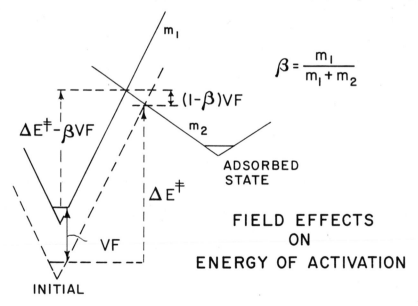

Fig. 17. Schematic representation of the significance of the symmetry factor β in terms of relative slopes of potential-energy profiles for reactant and product species (energy of initial state is a function of potential—for convenience of representation, the potential operative is written as V in this figure but has the quantitative significance of $z\Delta\phi_M$ as in the discussion on this page).

be deduced geometrically that

$$\beta = \frac{m_1}{m_1 + m_2} \tag{146}$$

Initial and final state curves which cross symmetrically give $\beta = 0.5$, i.e., $|m_1| = |m_2|$.

This treatment assumes implicitly that the behaviour of the reactant ion is unaffected by the field, and the electrons in the metal are made relatively more available by an energy $\Delta\phi_M zF$. If the field representation is used, e.g. as in the case of ionic migration in films and in field-ionisation theory (39), the field must be regarded as influencing the energy of the transferred particle throughout its activation and transfer displacement, e.g., as shown in Fig. 18 for discharge of H^+ out of the H_3O^+ ion (21,143, 144,145). The activation energy is changed by some fraction $\delta^{\ddagger}/\delta$ of the total energy change suffered by a charge zF passing down field $\mathcal{E}$ across a total distance δ. However, even if the curves are symmetrical, $\delta^{\ddagger}/\delta$ is not quite 0.5 and hence not quite equal to the β given by Equation 146, as is seen from Fig. 18. This effect arises since the crossing point, being lowered, also falls nearer to the final state, i.e. $\beta > 0.5$. The field representation is satisfactory for ion transfer processes that occur without neutralisation,* e.g. migration in oxides, since the ion-field interaction energy continues into the final-state curve (e.g., see ref.142). It also appears to be the better representation for H^+-ion discharge where the H^+—O bond in H_3O^+ is presumably stretched in the activation step. The formulation of Horiuti and Polanyi (20) and Butler (21) is probably most suitable for ionic redox reactions (146) where the formal concept of "ion transfer" is not clearly involved, and the rate is best regarded as being modified by the effect of electrode potential on the activation energy through an effect only on the electron energy levels as considered by Gurney (18).

The formal discussion of β resulting in Equations 143 and 144 is more consistent with the field representation than that in Fig.

* The same representation applies to field-assisted diffusion, e.g. in conductance by protons and other ions.

FIELD   REPRESENTATION

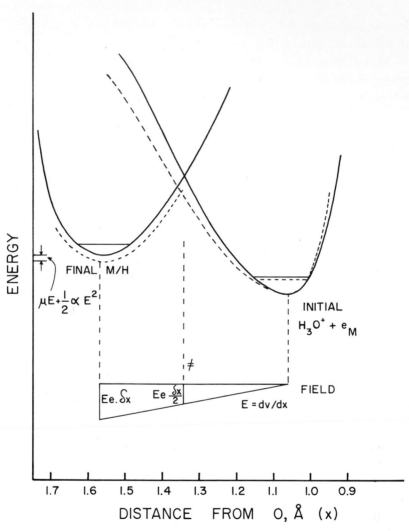

Fig. 18. "Field representation" of effects of applied potential on energy of activation of a charge-transfer process (e.g. particularly for proton transfer in the h.e.r.).

16, since β gives the fraction of the total double-layer p.d., $\phi_M - \psi_1$, operating between the activated and initial states. Symmetrical curves which would give $\beta = 0.5$ from Equation 146 would not give quite the same result on the basis of field effects unless at the same time $\delta^{\ddagger} = 0.5\delta$ which is not a necessary condition for the curves to have the same relative slopes at the region of intersection. Similarly, γ could be 0.5 ($= \delta^{\ddagger}/\delta$) without the two curves being symmetrical. The several approaches to electrical effects in charge-transfer kinetics will normally predict β as having a value near 0.5, but it is clear that, in detail, the various representations will not necessarily give identical results.

2. OVER-ALL KINETIC RATE EQUATION

(i) Formulation. From the principles discussed above, it is now possible to write the rate equation for an ion-neutralisation step* from Equations 135, 136, 137 and 144 as

$$i = \tau \frac{kTzF}{h} c_i \exp\left[-\frac{zF\psi_1}{RT}\right](1 - \theta)$$

$$\times \exp\left[-\frac{\Delta G^{0\ddagger}}{RT}\right]\exp\left[-\frac{\beta(\phi_M - \psi_1)zF}{RT}\right] \quad (147)$$

From this equation,† it is important to note that (a) the rate i in terms of current density at a given value of ϕ_M will depend on concentration c_i of ions through the term c_i and the two terms in ψ_1 (Equation 138); (b) the value of i will depend exponentially on ϕ_M at constant ψ_1. In practice, ψ_1 will depend to some extent (58)

* A similar result will follow for a molecule ionisation step such as $H_2O + M + e > MH + OH^-$. General formulations are given in references 117, 148, 149, 150 and 151, wherein double-layer effects are also examined.

† If the discharge step corresponds to part of a sequence of consecutive reactions in an electrochemical process and must occur ν times in order to produce the appropriate number of gram atoms or radicals for formation of one mole of products, then it is appropriate to include the stoichiometric number, ν, in Equation 147. The term ν will appear in place of z as Z/ν if Z is the *total* number of electrons involved in one act of the *over-all* reaction; z is the number of electrons involved in the discharge step. Detailed discussion of the significance of ν is given in refs. 151, 152 and 153, and applications have been made to the h.e.r. (154); see Chapter 8.

on ϕ_M but this effect is diminished for conditions of high ionic concentration (ψ_1 small) and high ϕ_M, at which ψ_1 varies relatively little with ϕ_M. It is convenient to replace ϕ_M by the quantity $\phi_{R,M} + \eta$, where $\phi_{R,M}$ is the rational potential of the electrode when the electrode process is behaving reversibly, and η is defined as the *overpotential*, i.e. the extra potential beyond the reversible value required to drive the electrode process at the net rate i faster than that for the forward direction of the process at the reversible potential. Then under conditions of constant c_i, ψ_1 and temperature, $\partial\eta/\partial(\ln i) = -RT/\beta zF = -b$, or

$$\eta = a - b \ln i \qquad (148)$$

the so-called Tafel equation; a is the value of η when i is 1 a. cm.$^{-2}$ and b is the Tafel slope taking into account the sign of z for cation or anion discharge, since η will formally be negative or positive for cathodic and anodic reactions, respectively.

(ii) **Concentration Dependence of Rate of a Discharge Step.** The dependence of i, expressed in terms of η from Equation 147, is

$$i = k_1 c_i \exp\left[-\frac{zF\psi_1}{RT}\right] \exp\left[-\frac{\beta(\phi_{R,M} + \eta - \psi_1)zF}{RT}\right] \qquad (149)$$

where other constant terms (including for convenience $1 - \theta$) have been included in k_1. The reversible potential $\phi_{R,M}$ will depend on c_i according to

$$\phi_{R,M} = \phi^0_{R,M} + \frac{RT}{zF} \ln \gamma_i c_i \doteqdot \phi^0_{R,M} + \frac{RT}{zF} \ln c_i \qquad (150)$$

where $\phi^0_{R,M}$ is a standard reversible potential on the rational scale and γ_i is a hypothetical single ion activity coefficient (in practice, the reversible potential will be expressed in terms of a *mean* ionic activity). It is seen that effects connected with the electrostatic adsorption of ions in the double-layer enter into the kinetics and, as in any heterogeneous reaction, the reactant adsorption isotherm must be considered. Recognition of the importance of double-layer effects in electrode kinetics was first made quantitatively by Frumkin in 1933 (19). The double-layer effects enter through the terms in ψ_1 and $\beta\psi_1$ in Equation 149.   If the reactant ions are specifically adsorbed, the ion adsorption term would involve the electrochemical adsorption energy given by (b) of Equation 137, and the term in $\beta\psi_1$ in the second exponential in Equation 149 would be replaced by $\beta\psi_2$.   Also strictly the rational scale of potentials on which $\phi_{R,M}$ is measured would then change with c_i, but $\phi_{R,M}$ could still be measured on a p.z.c. scale unaffected by specific adsorption effects if appropriate corrections are made.   Introducing Equation 138 for ψ_1 and Equation 150 for $\phi_{R,M}$ as $f(c_i)$ gives, from Equation 149 taken logarithmically term by term,

$$\ln i = k'_1 + \ln c_i - \ln c_i - \beta \ln c_i - \beta\eta \, \frac{zF}{RT} + \beta \ln c_i \quad (151)$$

where k'_1 is a new combined constant now involving terms in ψ_1^0 and $\phi_{R,M}^0$.   The result, using Equation 138, will be valid for dilute solutions in the absence of specific adsorption, and under these conditions the term $c_i \exp\left[-zF\psi_1/RT\right]$ will always be independent of c_i except in the presence of excess of other non-reacting ions.   Under the latter conditions, ψ_1 will be determined mainly by the concentration of the added "inert" ions rather than by c_i.   Similarly, the term $\beta \ln c_i$ from ϕ_M^0 cancels with that from ψ_1, so that the rate i in Equation 151 is *independent* of reactant ion concentration c_i.

In the presence of excess salt $[\psi_1 \neq f(c_i)]$, none of the terms in $\ln c_i$ and $\beta \ln c_i$ which arise from ψ_1 will appear in Equation 151, so that

$$\ln i = k'_1 + \ln c_i - \beta \ln c_i - \beta\eta \, \frac{zF}{RT} \quad (152)$$

The following characteristic derivatives may be then summarised:

$$\left[\frac{\partial(\ln i)}{\partial(\ln c_i)}\right]_\eta = 0; \qquad \left[\frac{\partial(\ln i)}{\partial(\ln c_i)}\right]_{\psi_1,\eta} = 1 - \beta$$

$$\left[\frac{\partial(\ln i)}{\partial(\ln c_i)}\right]_{\psi_1,\phi_M} = 1; \qquad \left[\frac{\partial(\ln i)}{\partial\eta}\right]_{c_i,\psi_1} = -\beta \, \frac{zF}{RT} \quad (153)$$

The derivative at constant ψ_1 and electrode potential ϕ_M is of special interest since this gives what may be termed the chemically significant reaction order, i.e., it gives the dependence of i on c_i in the absence of complicating double-layer ion distribution effects. This derivative will not necessarily be identical with the molecularity of the surface reaction particularly for cases of consecutive reactions involving adsorbed intermediates.

Electrochemical reaction orders for a number of processes have recently been discussed by Vetter (147) and Conway and Salomon (148), and the derivative $[\partial(\ln i)/\partial(\ln c_i)]_{\psi_i,\eta}$ has frequently been discussed as a diagnostic criterion of the rate-determining step in hydrogen evolution mechanisms. The derivative for the reciprocal of the Tafel slope, $-\beta z F/RT$, is written for constant c_i and ψ_1 conditions. The latter specification is necessary, though not always appreciated, since ψ_1 is moderately constant with ϕ_M only if the latter is fairly large and/or if the ionic strength is high. However, near the p.z.c. ψ_1 can vary significantly with η or ϕ_M and lead to changes of Tafel slope with η (67,149). If the electrode process involves reduction of anions e.g. $S_2O_8^{--}$ or polyvalent cations, the effect of variation of ψ_1 with η is particularly marked and leads to inflected or to S-shaped current-voltage curves (150). Here the anions are repelled from the surface at increasing cathodic potentials since the sign of the argument of the first exponential in Equation 147 is negative (both z and ψ_1 are negative); for normal cation reduction $\Delta \bar{G}_R^0$ will be negative and the argument in Equation 136 positive. Experimentally (96,150), rather more marked effects are observed than can be accounted for theoretically, and the rate of transfer of ions having the same sign of charge as that of the electrode through the double-layer to the electrode surface is rather higher than expected theoretically. It has been suggested by Frumkin (96) that this anomaly can be explained if allowance is made for specific ion-pair interaction between the reacting anions and the electrostatically adsorbed cations in the double-layer, or alternatively that the anions which react are not the typical bulk species but ion pairs of smaller charge, e.g. $M^+S_2O_8^{--}$, than that of the bulk species. The existence of such species in the double-layer may be enhanced by the lower local dielectric constant there (49,71,73); however, dissociation-field effects in the high field of the double-layer would tend to give effects in the opposite direction.

(iii) **Net Currents and Exchange Currents.** When the electrode potential reaches values near the reversible potential (i.e. $\eta \to 0$) for the over-all electrode process occurring, the back reaction can become kinetically significant and the *net* (say, cathodic) measured current density i_c is then the difference of the actual true partial cathodic and anodic current densities $\overrightarrow{i_c}$ and $\overleftarrow{i_a}$, respectively.   That is

$$i_c = \overrightarrow{i_c} - \overleftarrow{i_a} \tag{154}$$

The rate of the back reaction becomes significant when $\beta z F' \eta \approx RT$ or less.*   In practice, such conditions are not of great importance except for electrodes of high reversibility such as can be realised in some active fuel-cell systems.   When $\eta = 0$ and the electrode is then behaving reversibly, $\overrightarrow{i_c} = \overleftarrow{i_a}$ since the net current $i_c = 0$.   The partial current densities $\overrightarrow{i_c}$ and i_a are then the equal currents passing reversibly in both anodic and cathodic directions per square centimeter, and this quantity is referred to as the *exchange current density* i_0 for the electrode process.   For processes involving consecutive steps, i_0 is also the reversible rate of each of them at equilibrium, but the magnitude of i_0 will be determined by the step with the smallest electrochemical rate constant.   If alternative parallel pathways are available for an electrochemical reaction at equilibrium, the i_0 value will be largely characterised by the kinetics of the *most* reversible path with the largest rate constant.

Exchange currents can normally be obtained by extrapolation of a plot of $\ln i$ *vs.* the overpotential η to $\eta = 0$.   The value of $\ln i_0$ thus obtained will be characteristic of the electrode process

* η then becomes limitingly linear in i_c; when $\beta = 0.5$, the η-i_c relation can be written in a more general form as a hyperbolic sine function of $zF\eta/2RT$ which is applicable at all values of η.

kinetics over the range of potentials actually studied. It may or may not refer to the actual exchange current passing when $\eta = 0$, for several reasons: (a) a change of mechanism may occur between the lowest η values measured and $\eta = 0$; (b) the coverage factor in the kinetic rate expression may vary with potential and be different at $\eta = 0$ from that over the range of measured η values; (c) the Tafel slope may change with diminishing η values on account of double-layer effects, particularly if the range of potentials includes the p.z.c. or if, as $\eta \to 0$, the p.z.c. is approached as may be the case, for example, for the hydrogen evolution reaction at platinum. In some cases, the value of i_0 may be obtained directly from measurements of rates of isotope exchange, e.g. with some amalgam reactions (155). This can provide a useful check on the validity of data obtained by other methods, e.g. from the ohmic component of the a.c. impedance associated with electrodeposition reactions, after correction for diffusional resistive effects (156).

3. HEATS OF ACTIVATION AND FREQUENCY FACTORS

The kinetics of chemical reactions are often characterised by measurements of heats of activation and deduction of frequency factors A in the Arrhenius rate equation from

$$k = Ae^{-\Delta H^{\ddagger}/RT}$$

where k is the rate constant. Heats of activation in electrochemical reactions have often been measured (for data see ref. 157), but their significance is obscured by the complication that they must be deduced from measurements of current densities (e.g. i_0) at constant electrode potential referred to a reversible reference electrode in the system. As the temperature is varied, the absolute value of the metal-solution p.d. of this reference electrode will vary in an experimentally undeterminable manner. For example, if the hydrogen reversible electrode is used, its standard value of potential is arbitrarily zero at all temperatures, but it will in fact have a finite temperature coefficient of e.m.f. associated with the standard entropy change in the *half-cell* reaction

$$H_3O^+ + e \rightarrow H_2O + \tfrac{1}{2}H_2 \qquad (155)$$

If the reference electrode is maintained outside the part of the cell where the temperature of the test electrode is varied, an unknown electrolytic thermal junction potential (158) will be included in the measured e.m.f. Hence a true heat of activation at constant electrode potential cannot be determined, only a value at constant overpotential referred to the (temperature-dependent) reversible potential of the reaction being studied.

The relationship between the true and experimentally accessible apparent heat of activation at constant η may be considered as follows and was first examined by Temkin (159). By extracting concentration terms, etc., from Equation 147, the electrochemical *rate constant* $\bar{k}$ (*cf.* Equation 135) for an ion neutralisation process at a given ionic concentration is

$$\bar{k} = \tau \frac{kT}{h} \exp\left[-\frac{\Delta G^{0\ddagger}}{RT}\right] \exp\left[-\frac{\beta \phi_M zF}{RT}\right] \qquad (156)$$

where double-layer effects can be included in other constants in the expression for the corresponding rate. Equation 156 can be expressed in terms of $\Delta H^{0\ddagger}$, $\Delta S^{0\ddagger}$ and $\phi_{R,M}$, the reversible potential for the process concerned, by

$$\bar{k} = \frac{kT}{h} \tau \exp\left[\frac{\Delta S^{0\ddagger}}{R}\right] \exp\left[-\frac{\Delta H^{0\ddagger}}{RT}\right] \exp\left[-\frac{\beta(\phi_{R,M} + \eta)zF}{RT}\right]$$

$$(157)$$

Noting that $\phi_{R,M}$ may be expressed in terms of $\phi_{R,M}^0$ and hence as $-\Delta G^0/zF$, where ΔG^0 is the standard free energy for the half-cell reaction involved when the process is reversible, $d(\ln \bar{k})/d(1/T)$ taken at $\eta = 0$ $(\vec{i} = i_0)$ will give a quantity

$$-\frac{\Delta H^{0\ddagger}}{R} - \frac{zF\beta}{RT}\frac{\partial(\phi_{R,M}^0)}{\partial(1/T)} - \frac{zF\beta}{R}\phi_{R,M}^0$$

or

$$-\frac{\Delta H^{0\ddagger}}{R} + \frac{\beta T \Delta S^0}{R} + \frac{\beta \Delta G^0}{R}$$

neglecting the linear term in T in kT/h and assuming $\Delta S^{0\ddagger}$ is, to a first approximation, independent of T.   Then

$$\frac{\partial(\ln \bar{k})}{\partial(1/T)} = -\frac{\Delta H^{0\ddagger}}{R} + \frac{\beta}{R}\Delta H^0 = -\frac{1}{R}(\Delta H^{0\ddagger} - \beta\,\Delta H^0)$$

$$(158)$$

if ΔS^0 is independent of T.   Hence, if double-layer distribution effects and the $1 - \theta$ term are regarded as independent of temperature, then $\partial(\ln i_0)/\partial(1/T)$, which corresponds to $[\partial(\ln \bar{k})/\partial(1/T)]_{\eta=0}$, will give an *apparent* heat of activation*

$$\Delta W^{0\ddagger} = \Delta H^{0\ddagger} - \beta\,\Delta H^0 \qquad (159)$$

$\Delta H^{0\ddagger}$ can only be estimated from $\Delta W^{0\ddagger}$ by a non-thermodynamic calculation of ΔH^0 (β will be known from the Tafel slope), e.g., from the cycle:

$$M^{z+}_{(g)} + ze_{(g)} \xrightarrow{-I_{M,z+}} M_{(g)}$$

$$-\Delta H^0_{S,M^{z+}} \uparrow \qquad \uparrow z\Phi_e \qquad \downarrow -\Delta H_{\mathrm{sub}}$$

$$M^{z+}_{(S)} + ze_{(M)} \xrightarrow[\Delta H^0]{} M$$

where

$$\Delta H^0 = -\Delta H^0_{S,M^{z+}} + z\Phi_e - I_{M,z+} - \Delta H_{\mathrm{sub}} \qquad (160)$$

and $\Delta H^0_{S,M^{z+}}$ is the heat of solvation of the M^{z+} ion, $I_{M,z+}$ the ionisation energy of M to M^{z+}, ΔH_{sub} the heat of sublimation of M and Φ_e the electron work function of M.   Similar cycles can be written for other processes, e.g. the reaction 155.   Values of $\Delta H^0_{S,M^{z+}}$ and Φ_e are not known to better than 5–10 kcal. g. mole^{-1} (160), so that $\Delta H^{0\ddagger}$ could not be calculated very precisely from the measured $\Delta W^{0\ddagger}$.   Since $\Delta H^{0\ddagger}$ is not knowable, the true frequency factor $e(kT/h)\exp[\Delta S^{0\ddagger}/R]$ (137) in Equation 157 cannot be obtained from a measured i_0 or $\bar{k}$ value together with

---

* This is the result obtained by Temkin (159), but here the deduction is made in a simpler and more direct manner for conditions at the reversible potential.   The sign of the term in $\beta\Delta H^0$ in Equation 159 differs from that given by Temkin, who considered the reverse of reaction 155.   In practice, β is also usually a function of temperature, so that $\Delta W^{0\ddagger}$ will also contain a term depending on $d\beta/d(1/T)$.

$\Delta H^{0\ddagger}$, since only $\Delta W^{0\ddagger}$ is experimentally accessible. However, for the same over-all reaction (e.g. the hydrogen evolution reaction proceeding at different metals) or for isotopically analogous reactions (e.g. the "h.e.r." with H or D entities) proceeding at the same metal, the *differences* of true activation energies and the *ratio* of true frequency factors can be deduced and are, for example, useful in indicating different mechanisms for a given reaction at a series of metals (161) or for testing whether tunneling is significant in H^+, D^+ transfer steps (162). In considering kinetics of reactions involving H- and D-containing species, allowance must also be made for the significant difference of the reversible potentials for the isotopically analogous reactions.

Other factors which will lead to a difference between the measured apparent energy of activation and the kinetically significant quantity $\Delta H^{0\ddagger}$ are the temperature dependence of adsorption potentials ψ_1 or ψ_2 associated with the double-layer (163) and any variation of the $1 - \theta$ term with temperature which could be significant unless $\theta \ll 1$.

4.   TREATMENT FOR CONSECUTIVE AND ALTERNATIVE PROCESSES

(i) Methods of Approach. Most electrochemical reactions, except perhaps one-electron ionic redox steps, proceed by at least two consecutive steps, and in some cases alternative pathways in a given over-all reaction must also be considered as in the h.e.r. and o.e.r. (oxygen evolution reaction). Even electrolytic deposition of univalent metal ions, e.g. Ag^+, can proceed by consecutive ion discharge and lattice-building steps involving "adions" (156,164). As in consecutive chemical reactions, the kinetics for constant-current conditions may be examined in terms of either of two approaches: (a) *the steady-state method*, in which the rate of change of concentration of intermediates with time is equated to zero; or (b) the *quasi-equilibrium hypothesis*, in which it is supposed that all steps prior to the rate-determining one in the reaction sequence are almost in equilibrium, i.e., the rate constant of the rate-controlling step is, say, at least ten times smaller than that of all other antecedent steps in *both* directions. The steady-state method is, in general, to be preferred, but usually it will lead to cumbersome expressions for the rate of the reaction, and explicit results suitable for deduction of kinetic criteria diagnostic of rate-determining mechanisms can usually be obtained only by assuming that certain rate constants are negligible with respect to others. The results are then equivalent in most cases to those obtained directly by using the quasi-equilibrium hypothesis. Generally the aims of the kinetic calculation for consecutive reactions are the deduction of (a) Tafel slopes for consecutive steps and (b) reaction orders or equivalent derivatives, e.g. as in (148,154).

In consecutive reactions, it is always the step with the smallest rate constant (often referred to erroneously as the "slow" step; all steps in the steady state have of course the same velocity) that is rate-determining. In alternative pathways, it is the path which proceeds with the greatest velocity that characterises the kinetics. Since the electrochemical rate constants of various steps depend on potential, a step which is rate-controlling at one potential may not be the kinetically limiting step at another potential. For two consecutive steps, I and II, with Tafel slopes b_1 and b_2 ($b_2 > b_1$), the current-potential relation will be as in Fig. 19a where at high potentials the process II with the smaller electrochemical rate constant (larger Tafel slope) is rate-controlling, while at lower potentials step I is rate-controlling. This change of rate-controlling mechanism arises because the electrochemical rate constant of process I in this example changes more rapidly with potential by the factor $\exp\left[-\eta/b_1\right]$ than does process II, which can change only by the factor $\exp\left[-\eta/b_2\right]$. Thus, for a given change of overpotential η, a smaller change of electrochemical rate constant will arise for process II than that for I for the same change of η, b_2 being supposed greater than b_1. Conversely, for alternative processes I and II, the faster character-ises the kinetics and the current-potential relation will be as shown in Fig. 19b. At a critical potential, the two processes will have comparable rates, and a smooth inflection in the ln i *vs.* η

CHANGES OF MECHANISM

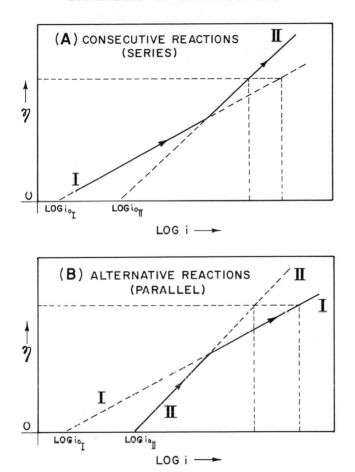

Fig. 19. Current-potential relation for consecutive and alternative electrode processes with exchange currents $i_{0,\mathrm{I}}$ and $i_{0,\mathrm{II}}$ and Tafel slopes b_1 and b_2. In (A), reaction I is slower than II, but its rate is more potential-dependent than that of II. II becomes rate-determining at high potentials even though $i_{0,\mathrm{II}} > i_{0,\mathrm{I}}$. In (B), if I and II are alternative, I passes more current than II even though $i_{0,\mathrm{I}} < i_{0,\mathrm{II}}$. (After Parsons, 151; Conway, 161.)

relations will arise over a small potential range. Examples of both types of behaviour discussed above arise in the electro-chemistry of anodic reactions at the nickel oxide electrode studied by Conway and Bourgault (165), and in the h.e.r. at silver, platinum and palladium-gold alloys.

(ii) **Steady-State Method.** Here it will be best to consider a specific case, e.g. the h.e.r. proceeding by the H atom–H^+ ion desorption mechanism:

$$H_3O^+ + e + M \rightleftarrows MH + H_2O \qquad\qquad I, -I$$

$$MH + H_3O^+ + e \rightarrow H_2 + H_2O \qquad\qquad II$$

In the state of steady current, the surface concentration of adsorbed H will be constant, and this condition may be written in terms of the velocities v of the indicated steps

$$\frac{d\theta_H}{dt} = 0 = v_1 - v_{-1} - v_2 \qquad\qquad (161)$$

Using abbreviated representation for the velocities v_1, v_{-1} and v_2 of the steps involved, but basing the expressions on Equation 149 with double-layer effects regarded as constant, we have

$$v_1 = k_1 c_{H^+}(1 - \theta_H)e^{-\beta\eta F/RT} \qquad\qquad (162a)$$

$$v_{-1} = k_{-1}\theta_H e^{(1-\beta)\eta F/RT} \qquad\qquad (162b)$$

$$v_2 = k_2\theta_H c_{H^+}e^{-\beta\eta F/RT} \qquad\qquad (162c)$$

where c_{H^+} is the concentration of hydrogen ions in solution. Applying the condition 161, and assuming β to be the same for I and II,

$$0 = k_1 c_{H^+}(1 - \theta_H)e^{-\beta\eta F/RT} - k_{-1}\theta_H e^{(1-\beta)\eta F/RT}$$
$$- k_2\theta_H c_{H^+}e^{-\beta\eta F/RT} \qquad (163)$$

If $\beta = \frac{1}{2}$, then, denoting $2RT/F$ as b, we have

$$\theta_H = \frac{k_1 c_{H^+}e^{-\eta/b}}{k_1 c_{H^+}e^{-\eta/b} + k_{-1}e^{\eta/b} + k_2 c_{H^+}e^{-\eta/b}} \qquad (164)$$

and the velocity of II, if rate-determining, will be given by Equation 162c with θ from Equation 164. The general expression 164 for θ will not lead to any simple explicit relation for v_2 as $f(\eta)$. However, if two alternative limiting conditions are applied, explicit results follow. Thus (a) if II is rate-controlling, $k_{-1}e^{\eta/b} \gg k_1 c_{H^+} e^{-\eta/b}$ and k_2 is small, so that θ_H can be expressed by $(k_1/k_{-1})c_{H^+}e^{-2\eta/b}$, i.e.

$$v_2 = k_2 K_1 c_{H^+}^2 e^{-\eta F/RT} e^{-\eta F/2RT} \qquad (165)$$

where $K_1 (= k_1/k_{-1})$ is the quasi-equilibrium constant for step I and $\beta = 0.5$. Since the current i_2 passing for mechanism II is proportional to v_2, the Tafel slope is given by

$$\left[\frac{\partial \eta}{\partial (\ln i_2)} \right]_{c_{H^+}} = -\frac{2RT}{3F} \qquad (166)$$

If β had been retained without the numerical substitution $\beta = 0.5$, the result for the Tafel slope would have been $-RT/(1 + \beta)F$. It is seen that the assumption $k_{-1}e^{\eta/b} \gg k_1 c_{H^+} e^{-\eta/b}$ will correspond almost to a hypothetical equilibrium in step I, in which the equilibrium is far to the left-hand side, i.e., the surface concentration of adsorbed H, to which θ_H is proportional, is small.

The second condition (b) is $k_1 c_{H^+} e^{-\eta/b} \gg k_{-1} e^{\eta/b}$ or $\gg k_2 c_{H^+} e^{-\eta/b}$, which corresponds to high cathodic potentials and/or an "equilibrium" constant for step I, which is greater than 1. Then θ_H tends to become equal to unity and, with $\beta = 0.5$,

$$v_2 = k_2 c_{H^+} e^{-\eta F/2RT} \qquad (167)$$

which gives a Tafel slope

$$\left[\frac{\partial \eta}{\partial (\ln i_2)} \right]_{c_{H^+}} = -\frac{2RT}{F} \qquad (168)$$

Further calculation shows that conditions for which the general expression 164 for θ_H will apply are strictly limited, since it may be shown (see Chapter 7) that θ_H will vary from <0.1 to >0.9 over a range of potential of only some 240 mv., i.e. over a current density range of about two decades if $b = -2.3(2RT/F)$. Hence the limiting conditions are justified, respectively, for current densities above and below the critical range. The analysis of the kinetics of consecutive steps thus gives Tafel slopes which in some cases can be characteristic of mechanism and coverage conditions. The reaction order values, $\partial(\ln i)/\partial(\ln c_{H^+})$, may be deduced also for conditions under which ψ_1 is constant; it will be necessary also to take into account variation of $\phi_{R,M}$ with concentration c_{H^+} if the rate expressions are kept in a form involving η (see Equation 149). The "chemically significant" reaction orders (148) taken as $[\partial(\ln i_2)/\partial(\ln c_{H^+})]_{\phi_M, v_1}$ will then be 2 for the first condition and 1 for the second. The difference arises since, when $\theta_H \ll 1$ and θ_H is potential-dependent, it involves a term in c_{H^+}, whereas when $\theta_H \to 1$, only the kinetic rate term in c_{H^+} in Equation 162c determines the order in c_{H^+}.

If the reaction mechanism were I with

$$\text{HM} + \text{MH} \to \text{H}_2 \qquad\qquad \text{III}$$

as the rate-determining desorption step, the steady-state condition would give a complex square-root function for θ, since

$$v_3 = k_3 \theta_H{}^2 \qquad\qquad (169)$$

Simple results are obtained only if it is again assumed that $k_1 c_{H^+} e^{-\eta/b} \ll k_{-1} e^{\eta/b}$ and k_2 is negligible. Then

$$v_3 = k_3 K_1^2 c_{H^+}^2 e^{-2\eta F/RT} \qquad\qquad (170)$$

which leads to a Tafel slope $[\partial\eta/\partial(\ln i_3)]c_{H^+} = -RT/2F$ and a reaction order of 2. The other limiting condition is $\theta \to 1$, and a kinetically controlled limiting current (in distinction from a diffusion-controlled one) arises, corresponding to $[\partial\eta/\partial(\ln i_3)]_{c_{H^+}} = \infty$ with a corresponding reaction order of zero. Intermediate conditions are again of little interest. It may be noted that, for a chemical step such as III, the dependence of rate upon potential arises indirectly from the dependence of coverage of the reacting intermediate on potential.

In the two cases considered above, it is seen that the significant limiting results can be readily obtained without much mathematical difficulty. However, in more complex reactions such as the o.e.r., involving three or four consecutive steps, the steady-state calculation becomes more difficult.   In such cases, the Christiansen method (166), originally developed for chemical reactions, may be applied (167) to obtain the general kinetic equation from which limiting results for Tafel slopes and reaction orders may be deduced by appropriate choice of relative values of the rate constants.   This method is a mathematical device for solution of simultaneous equations, but the limiting conditions which must be examined, to give kinetically useful diagnostic values of Tafel slopes and reaction orders, can be shown to be equivalent in most cases to those involved as assumptions in setting up the "quasi-equilibrium" hypothesis, by means of which the same results are more easily deduced.

(iii) Quasi-equilibrium Method.   Here steps prior to the rate-determining one are assumed to be almost in equilibrium.   This assumption will be valid if at least 90 per cent of particles are in equilibrium for at the most 10 per cent passing as activated complexes through the rate-controlling step to products.   This is equivalent to stating that all rate constants for steps (in both directions) antecedent to the rate-controlling step are at least ten times greater than that of the latter step.   Then, e.g. for step I, when either II or III is rate-controlling, θ_H can be written directly as

$$\frac{\theta_H}{1 - \theta_H} = K_1 c_{H^+} e^{-\eta F/RT} \tag{171}$$

which is identical with the result of applying condition (a) above in the steady-state method if $\theta_H \ll 1$.   The term $K_1 e^{-\eta F/RT}$ is seen to be an *electrochemical* equilibrium constant for reaction I. It will be noted that the result (Equation 171) is independent of β, since this will always cancel in any electrochemical equilibrium condition of the form

$$k_1(1 - \theta_H)c_{H^+} e^{-\beta \eta F/RT} = k_{-1} \theta_H e^{(1-\beta)\eta F/RT} \tag{172}$$

Similarly, if double-layer effects had been included in the electrochemical expressions for v_1 and v_{-1}, these would also cancel out.

These results are expected, since the equilibrium expression (Equation 171) is a thermodynamic result for the surface and bulk species and must hence be independent of both β and the double-layer potential ψ_1. In the steady-state method, however, such factors will not cancel out unless assumptions equivalent to the quasi-equilibrium hypothesis are made as approximations.

It will be useful to examine the application of these approaches to a more complex reaction, e.g. that in anodic oxygen evolution. Various pathways have been suggested (167,168,169); as an example, the following particular series of steps will be considered for alkaline solution conditions (where OH^- ions can be the source of O_2):

$$OH^- + M \rightarrow MOH + e \qquad\qquad IV$$

$$MOH + OH^- \rightarrow MO + H_2O + e \qquad\qquad V$$

$$2MO \rightarrow O_2 \qquad\qquad VI$$

where MO and MOH represent intermediate adsorbed radicals. If step IV were rate-controlling and no equilibrium in other steps with molecular oxygen were involved which could lead to significant coverage by O, e.g. in step VI, the result is obtained directly that the rate follows a simple electrochemical ion discharge relation such as Equation 149 with Tafel slope $RT/\beta F$. If step V were rate-controlling, the quasi-equilibrium expression applied to IV would lead to an equation for θ_{OH} analogous to Equation 171, i.e.

$$\frac{\theta_{OH}}{1 - \theta_{OH}} = K_4 c_{OH} - e^{\eta F/RT} \qquad\qquad (173)$$

where the sign of ηF is now positive (ηF is negative in Equation 171 for the cathodic reaction). The numerical results for the Tafel slopes and reaction orders will then be exactly similar to those deduced for the h.e.r. proceeding by step II, i.e., two kinds of results will arise for high and low θ_{MOH}.

If reaction VI were rate-controlling, both steps IV and V would be considered in quasi-equilibrium. For step V, this condition gives,* at low total coverages,

$$\theta_{MO} = K_5 \theta_{MOH} c_{OH^-} e^{\eta F/RT} \tag{174}$$

and, with Equation 173 for θ_{MOH},

$$\theta_{MO} = K_4 K_5 (c_{OH^-})^2 e^{2\eta F/RT} \tag{175}$$

and the electrochemical rate of step VI is then

$$v_6 = k_6 \theta_{MO}^2 = k_6 (K_4 K_5)^2 (c_{OH^-})^4 e^{4\eta F/RT} \tag{176}$$

The resulting Tafel slope is $RT/4F$ and the reaction order at low coverage by MO is 4 in c_{OH^-}. The constant k_6 includes a term $4F$ per mole of O_2 produced per square centimeter per second. If $\theta_{MO} \to 1$, a limiting current condition, as in step III for the h.e.r., would arise. Various other steps have been considered in refs. 167, 168, and 169. The above serves to exemplify the method of treatment for more complex reactions.

Calculations of the rate expressions using the Christiansen steady-state method for reaction V leads (167), with $\beta = 0.5$ and k_5 and $k_{-5} \ll k_4$, to

$$v_5 = \frac{k_4 k_5 (c_{OH^-})^2 e^{\eta F/RT}}{k_{-4} e^{-\eta F/2RT} + k_4 c_{OH^-} e^{\eta F/2RT}} \tag{177}$$

Limiting results which are the same as those obtained by the quasi-equilibrium method follow if further approximations are introduced into Equation 177, viz., $k_{-4} e^{-\eta F/2RT} \gg k_4 c_{OH^-} e^{\eta F/2RT}$, or at high potentials where $\theta_{MOH} \neq f(\eta)$, $v_5 = k_5 c_{OH^-} e^{\eta F/2RT}$. Similarly the result for step VI follows from other approximations involving the assumption of relatively low values of k_6 when VI is rate-determining.

---

* In practice, coverage by MOH and MO species cannot be distinguished, and there is a more or less continuous linear increase of degree of surface oxidation, e.g. at Pt, with increasing potential (cf. Temkin conditions discussed on p. 118).

5. KINETICS UNDER TEMKIN-TYPE ADSORP-
TION CONDITIONS

In most cases, the quasi-equilibrium method allows estimation of limiting Tafel slopes and reaction orders virtually "by inspection," after several typical cases, such as those above, have been explored. Implicit in the above discussion, however, has been the assumption that the relations for coverage by inter-mediates, e.g. Equation 171 or 173, involve equilibrium constants independent of coverage; in fact, Equations 171 and 173 can be regarded as electrochemical Langmuir isotherms.. It is more realistic, however, to regard the energy of adsorption of inter-mediates as dependent upon coverage, e.g., through a Temkin type of isotherm (*cf.* Chapter 5). Such a treatment has been given by the present (124) and other authors (170,171), and was first developed by Frumkin, Dolin and Ershler (172) and Temkin (125).

The limitations of the Langmuir isotherm have been discussed in Chapter 5, where it was shown that for real adsorbate systems such an isotherm would not generally be applicable at inter-mediate values of the coverage.   In a recent paper, Thomas (171) has discussed several experimental studies on the h.e.r., the results of which are not compatible with kinetic equations such as those derived above, assuming limiting Langmuir conditions. Thus a Tafel slope of less than $RT/\beta F$ for the h.e.r. can be predicted only, for example, for atom-ion desorption and the atom-atom recombination mechanism if $\theta < 0.1$, while such slopes have been observed at Pt and Pd cathodes on which the coverage was found to be appreciably greater than 0.1. A similar argument applies to the o.e.r., where low Tafel slopes have been established (168) in the range where $\theta > 0.5$. Also, in several cases, Tafel slopes having a value close to RT/F have been observed for the h.e.r. (173), which cannot be accounted for if Langmuir adsorption occurs.* Moreover, it should be

---

* It should be noted, however, that such a slope could arise if surface diffusion of adsorbed (H) atoms to recombination sites were rate-controlling (174).

pointed out that a treatment based on the Langmuir isotherm predicts linear Tafel relationships over appreciable ranges of potential only at extreme values* of the coverage ($\theta < 0.1$; $\theta > 0.9$), while such linear relationships are actually observed (171,175) when the coverage by adsorbed species has intermediate values around 0.5.

It is surprising that much experimental data in electrode kinetics is still interpreted exclusively in terms of the Langmuir isotherm, even though the Temkin and Temkin-type isotherms and the corresponding modified rate equations have been available for over twenty years and the applications which have been made have been restricted, until very recently (176,177,178), to the case of the h.e.r.

It was shown by Temkin that the change in ΔG_θ^0 with coverage (see Equation 116) should generally be accompanied by a proportional change in the apparent standard free energy of activation $\Delta G_\theta^{0\ddagger}$ for the adsorption and desorption steps. Thus, by analogy with Equation 118,

$$\alpha f RT = \frac{d\,\Delta G_\theta^{0\ddagger}}{d\theta} \tag{178}$$

where α is a proportionality constant† ($0 < \alpha < 1$) the magnitude of which depends on the form of the energy barrier for the activation controlled process and has the significance of a symmetry factor. Usually α will be equal to $1 - \beta$, if β is the symmetry factor for potential effects (see Fig. 16) on the ion-discharge rate. Temkin's representation was based on the experimentally observed correlation between the logarithm of the rate constant and the logarithm of the equilibrium constant in various series of analogous reactions. It is convenient to

---

* Thus, under Langmuir conditions, the coverage by univalent intermediates will change from a small value (<0.1) to a large value (>0.9) over a potential range of ca. 240 mv (cf. Equation 203 and Fig. 26).

† The α used here is not to be confused with the quantity α taken as the transfer coefficient in the definition of Tafel slopes $b = \pm RT/\alpha z F$.

consider a general sequence of steps in an anodic reaction, e.g.

$$M + X^- \rightarrow MX + e \qquad\qquad\qquad VII$$

$$2MX \rightarrow M + X_2 \qquad\qquad\qquad VIII$$

The rate equations for steps VII and VIII above will be written in a form applicable, at intermediate values of the coverage, to a case in which the apparent standard free energy of activation $\Delta \bar{G}_\theta^{0\ddagger}$ expressed for a given coverage θ is also potential-dependent. Similar kinetic equations may be written for other particular reaction sequences involving a single adsorbed intermediate, but a somewhat modified form of the rate equation will result if several adsorbed intermediates are involved in the over-all reaction sequence, as will be discussed below.

For a simple ion-discharge step (e.g. step VII above), the rate equations are

$$v_7 = k_7(1 - \theta)c_{X^-} \exp\left(\frac{\beta \eta F}{RT}\right) \exp\left[-\alpha f\theta\right] \qquad (179)$$

$$v_{-7} = k_{-7}\theta \exp\left[-\frac{(1 - \beta)\eta F}{RT}\right] \exp\left[(1 - \alpha)f\theta\right] \qquad (180)$$

The term $f\theta RT$ is the change of apparent standard free energy of adsorption of X with θ from $\theta = 0$ to $\theta = \theta$, and $\alpha f\theta RT$ is the corresponding change of $\Delta \bar{G}_\theta^{0\ddagger}$ where θ is the coverage by X and a coverage-dependent (as well as a potential-dependent) activation energy has been introduced through Equation 178.

These equations may be written in a simplified form for intermediate values of coverage by X as

$$v_7 \doteqdot k'_7 c_{X^-} \exp\left[\frac{\beta \eta F}{RT}\right] \exp\left(-\alpha f\theta\right) \qquad (181)$$

$$v_{-7} \doteqdot k'_{-7} \exp\left[-\frac{(1 - \beta)\eta}{RT}\right] \exp\left[(1 - \alpha)f\theta\right] \qquad (182)$$

since the concentration θ of intermediate X now affects the rates of these reactions primarily through the *exponential* terms in θ in Equations 179 and 180 and the effect of the pre-exponential terms involving θ in these equations is then relatively negligible (170) at intermediate values of the coverage (say, $0.2 < \theta < 0.8$) if f is appreciable. If a step following reaction VII is rate-determining, step VII may be regarded as practically at equilibrium (see above) and then, from Equations 181 and 182,

$$f\theta = \frac{\eta F}{RT} + \ln K_7 \qquad (183)$$

for unit c_{X^-} and $k'_7/k'_{-7} = K_7$, the equilibrium constant for step VII.

If it is now assumed that reaction VIII, which is a final desorption step giving rise to a gaseous product, is rate-determining, it is necessary first to consider the process of dissociative chemisorption. The problem is approached by first considering the process of adsorption: The molecule X_2 (this could represent H_2, O_2 for example) first approaches the surface and becomes physically adsorbed without dissociation. This process usually requires no energy of activation. The physically adsorbed molecules can then undergo dissociation on the surface and become chemisorbed. Depending on whether the potential energy curves for $X_2 \rightarrow MX_2$ and $2X \rightarrow 2MX$ cross above or below the line for zero energy (referred to that of X_2 molecules at an infinite distance from the surface), activated or non-activated adsorption of X, respectively, will arise. The situation is represented schematically in Figs. 20a and b. (Figure 20c represents an intermediate case in which adsorption is non-activated at low or zero coverage and becomes activated as the coverage is increased,* so that the potential energy curve for $2X \rightarrow 2MX$ becomes shallower.) It is obvious from these figures that if adsorption is non-activated, the change in $\Delta \bar{G}^{0\ddagger}$ for a given increment in θ will be equal to the change in ΔG_θ^0, namely $\alpha = 1$. For the case of activated adsorption, α is less than unity and will normally be close to 0.5. Thus the forward rate for step VIII will be written

$$v_8 = k_8 \theta^2 \exp [2f\theta] \doteqdot k_8 \exp [2f\theta] \qquad (184)$$

---

* In an electrochemical reaction, this would be equivalent to a change in mechanism if the desorption step were rate-controlling.

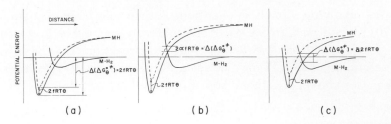

Fig. 20. Activated and non-activated adsorption of intermediates in an electrode process in relation to the potential-energy profile; (a) non-activated; (b) activated (symmetry factor α); (c) change from non-activated to activated adsorption as coverage by the intermediate increases and energy of its adsorption decreases (variable symmetry factor α).

if adsorption is non-activated; and

$$v_8 = k_8' \theta^2 \exp\left[2\alpha f\theta\right] \doteq k_8' \exp\left[2\alpha f\theta\right] \qquad (185)$$

for the case of activated adsorption, when $\theta \approx 0.5$.

Substituting $f\theta$ from Equation 183 into these equations gives

$$v_8 = k_8 \exp\left[\frac{2\eta F}{RT}\right] \qquad (186)$$

$$v_8 = k_8' \exp\left[\frac{2\alpha\eta F}{RT}\right] \qquad (187)$$

for non-activated and activated adsorption, respectively, where k_8 and k_8' contain all constant terms independent of η or θ. Thus, the dependence on overpotential of the concentration of intermediates directly determines, in this case, the dependence of the rate of the over-all reaction on potential. Since the currents measured are proportional to the rates, the Tafel slopes for relations 186 and 187 are $RT/2F$ and $RT/2\alpha F$ (171), respectively.

A Tafel slope of $RT/2F$ is predicted for this mechanism, assuming limiting Langmuir conditions, only if $\theta < 0.1$, while the present derivation (cf. 171) allows the same Tafel slope to arise over a range of coverage from zero up to $\theta \doteqdot 0.8$.   When $f = 0$, it is immaterial whether activated or non-activated adsorption arises.

The treatment of electrode kinetics in terms of the Temkin isotherm or "Temkin-type" isotherms can be criticised on the grounds that in most cases the observed heat of adsorption does not decrease exactly linearly with coverage and, moreover, some of the models proposed above do not predict such a linear dependence on θ except as a first approximation.   If a more general equation is written for $\Delta \bar{G}_\theta^0$ as a function of θ, e.g.

$$\frac{1}{RT} \frac{d \, \Delta \bar{G}_\theta^0}{d\theta} = g(\theta) \tag{188}$$

where $g(\theta)$ is a simple but non-linear function of θ which need not be specified now, the rate equations may be written out as before, but in terms of $g(\theta)$.   Instead of Equation 183, there now results

$$g(\theta) = \frac{\eta F}{RT} + \ln K_7 \tag{189}$$

and substitution of $g(\theta)$, whatever its form, in the original rate expressions such as 184, gives the same dependence of v_8 on overpotential as obtained in Equations 186 and 187.   Thus the final kinetic rate equations (and consequently the resulting Tafel slopes) are *independent of the form* of the function $g(\theta)$ which defines the rate of change of the apparent standard free energy of adsorption with coverage.   The variation of coverage with potential may, however, depend strongly on the form of the function $g(\theta)$, as will be discussed in Chapter 7.

6.   KINETIC EQUATIONS UNDER TEMKIN CONDITIONS WHEN SEVERAL ADSORBED INTERMEDIATES ARE INVOLVED

A more complex reaction scheme may now be considered, in which at least two adsorbed intermediates are produced, for example:

$$M + A^- \rightarrow MA + e \qquad\qquad IX$$

$$MA + A^- \rightarrow MB + C + e \qquad\qquad X$$

$$2MB \rightarrow 2M + B_2 \qquad\qquad XI$$

Assuming that the induced heterogeneity model (see p. 83) can account for most of the decrease of $\Delta\bar{G}^0_\theta$ with coverage, then

$$\Delta\bar{G}^0_{\theta,A} = \Delta G^0_{0,A} - f_A RT\theta_A - f_B RT\theta_B \qquad (190)$$

$$\Delta\bar{G}^0_{\theta,B} = \Delta G^0_{0,B} - f_A RT\theta_A - f_B RT\theta_B \qquad (191)$$

which follows since ΔG^0_θ for species A and B will depend on effects arising from both A and B surface dipoles. Thus, while the apparent standard free energies of adsorption of the various species may be quite different, the rate of change of these quantities with coverage by either species can be the same, if the two adsorbed species contribute simultaneously to a common surface dipole potential (111, 179) which determines the energy of adsorption of both species together. Thus, Equations 190 and 191 may be rewritten as

$$\Delta\bar{G}^0_{\theta,A} = \Delta G^0_{0,A} - g(\theta); \qquad \Delta\bar{G}^0_{\theta,B} = \Delta G^0_{0,B} - g(\theta) \quad (192)$$

where $g(\theta)$ is the *same* function of θ in both equations. Equation 189 relating coverage to potential will hence be just as valid in this case as in the case for which a single adsorbed intermediate is involved, and $g(\theta)$ will be replaced by a term in η as in the previous treatment above. At electrodes, the function $g(\theta)$ will also be determined by the influence of adsorbed solvent molecules on the adsorption behaviour of the reaction intermediates.

When reaction sequences involving more than two steps are involved, and coverage conditions can correspond to Temkin-type behaviour, the kinetic analysis is more difficult, but it has been treated in detail by Conway and co-workers in various papers (112,113,176,177) for several types of reaction. The general result is that the kinetics (reaction orders and Tafel slopes) can depend on relative coverages by the several inter-mediates and the *same* Tafel slopes may now arise for different reaction steps in a given sequence.   In this respect, the deduction differs from those which follow for Langmuir behaviour, where, at low coverage, successive steps down a consecutive reaction sequence are associated with characteristically decreasing slopes, depending on whether they are radical-radical or radical-ion discharge processes.

7.   KINETIC EQUATIONS ARISING FOR
A PRIORI HETEROGENEITY

Here the consequences of assuming that the variation of apparent standard free energy of adsorption with coverage arises from an intrinsic heterogeneity of the surface will be examined.   If there is no specificity of surface sites for two or more adsorbed intermediates at total coverage θ_T (i.e., when the species are chemically similar, as in the o.e.r.), then the following definitions   hold: $\Delta \bar{G}^0_{\theta,A} = \Delta G^0_{0,A} - f_A RT\theta_T$,   and $\Delta \bar{G}^0_{\theta,B} = \Delta G^0_{0,B} - f_B RT\theta_T$ since the energy of adsorption of a given species will depend on the sites remaining just beyond the coverage θ_T.   If specificity of site occupation occurs, then θ_T in the above two expressions must be replaced by θ_A and θ_B, respectively, and the surface behaves essentially as a mixture of two types of surface with independent properties.   Proceeding as in Equations 189 for evaluation of $\int \theta_T$ terms, and applying the method to the steps IV and V in the o.e.r. (p. 116) at intermediate coverages using equations of the form of 179 and 180 for step IV, leads to a Tafel slope for step V of $(2RT/F)f_{OH}/(2f_{OH} - f_O)$, $\alpha = \beta = 0.5$.   If the coverage factors f for adsorbed OH and O species in the mechanism IV, V, VI (p. 116) are assumed to be equal, then the Tafel slope for V is $2RT/F$, which is the same result as would be obtained with the surface dipole model for variation of energy of adsorption with coverage.   In practice, it is likely that both intrinsic heterogeneity and dipole induction effects are operative at appreciable coverages on polycrystalline metals, so that the above treatment allows the possibility that Tafel slopes may arise with significant variations of value from integral or simple fractional values of RT/F.

8. ENERGETICS OF IRREVERSIBLE PROCESSES

(I) **Thermodynamic Principles.** In Chapter 2, the energetics of reversible processes were considered. For irreversible processes, different energetic factors are involved which determine the rates of electrode reactions through the free energies of activation. In a simple ionic redox reaction such as $M^{n+} + ze \rightarrow M^{(n-z)+}$, the factors which determine the ΔG^0 for this *half-cell* reaction are the free energies of solvation of the ions M^{z+} and $M^{(n-z)+}$ the energy of neutralisation of the ion M^{n+} by z electrons in the gas phase and the electron work function of the electrode metal at which the reaction is proceeding. At equilibrium, the *electro-chemical* potentials of $M^{n+} + ze$ and $M^{(n-z)+}$ must be equal and the electrical potentials at which M^{n+} and $M^{(n-z)+}$ exist in the bulk solution must be identical. The chemical potentials of $M^{n+} + ze$ and $M^{(n-z)+}$ will hence not generally be identical, and this will determine a difference of "chemical" free energy of the ions in the initial and final states. The free energy of activation will be determined by the way in which the energy of the state $M^{n+} + ze$ varies as a critical configuration is approached from which the final-state ion can be formed with electron transfer (18,180). Generally the energy of activation involved in a process such as this will be associated with thermal and field-assisted modification of the configuration of solvent molecules around M^{n+} until suitable configurations are reached to (or from) which electron transfer may occur by a tunneling process* (140,141,181).

Under reversible conditions ($\eta = 0$), the exchange current is determined by the (equal) *electrochemical* free energies of activation $\Delta \bar{G}^{\ddagger}$ for the forward and backward directions of the reaction; the *chemical* free energies of activation $\Delta G^{\ddagger}$ for these two directions of reaction at equilibrium will not generally be the same, but are modified by the finite, single metal-solution p.d. ϕ_R^0 existing at the interface when the reaction is proceeding reversibly, so that the electrochemical $\Delta \bar{G}^{\ddagger}$ becomes the same for the anodic and cathodic directions of reaction. It is hence seen

---

* Usually a distribution of configurations will be involved, with corresponding tunneling probabilities, so that the rate must be obtained by an appropriate integration (18,21).

that the $\Delta\bar{G}^{\ddagger}$ is determined by the chemical factor $\Delta G^{\ddagger}$ modified by a term $\beta\phi_R^0 zF$. The chemical factor will be determined by the energy quantities which are changed in the activation process and in some cases indirectly by the value of ΔG_R for the over-all half-cell process; e.g., when ΔG_R is a positive quantity, $\Delta G^{\ddagger}$ must be at least equal to ΔG_R. These factors are illustrated in Fig. 21. At equilibrium $\Delta\vec{\bar{G}}^{\ddagger} = \Delta\overleftarrow{\bar{G}}^{\ddagger}$ (see Fig. 21), but the condition of equality does not apply to $\Delta\vec{G}^{\ddagger}$ and $\Delta\overleftarrow{G}^{\ddagger}$; it will, however, apply also to the standard quantities $\Delta\vec{\bar{G}}^{0\ddagger}$ and $\Delta\overleftarrow{\bar{G}}^{0\ddagger}$ when reactants, products and activated complexes are in their standard states, as can be seen from Fig. 21, since the $\Delta\bar{G}^{\ddagger}$ quantities differ from $\Delta G^{\ddagger}$ quantities by the same energy as $\Delta\bar{G}^{0\ddagger}$ quantities differ from $\Delta G^{0\ddagger}$ terms.

(ii) **Role of Electron Work Function.** In the simple half-cell electron transfer reaction discussed above, the "chemical" energetic quantities determining the relative energies of initial and final states follow from the cycle

$$
\begin{array}{ccc}
M_g^{n+} + ze_y & \xrightarrow{\;-I\;} & M_g^{(n-z)+} \\
{\scriptstyle -\Delta G_{S,M^{n+}}^0}\Big\uparrow & {\scriptstyle z\Phi_e}\Big\uparrow \quad {\scriptstyle \Delta G_R^0} & \Big\downarrow{\scriptstyle \Delta G_{S,M^{(n-z)+}}^0} \\
M_l^{n+} + ze_M & \xrightarrow{} & M_l^{(n-z)+}
\end{array}
$$

where ΔG_S^0 quantities are the standard free energies of solvation of the indicated ions, Φ_e the numerical value of the electrode work function in e.v. and I the ionisation energy of $M^{(n-z)+} \rightarrow M^{n+}$. Obviously, from the cycle,

$$\Delta G_R^0 = -zF\phi_R^0 = \Delta G_{S,M^{(n-z)+}}^0 - I + z\Phi_e - \Delta G_{S,M^{n+}}^0 \quad (193)$$

The standard free energy of the initial state relative to that of the final state will hence vary directly with Φ_e *for a given reaction*, and will be lower the higher is Φ_e. Hence $\Delta G^{0\ddagger}$ will vary with $z\beta\,\Delta\Phi_e$ as Φ_e is changed by $\Delta\Phi_e$ on going from one electrode metal to another, since changes of G^0 for the initial state will be reflected as changes of $\Delta\vec{\bar{G}}^{0\ddagger}$ by βz times the change in Φ_e. However,

$$\Delta\vec{\bar{G}}^{0\ddagger} = \Delta\vec{G}^{0\ddagger} - \beta\phi_R^0 zF \quad (194)$$

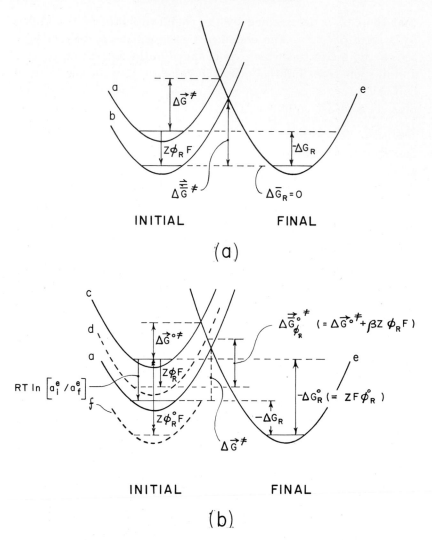

Fig. 21. Free-energy profiles for the course of a single electrode process involving a discharge step: (a) $\Delta G^{\ddagger}$ is the free energy of activation and $\Delta \overleftrightarrow{G}^{\ddagger}$ the electrochemical free energy of activation at equilibrium when the equilibrium potential is ϕ_R and the electrochemical free energy change in the over-all reaction $\Delta \overline{G}_R$ is zero. Curve a is for chemical-energy changes of the initial state as a function

and ϕ_R^0 is also determined by Φ_e from Equation 193. Hence changes of Φ_e change $\Delta\vec{G}^{0\ddagger}$ by $z\beta\Phi_e$ and $-zF\phi_R^0$ by $z\Phi_e$, so that the electrochemical standard free energy of activation $\Delta\vec{G}^{0\ddagger}$ in Equation 194 is *independent* of work function Φ_e; hence the exchange current i_0 is also independent of Φ_e. It is not, however, independent of the ion solvation energies since these enter indirectly in determining the *shape* of the potential functions in Fig. 21, whereas Φ_e affects only the *position* of the curves. The difference between the standard quantity ΔG_R^0 and ΔG_R in Fig. 21b will be $RT\ln(a_i^e/a_f^e)$ where a^e terms are the equilibrium activities of ions in the final state (f) and the initial state (i). It will be noted that at the reversible potential, $\Delta\vec{G}^{\ddagger}$ is always equal to $\Delta\vec{G}^{0\ddagger}$ because of compensating effects of concentration in the G terms and the half-cell reversible potential ϕ_R.

The independence of i_0 on Φ_e for the simple reaction discussed will be valid irrespective of how i_0 is measured, i.e., whether it is deduced from currents recorded as a function of a measured overpotential involving two metal electrodes, or whether it is obtained chemically by measurements of isotope exchange rates (155) on open circuit.

The situation for measured overpotentials is similar. Thus, for an electrode M at which there is a net cathodic current, the metal-solution p.d. ϕ_M may be written, using the result in

---

of position of the reacting particle along the reaction coordinate and curve *b* is that for electrochemical-energy changes. (b) Corresponding curves for initial-state free energies, showing the difference of profiles for the standard free-energy quantities and the free-energy quantities, and for the effect of the standard reversible potential ϕ_R^0 and an actual reversible potential ϕ_R; a_i^e and a_f^e are the activities of initial- and final-state entities when the reaction is at *equilibrium:*

Curve *a*: free-energy profile.

Curve *c*: standard free-energy profile.

Curve *d*: curve *c* corrected by $z\phi_R F$ giving the standard $\Delta\vec{G}_{\phi_R}^0$ at general potential ϕ_R.

Curve *f*: curve *a* corrected by $z\phi_R^0 F$, giving the standard $\Delta\vec{G}_{\phi_R^0}^{0\ddagger}$.

Equation 193,

$$\phi_{\mathrm{M}} = \phi_{R,\mathrm{M}} + \eta = \phi'_{R,\mathrm{M}} + \eta - \frac{\Phi_{e,\mathrm{M}}}{F} \qquad (195)$$

where the work function term $\Phi_{e,\mathrm{M}}$ has been separated out and $\phi'_{R,\mathrm{M}}$ is a constant term for a given reaction. For two metals *1, 2* at which the same current is passing by the same reaction, but at different overpotentials η_1 and η_2,

$$i = k \exp\left[-\frac{\Delta G_1^{0\ddagger}}{RT}\right] \exp\left[-\frac{\beta z F \phi_{\mathrm{M}_1}}{RT}\right]$$

$$= k \exp\left[-\frac{\Delta G_2^{0\ddagger}}{RT}\right] \exp\left[-\frac{\beta z F \phi_{\mathrm{M}_2}}{RT}\right] \qquad (196)$$

i.e.,

$$\Delta G_1^{0\ddagger} - \Delta G_2^{0\ddagger} + \beta z F(\phi_{R,\mathrm{M}_1} + \eta_1 - \phi_{R,\mathrm{M}_2} - \eta_2) = 0 \qquad (197)$$

Hence,

$$\eta_1 - \eta_2 = -(\phi_{R,\mathrm{M}_1} - \phi_{R,\mathrm{M}_2}) - \frac{\Delta G_1^{0\ddagger} - \Delta G_2^{0\ddagger}}{\beta z F} \qquad (198)$$

For the reaction at two different metals, $\Delta G_1^{0\ddagger}$ and $\Delta G_2^{0\ddagger}$ differ only by $|z| \beta$ times the difference of the work function terms in the corresponding initial states, as was shown above, and $1 - \beta$ times any difference in energy quantities for the final states in the two reactions. Since ϕ_{R,M_1} and ϕ_{R,M_2} involve $-\Phi_{e,\mathrm{M}_1}/F$ and $-\Phi_{e,\mathrm{M}_2}/F$, it is clear that $\eta_1 - \eta_2$ is then independent of the work functions, as also expected in terms of the independence of i_0 on work function shown above. Experimentally, e.g. in the h.e.r., i_0 or η, in fact, *is* found to depend on Φ_e (182,183), so that this effect must arise indirectly (184), as discussed below. Since $\eta_1 - \eta_2$ is a difference of measured cell potential using a given reference electrode, any work function effects at the single electrode-solution interfaces and at the metal contact (if any) in the external circuit cancel out. Also, for a given process, e.g. the h.e.r., set up reversibly at two different metals, the *measured* potential difference is zero and independent of the metal; however, the individual metal-solution p.d.'s at the two metals are, of course, different on account of the difference of work functions, but this effect is cancelled at the metal-metal contact in the external circuit, as discussed in Chapter 2.

(iii) Energetic Factors in the H.E.R.   For the step of discharge of hydrogen ions, the immediate product is an adsorbed H atom. The energy factors involved in the discharge step I (p. 112) then follow (20,21) from the cycle:

$$(H^+)_g + (H_2O_s) + e_g \xrightarrow{\quad -I_H \quad} H_g + (H_2O)_s$$

$$\left. -\Delta G^0_{S,H^+} \right\uparrow \qquad \nearrow \Phi_e \qquad \downarrow \Delta G^0_{ads\,H} \qquad\qquad (199)$$

$$\Delta G^0_R$$

$$(H_3O^+)_s + e_M \xrightarrow{\qquad\qquad} MH + (H_2O)_s$$

The only difference from the general case considered above is the presence of a term $\Delta G^0_{ads\,H}$, the standard free energy of adsorption of H atoms.   The latter quantity can be expressed in terms of a measurable molecular standard free energy of adsorption $\frac{1}{2}\Delta G^0_{ads\,H_2}$ which is equal to the standard free energy of dissociation of $\frac{1}{2}H_2$ plus $\Delta G^0_{ads\,H}$, so that the latter quantity can be obtained. The relative positions of potential-energy curves for initial and final states (Fig. 16) may be estimated by various procedures, e.g., by using $H_2 + H_2O$ as a common energy reference state or by calculating the relative position under conditions of equilibrium at the potential of zero charge (185).   The quantities which are dependent on the position of the reacting particle H along the reaction coordinate are (a) the energy of solvation of the proton $\Delta H^0_{S,H^+}$, (b) the energy of adsorption of H at the metal and (c) the repulsion energy between the H atom and the water molecule resulting from the neutralisation of the H_3O^+ ion.   The quantities which fix the relative positions of the two curves (for H^+-H_2O and M-H interactions) are Φ_e, I_H and the values of $\Delta H^0_{ads\,H}$ and $\Delta H^0_{S,H^+}$ at the equilibrium internuclear separations.   The energy of activation is then determined by molecular parameters for H_3O^+ and MH and the work function of the metal.   For this

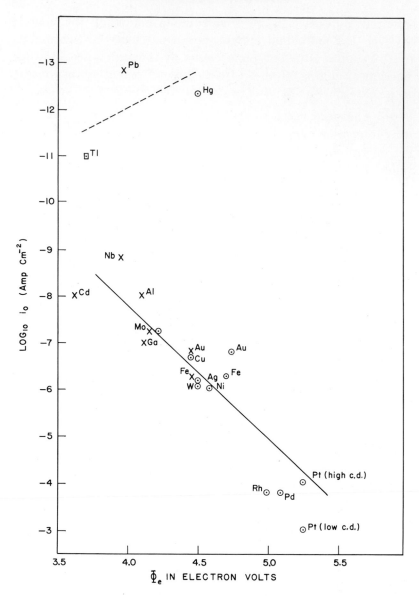

Fig. 22. Relation between electronic work function and log [exchange current] for the h.e.r. at various metals. (After Conway and Bockris, 182.)

H_3O^+ ion-discharge step, the activation energy will tend to *decrease* with increasing H adsorption energy. In the final kinetic equation for the rate of hydrogen evolution by this rate-controlling mechanism, the work function effects will cancel out, as discussed above. Since i_0 for the h.e.r. is observed to depend on Φ_e for a series of metals (Fig. 22), an indirect dependence must be sought. Conway and Bockris (182) showed that this arose from the dependence of the H adsorption energy on the work function of the metal; experimentally analogous relations were found by Conway *et al.* (183) between i_0 and the number of d-holes per atom in transition metal alloys. This matter was first examined by Delahay and Ruetschi (182) following the principles of the analysis of Horiuti and Polanyi (20).

For the h.e.r. proceeding by the rate-controlling step II (p. 112), the energetics are analogous to those considered above for step I, except that the H adsorption energy appears in the energy for the initial-state and that for H_2 formation in the final-state quantity. When the kinetics are controlled by step II, the activation energy will tend to *increase* with increasing H adsorption energy (184). The adsorption energy of H at electrode surfaces, where co-adsorption of solvent must occur, will generally be less than that for the corresponding gas-metal interface, and can be obtained from studies of charging curves at various temperatures (see Chapter 7).

Generally the heat of adsorption will depend on coverage, and Temkin-type adsorption can arise. Under these conditions, the exchange current can show a region of independence of standard free energy of adsorption of H, as shown by Parsons (170) (see Fig. 23). At the reversible potential, the coverage will be determined by equilibrium between MH, H_2 and H_3O^+ ions, since when the over-all reaction is at equilibrium, each of the steps must also be at equilibrium.

(iv) Calculation of Activation Energies. The *a priori* calculation of activation energies (21,185,186) has been attempted for several types of electrode reaction, including metal-deposition processes occurring by various steps (187), for which comparative

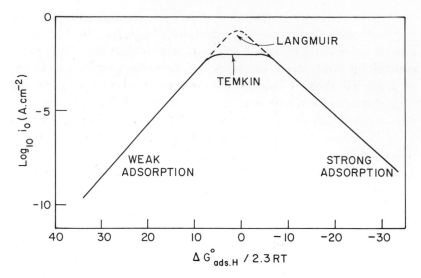

Fig. 23. Theoretical relations between exchange current and standard free energy of adsorption of hydrogen. (After Parsons, 170; based on his Figs. I and 2.)

calculations were made. The first semi-quantitative calculations for the discharge step in the h.e.r. were made by Butler (21), based on principles discussed by Horiuti and Polanyi (20). Bockris and Parsons (185) made a similar but thermodynamically more complete calculation (185) and examined the uncertainties in the treatment. Keii and Kodera (186) calculated a potential-energy surface for step I, and Horiuti *et al.* (188) examined the potential-energy surface for reaction steps in the h.e.r. at a nickel cathode. All these calculations give only a very approximate value of the heat of activation, but a rather better estimate of the symmetry factor β. Temkin (159) has examined the significance of theoretical calculations of activation energy in relation to the experimentally accessible value obtained from $[\partial(\ln i_0)/\partial(1/T)]_{\eta=0}$. The true activation energy $\Delta H^{0\ddagger}$ cannot be calculated, since the relative positions of the curves for initial and final states cannot be determined unambiguously, as the heat content change in the single electrode process (Equation 155) is unknown. However,

Bockris and Parsons (185) suggested that this difficulty could be avoided by treating the problem for conditions of equilibrium at the p.z.c.   In Temkin's treatment, the apparent heat of activation is calculated by placing the curves so that the zero-point level for the initial state lies above a reference level (energy of H_2) by ηF and that for the final state lies at an energy $\Delta H_{ads\ H_2}$ (referred to $\frac{1}{2}H_2$) below the reference energy.   The distance-dependent energy quantities are treated as in Butler's theory, and the apparent activation energy results.

7

Adsorbed Intermediates
at Electrodes

1. INTRODUCTION

Chemisorbed species (apart from certain reactant ions, e.g. I^-, CNS^- which are specifically adsorbed) can arise in electrochemical reactions by two types of process:

(a) In an ion- or molecule-discharge step or in some subsequent step in a sequence of consecutive reactions. In some cases, several chemisorbed species may arise in the same over-all reaction, e.g. OH, O and HO_2 in the o.e.r.; NH_2, NH and N in the oxidation of ammonia at electrodes; and CH_3COO and CH_3 radicals in the Kolbe electrosynthesis.

(b) In reactions in which a chemical step occurs before the electrochemical charge-transfer process. Reactions of this kind are the ionisation of H produced by dissociative chemisorption of hydrogen, or the electrochemical oxidations of hydrocarbons and other molecules at catalytically active anodes, e.g., as in fuel cells.

In case (a), the concentration of species on the surface will depend on the electrochemical rate constants of the radical producing and removal steps, and will depend on potential. In case (b), the surface concentration will depend on the rate constants for the chemical catalysed dissociation and the electrochemical rate constants for subsequent radical ionisation or radical removal steps. In this case, the dissociating molecules must usually reach the electrode by diffusion or convective mass transfer from the solution and the electrochemical reaction can become diffusion-controlled as the current density is increased.

The first case is of particular importance, since information concerning the adsorption behaviour of the intermediates can be obtained from suitable kinetic studies involving measurements of electrode capacitance. In the second case, the study of the ad-species can be more difficult owing to continuing chemisorption from the chemical catalytic reaction during the electrochemical measurements, e.g., in studies of H adsorption from molecular hydrogen at active platinum electrodes.

2. CONDITIONS FOR INTERMEDIATE COVERAGE
$$(0.8 > \theta > 0.2)$$

For quasi-equilibrium in a radical-producing discharge step such as I (see p. 112) the coverage θ by H is given by

$$\frac{\theta}{1-\theta} \exp\left[f\theta\right] = K_1(C_{H^+}) \exp\left[-\frac{\phi_M F}{RT}\right] \qquad (200)$$

and the limiting conditions for $0.8 > \theta > 0.2$ are

$$\ln C_{H^+} + \ln K_1 - \phi_{M,0.2} \frac{F}{RT} = 0.2f - 1.38 \quad \text{for } \theta = 0.2 \quad (201)$$

and

$$\ln C_{H^+} + \ln K_1 - \phi_{M,0.8} \frac{F}{RT} = 0.8f + 1.38 \quad \text{for } \theta = 0.8 \quad (202)$$

For a given value of the equilibrium constant, the range $\Delta\phi_M$ ($= \phi_{M,0.2} - \phi_{M,0.8}$) of potentials over which the above condition for θ is applicable will be determined partly by f according to

$$\Delta\phi_M = \frac{RT}{F}(0.6f + 2.76) \qquad (203)$$

and the lower value $\phi_{M,0.2}$ of potential at which θ begins to become appreciable (>0.2) is

$$\phi_{M,0.2} = \frac{RT}{F} \ln K_1 + \ln C_{H^+} - 0.2f + 1.38 \qquad (204)$$

where K_1 is defined appropriately for the units of C_{H^+} taken. Hence, the potential at which onset of appreciable coverage and associated pseudocapacitance (see below) arises, and Temkin conditions possibly apply, will mainly depend on $\ln K_1$ since f may not usually be greater than 10–15. Thus, in the cathodic h.e.r., appreciable coverage at Pt and related group VIII metals already occurs at potentials *anodic* to the reversible hydrogen potential, while in the anodic formate decarboxylation (177), intermediate coverage and significant pseudocapacity do not arise until high (anodic) overpotentials are attained.

3. RELATION BETWEEN COVERAGE, CHARGE AND CAPACITANCE ASSOCIATED WITH INTERMEDIATES

In a reaction scheme such as I–III (see Chapter 5), the partial surface coverage θ for adsorbed H is usually potential-dependent. Each value of the coverage corresponds to a charge q required to reach that coverage from a previously uncovered electrode surface, i.e., $q = k'\theta$ (where k' is a constant) since the adsorbed intermediates are formed in a faradaic process involving charge transfer, e.g. step I. The variation of θ (and hence q) with potential gives rise to a capacity defined by

$$C = \frac{dq}{d\phi_M} = k' \frac{d\theta}{d\phi_M} \qquad (205)$$

It is important to note that this capacitance arises in a different way from the ionic double-layer capacitance C_{dl}. The coverage θ can be changed only by passage of charge *across* the double-layer (see Fig. 24a,b) in a *non*-ideally polarisable electrode, while C_{dl} alone represents an ideally polarisable electrode (54). In other ways, however, C behaves electrically like a capacitance,

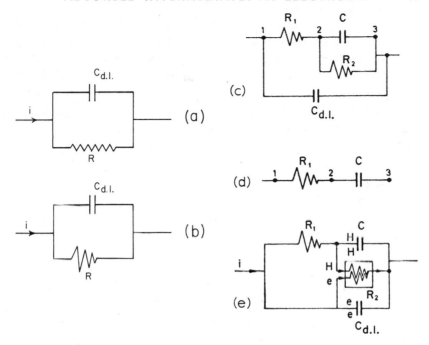

Fig. 24.   Equivalent circuits for processes involving two consecutive reaction steps, a charge transfer followed by a desorption: (a) basic circuit for discharge step occurring across double-layer (capacitance C_{dl}); (b) modification to indicate non-ohmic character of the reaction resistance R; (c) basic circuit for charge-transfer step and pseudo-capacitance discharged by following rate-determining step; (d) initial charging equivalent circuit, when $R_2 \gg R_1$; (e) circuit for electro-chemical atom (H) and ion (H_3O^+) desorption reaction following proton discharge to produce adsorbed H.

except that it may vary extensively with potential and a.c. signal frequency or d.c. charging rate. The role of C in the impedance presented to an external signal by the electrode interface may be considered by reference to equivalent circuits.

In Chapter 3, the behaviour of the distribution of ions at an electrode interface as a function of electrode charge and potential was referred to in terms of a capacitance, or more precisely in terms of a series combination of capacitances for the diffuse, inner and/or outer Helmholtz layers.   Implicit in this representation is the idea that the electrochemical behaviour of the interface can be represented by the electrical behaviour of equivalent circuit elements. So long as an ideal polarised electrode is considered and no faradaic charge-transfer process is concerned, the capacitative representation of the double-layer is adequate, although some frequency dependence of the capacitance must in reality be allowed for, even at the mercury electrode.

When a charge-transfer process can occur at a rate dependent on electrode potential, a purely capacitative representation of the electrochemical behaviour is inadequate since a net flow of d.c. current cannot pass a capacitance. The behaviour of a discharge step occurring at a current i at an electrode at which a double-layer can be set up can therefore be approximated by a combination of a capacitance C_{dl} and a reaction resistance R in parallel as shown in Fig. 24a, neglecting diffusional components (156).   Usually R will not simply be an ohmic resistance* but must represent a current-potential (i-V) relation of the form $dV/d(\ln i) = $ constant,   rather   than $dV/di = $ constant   (ohmic behaviour).   Consequently, it is convenient to adopt the symbol ⌁ for R, to stress its non-ohmic character under most conditions (at low overpotentials when $\beta\eta F/RT < 1$, an approximately linear current-potential relation can arise), whence circuit a will be better drawn as shown in Fig. 24b.   While equivalent circuits are useful for purposes of considering the behaviour of an electrode reaction, it must be stressed that no electrical circuit can give a complete quantitative representation of the electrochemical behaviour of an electrode reaction particularly with respect to varying frequency of applied voltage and corresponding current.

When adsorbed intermediates are involved, it has been shown above that another (adsorption) capacitance C is involved, in

---

* The reaction resistances R are differential resistances defined by $d\phi_M/di$; cf. Ohm's law $R = E/I$ for a p.d. E passing current I through a resistance R.   When i depends exponentially on ϕ_M (Tafel behaviour), R will depend on ϕ_M (non-ohmic behaviour).

addition to that associated with the ionic double-layer. This capacitance arises, however, from the dependence of charge required to change the steady-state coverage by $\Delta\theta$ when the potential is changed by $\Delta\phi_M$, i.e., when a faradaic charging or discharging process is required, to give rise to this change of coverage. The adsorption "pseudocapacitance" is thus less like a true capacitance than is the ionic double-layer capacitance, though it behaves electrically like a capacitance except that it can depend markedly on electrode potential and frequency. The adsorption pseudocapacitance C must be "charged up" through a faradaic discharge step, and hence through a corresponding faradaic discharge resistance R_1 which may be non-ohmic; it will correspond, at a given potential, to the reciprocal of the rate of the discharge step producing an adsorbed intermediate, e.g. H in the h.e.r. The whole combination of C and R must be in parallel with C_{dl} since it provides a leakage path across the double-layer. The representation is hence as shown in Fig. 24c. Usually for ranges of potential in which the faradaic process corresponding to R_1 is significant and C can be charged, C will be much larger than C_{dl} and the charging behaviour will be characterised limitingly by R_1 and C in series (Fig. 24d). Since C corresponds to change of coverage by some intermediate, at least one subsequent step (usually rate-determining if C is to be appreciable) must also be involved in its removal in the steady state to produce products of the over-all reaction. Hence, C is also short-circuited by a second non-ohmic resistive component R_2 (circuit c). In the steady state, the current passes through R_1 and R_2 and is limited normally by R_2 if, for the rate-controlling step, $R_2 \gg R_1$. R_2 becomes rapidly less with increasing potential, and the charging process through R_1 becomes less and less efficient with respect to charging C as the steady-current condition is approached, when, in the limit, the net charging current is zero. The whole of the combination of R_1, C and R_2 is, as above, in parallel across C_{dl} in the case of a non-ideally polarisable electrode. In the initial stages of a charging process, or one corresponding to potentials below the reversible potential of the over-all reaction, $R_2 \gg R_1$ and the charging of C occurs by almost the whole current provided through R_1; the equivalent circuit is then limitingly R_1 (circuit d) in series with C and both in parallel with C_{dl}; this is the case considered by Dolin and Ershler (189). Circuit d cannot, however, apply to the steady state. In a number of experimental cases, e.g. in the charging of the nickel oxide electrode (168,176), the complete equivalent circuit e must be retained.

For a rate-controlling electrochemical atom-ion type of desorption (reaction II), the circuit c must be inapplicable, since H atoms are formed through a process corresponding to R_1 but are removed by another faradaic step, electrons and H^+ ions being provided from the metal electrode side and the solution side, respectively, of C_{dl} and H atoms from the pseudocapacitor C. A special kind of representation is hence necessary for this reaction and is shown in circuit e (Fig. 24), where the non-ohmic resistance corresponding to the rate-controlling desorption step R_2 is written with two "input channels," one for electrons and H^+ ions and the other for the H atoms removed as equivalent charge from C.

In other types of reaction where diffusion plays an important role in the kinetics, the equivalent circuit must contain additional components (the so-called Warburg impedance) associated with diffusional pseudocapacitance and diffusional resistance as required in the treatment of a.c. impedance (see Chapter 8) of partly diffusion-controlled reactions. The values of these equivalent-circuit components vary with the reciprocal square root of frequency ω of the a.c. signal and can usually be eliminated by suitable extrapolations of $(1/\omega)^{1/2}$ to zero ($\omega \to \infty$).

4.   ADSORPTION PSEUDOCAPACITANCE FROM KINETIC EQUATIONS

Two general types of isotherms may be considered, the Langmuir and Temkin types, as discussed in Chapter 5. Also, behaviour corresponding to (a) steady-state and (b) quasi-equilibrium conditions in the radical-producing step (e.g. I in the h.e.r. sequence) can be distinguished, but (b) will normally be a special case of (a). The Langmuir case for quasi-equilibrium conditions will first be examined, since the treatment illustrates in a simple way the principles involved.

(i) Langmuir, Quasi-equilibrium Case. If an ion-discharge step such as I is at equilibrium when, for example, the following step II is rate-controlling, a pseudocapacitance C associated with the dependence of θ for adsorbed H on ϕ_M arises (200). From Equations 162a and 162b, when $v_1 \doteq v_{-1}$ (i.e., for $k_2 \ll k_1, k_{-1}$),

$$\frac{k'}{C} = -\frac{d\phi_M}{d\theta} = \frac{RT}{F} \frac{d}{d\theta}\left(\ln \frac{\theta}{1-\theta}\right) \tag{206}$$

and ϕ_M is increasingly negative for increasing cathodic currents in the h.e.r. Hence,

$$C = \frac{k'F}{RT}\theta(1-\theta) \tag{207}$$

which obviously has a maximum value of $k'F/4RT$ farad cm.$^{-2}$ at $\theta = 0.5$ and must be symmetrical with respect to θ as θ goes from 0 through 0.5 to 1. In terms of potential, Equations 162a and 162b give

$$C = \frac{k'F}{RT} \frac{K_1 \exp\left[-\phi_M F/RT\right]}{(1 + K_1 \exp\left[-\phi_M F/RT\right])^2} \tag{208}$$

which is also symmetrical with respect to the electrode potential at which $\theta = 0.5$; K_1 in Equation 208 is an equilibrium constant for reaction 1, and ϕ_M will be negative. C has a maximum value, for example for hydrogen adsorption (ca. 10^{15} sites per square centimeter of real surface area) of 1.6×10^3 μf. cm.$^{-2}$. It is seen from Equation 208 that at low coverage when ϕ_M is small or positive, $C > 0$ and varies as $\exp\left[-\phi_M F/RT\right]$, whereas, when $\theta \to 1$ at high potentials, C varies as $\exp\left[\phi_M F/RT\right]$. Both cases have been observed experimentally (168,177). The relation of C to θ and ϕ_M is shown in Figs. 25a and 25b, and the physical

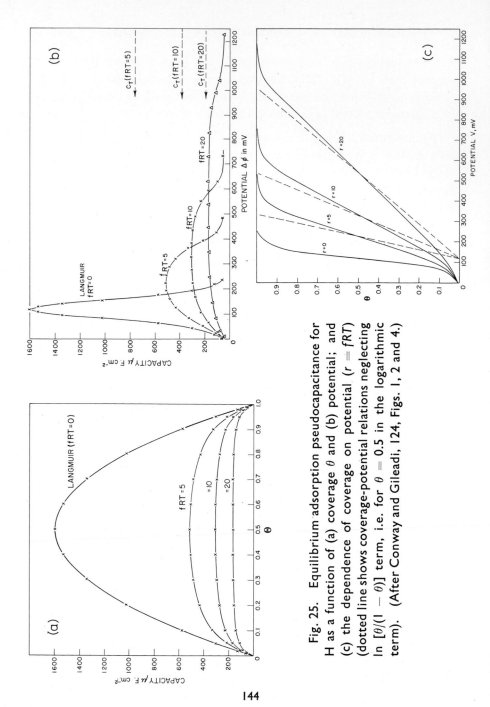

Fig. 25. Equilibrium adsorption pseudocapacitance for H as a function of (a) coverage θ and (b) potential; and (c) the dependence of coverage on potential ($r = fRT$) (dotted line shows coverage-potential relations neglecting ln $[\theta/(1-\theta)]$ term, i.e. for $\theta = 0.5$ in the logarithmic term). (After Conway and Gileadi, 124, Figs. 1, 2 and 4.)

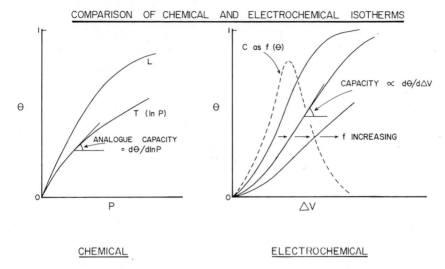

COMPARISON OF CHEMICAL AND ELECTROCHEMICAL ISOTHERMS

CHEMICAL   ELECTROCHEMICAL

Fig. 26. Comparison of chemical and electrochemical adsorption isotherms showing the significance of adsorption pseudocapacitance and its dependence on the interaction and/or heterogeneity parameter f.

significance of C in relation to chemical and electrochemical isotherms is shown in Fig. 26.

(II) Temkin-Type Isotherm, Quasi-equilibrium Case. Here equations similar to 181 and 182 are used instead of Equations 162a and 162b, for quasi-equilibrium in step I, so that

$$\frac{k'}{C} = \frac{d\phi_M}{d\theta} - \frac{RT}{F}\frac{d}{d\theta}\left(\ln\frac{\theta}{1-\theta}\right) + \frac{RTf}{F} \tag{209}$$

and the significance of the parameter f in terms of heterogeneity or interaction effects has been discussed in Chapter 5.

Equation 209 cannot be explicitly solved for C as a function of ϕ_M, but numerical evaluation can be made for an assumed value of K_1. Plots for various values of f are shown in Figs. 25a and 25b. Even a relatively small value of f is sufficient to cause the maximum value of C to diminish and C to have an appreciable dependence on potential over a wider range of potentials (Fig. 25b) than in the Langmuir case for which $f = 0$. At high values of f, the pseudocapacity C tends to become more independent of ϕ_M as discussed by Temkin (109) and other Russian workers (172) for H adsorption at platinum. In most cases, over a certain range of potentials determined by K_1 and f, C will be much larger than C_{dl} unless f is very large; however, C_{max} will approach C_{dl} only for impossibly large values of f.

(iii) **Steady-State Cases.** In the kinetics of consecutive reactions, it is usually sufficient that one rate constant is, say, ten times less than another for the step with the smaller rate constant to be unambiguously rate-controlling, and this is the usual basis for simplifying assumptions which are introduced in general steady-state rate equations (*cf.* Chapter 6). In the case of the adsorption pseudocapacitance, however, the values of C obtained for a given reaction mechanism at a given potential were shown by Conway and Gileadi (190) to be very sensitive to the ratio of rate constants, K_{NE} (*K-non-equilibrium*), for the rate-determining and the prior radical-producing step; K_{NE} is then a measure of the extent to which "equilibrium" in a radical-producing step is disturbed in the steady-state when a following step is rate-controlling.

The only case for which the steady-state treatment gives an explicit result for C as a function of θ or ϕ_M is under Langmuir conditions when a radical-ion desorption reaction sequence is involved, such as in the hydrogen evolution reaction proceeding by step III (190).

The steady-state equation for θ can be deduced for this case and differentiated with respect to electrode potential to obtain C/k'. For steps I and II with II rate-controlling, the steady-state result for θ is

$$\theta = \frac{k_1 e^{-\beta \phi_M F/RT}}{k_1 e^{-\beta \phi_M F/RT} + k_{-1} e^{(1-\beta)\phi_M F/RT} + k_2 e^{-\beta \phi_M F/RT}} \tag{210}$$

giving C as

$$C = k' \frac{2k_1 k_{-1}/b}{(k_1 e^{-\phi_M/b} + k_{-1} e^{\phi_M/b} + k_2 e^{-\phi_M/b})^2} \tag{211}$$

where $b = RT/0.5F$, the Tafel slope for the discharge step, taking $\beta = 0.5$. The result for C for a given value of K_1 depends on the ratio k_2/k_1, i.e. a factor which measures the extent to which step I is in quasi-equilibrium; thus if $k_2/k_1 = 0$, complete equilibrium can be maintained, whereas if k_2 is only somewhat less than k_1 and k_{-1}, then equilibrium is appreciably disturbed and the steady-state result must be used. The effect of variations of the ratio k_2/k_1, i.e. of K_{NE}, is shown in Fig. 27. When significant dependence of the apparent standard free energy of adsorption on coverage arises, and Temkin kinetic equations (e.g. Equations 181 and 182) must be used, a more complex result for C follows (190). The extent to which C depends on K_{NE} is then found to be relatively more important than in the Langmuir case, and increasingly so the larger is the "heterogeneity" parameter f. Even for large ratios of k_1/k_2 (> 10) (i.e. $k_1, k_{-1} \gg k_2$), the dependence of C on ϕ_M and θ is significantly different from that resulting for the equilibrium case, whereas in the current-potential relations the "rate-controlling" step is already more or less unambiguously rate-determining when $k_1 \geqslant 10k_2$. Similar conclusions apply to other reaction sequences (190) except that the forms of the steady-state C-ϕ_M profiles, which must be evaluated numerically, can be characteristic of the reaction mechanism, e.g., in the h.e.r., whether step II or step III is rate-limiting. The capacity behaviour can thus be a more sensitive indication of kinetic conditions in consecutive reaction sequences than is the steady current-potential behaviour.

5. CHEMICAL FACTORS

Most intermediates involved in electrochemical processes, particularly the gas evolution reactions, must be considered chemisorbed at the metal. They can arise in the discharge step as radicals which combine in a transitory chemical manner with the electrode metal. In the reverse direction of some of these reactions, the same species arise from a chemical dissociative adsorption of stable molecules catalysed by the surface of the electrode metal, e.g. as in the h.e.r. In most of these cases, the adsorbed intermediates are probably not "free" radicals in the sense involved in

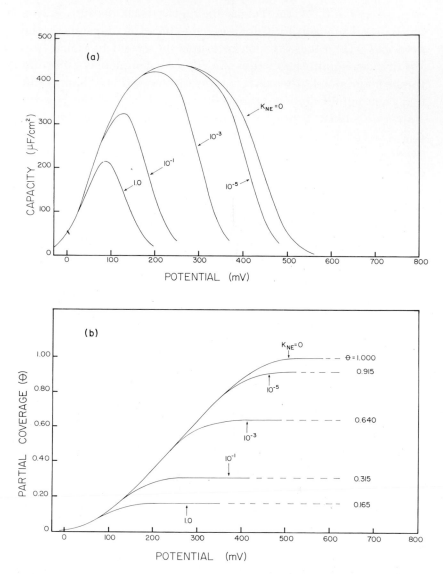

Fig. 27.   (a) Non-equilibrium adsorption pseudocapacitance for H (desorption by step II, atom-ion mechanism). K_{NE} indicates the ratio of k_2 to k_1 for steps II and I, respectively.   (b) Corresponding coverage-potential behaviour with limiting maximum coverages indicated.   (After Gileadi and Conway, 190.)

certain gas reactions, but are combined with the surface through a covalent or possibly, in the case of hydrogen, by a kind of surface metallic bond (*cf.* the Pd-H system) in the surface of the metal.   At the gas-solid interface, chemisorptions of O, H, N are usually associated at low coverage with large exothermic heats of adsorption in the range 60–75 Kcal. g. atom^{-1}.   In the presence of solvent molecules at electrodes, the magnitude of this energy may be expected to be appreciably diminished.   The heat of adsorption of intermediates, e.g. H, can, however, be indirectly determined at electrodes by studying the temperature dependence of equilibrium adsorption of hydrogen at catalytically active metals by measuring the charge required to remove the ad-layer at various temperatures (191).   The heats of adsorption vary from about 22 to 8 Kcal. mole^{-1} (referred to H_2) for Pt, Rh and Ir electrodes, and decrease with increasing coverage by about 5–10 Kcal. mole^{-1} from $\theta = 0$ to $\theta = 0.5$.   This confirms that a Temkin type of treatment in kinetic equations will be appropriate for these metals, and be preferable to the use of the Langmuir isotherm (i.e., when it is assumed that the electrochemical free energy of activation is independent of coverage).

The heats of dissociative chemisorption will usually depend on the electron-accepting or -donating properties of the metal, e.g. as measured by the work function Φ_e.   If the energy of adsorption is referred to that of the molecule undergoing the dissociation, the energy of adsorption will also be dependent on the bond-dissociation energy of the species involved.   The energy of adsorption will usually tend to have a range of values depending on what crystal planes are occupied, if only because the electronic work function can vary appreciably from one type of crystal plane exposure to another.   More specifically "chemical" effects may be associated with electrochemical adsorption at the transition metals where d-band character and the number of "d-holes" per atom of the metal (i.e. the paramagnetic susceptibility in Bohr magnetons) as well as surface ligand field effects, can be the important quantities (182,183,192,193).   The adsorption behaviour of intermediates will depend also on their own chemical properties, e.g. the relative electronegativity with respect to that of the metal crystal face at which they are adsorbed and the extent of interaction with solvent dipoles at the interface and with like chemisorbed species at the surface (*cf*. the dipole induction effects discussed above). Usually the properties of the electrode metal and those of the species adsorbed cannot be considered separately, since the nature of the chemisorption at the metal depends both on the properties of the latter and of the adsorbate.

6. METHODS FOR STUDY OF INTERMEDIATES

(i) Electrical Methods. The most generally applicable methods are based on observation of the electrical effects associated with causing changes in the extent of coverage of the electrode by the intermediates involved (194,195,196,197). This can be achieved by "charging" or "discharging" the surface layer by either of two methods: (a) the *galvanostatic* method, in which the charging current is maintained constant through a resistance having a value large compared with that of the electrochemical cell used; or (b) the *potentiostatic* method, in which a rapid change of potential (in less than several μsec.) is applied to the electrode from a potentiostat, and the time-dependent charging current associated with the electrode capacitance is recorded by means of an oscilloscope (197). Usually the steady current passing at the end of the charging process will be different from that at the beginning, because the metal-solution p.d. has been changed. The method can be applied over a wide range of potentials by using a potential step technique developed by Gerischer (197) and discussed by Gileadi and Conway (128,194). During any given transient, the charge passed will be $\int i\, dt$ over the time interval involved,* i.e. the area under the i-t relation (see Fig. 28).

The galvanostatic method originated in studies of the double-layer capacity by Bowden and Rideal (195), was extended by

---

* Under conditions where a faradaic process corresponding to the over-all reaction can proceed, allowance must be made for the charge passed during the transient by this process. A full non-steady-state calculation is then required.

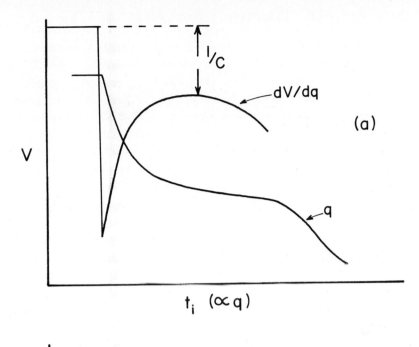

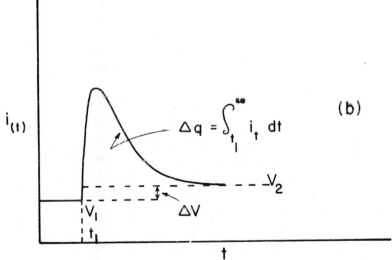

Fig. 28. Charging transients: (a) galvanostatic and differential galvanostatic at current i; and (b) potentiostatic i-t transient from potential V_1 to potential V_2. Ideally the spike in (b) should be sharp.

Frumkin and co-workers in a number of papers (196), particularly for studies of H adsorption and has been developed in specialised ways by various other workers (198,199).

The charge q passed as a function of potential obtained gives the coverage θ as a function of potential since q is proportional to θ through the constant k' (Equation 205). If the charging process occurs at potentials above the reversible potential for the over-all reaction occurring, then the total current passing is made up of a non-faradaic current (i.e. one not involving electron transfer) associated with charging of the double-layer, and a faradaic current made up of two components: (a) the current associated with discharge of ions to form intermediates, the coverage by which is changing with potential (and hence time) in the non-steady state, and (b) the current associated with the rate of the over-all process, e.g. in the reaction sequence I, II, at the various potentials attained during the transient. Usually the latter current is significant only towards the end of the transient at high overpotentials. The equation for the time-dependent potential η at constant total current i_T is formally

$$i_T = C_{dl} \frac{d\eta}{dt} + C_{ads} \frac{d\eta}{dt} + i_0 \exp \left[\frac{\eta}{b} \right] \tag{212}$$

The middle term, associated with faradaic charging,* is determined by the adsorption capacitance C_{ads}, which itself will usually be a function of potential (e.g., see Equation 211). In the range of potentials over which adsorption of intermediates is appreciable, $C_{ads} \gg C_{dl}$, and if η is not too large ($i_0 \exp [\eta/b] \ll i_T$), i_T is determined largely by $C_{ads} d\eta/dt$ and the charge passed is $\int i_T \, dt$ over the relevant duration of charging. Since $C_{ads} d\eta$ is dq, the charge associated with changing the coverage by $d\theta$, the capacitance is determined by the slope $(\partial t/\partial \eta)_{i_T}$. Since such a slope is graphically difficult to determine with satisfactory precision from

---

* Since this is the current for charging the adsorption pseudocapacitance, it may be suggested that it be called the "pseudofaradaic" current contribution in order to distinguish it from any over-all faradaic currents that may pass, and any non-faradaic current $C_{dl} d\eta/dt$.

oscilloscope photos, a more direct method is desirable, as described below.

A fast differential d.c. charging method has been described by Kozlowska and Conway (199), in which the charging curve and its time-differential coefficient are recorded simultaneously by means of a dual-beam oscilloscope. The differential curve gives directly a quantity which is the reciprocal of the capacitance as a function of the potential. It has the advantage of giving the detailed form of the potential dependence of the capacitance associated with the charging process and can indicate the presence of two or more intermediates on the surface in more complex reactions, e.g. in the formate oxidation reaction. From the charging curves themselves, which often show only some inflections, it is usually difficult to deduce capacitance sufficiently accurately by taking tangents. The types of results obtained with the three methods are illustrated schematically in Fig. 28, and a typical charging curve for the transition from H adsorption to oxygen adsorption is shown in Fig. 29. Usually there is some hysteresis between the charging curve taken from the cathodic to the anodic direction and that taken in the reverse direction (196). A complementary method for studying adsorption of intermediates as a function of electrode potential is afforded by the a.c. capacitance method in which the capacitative component of the impedance of the electrode to an a.c. signal is deduced as a function of frequency after allowance for diffusional effects. This method was developed by several of the Russian workers (189, based on 107) and applied by Eucken and Weblus (200) and Breiter (201). The results for H adsorption at Pt (201) are found to be strongly frequency-dependent (201), which may reflect a wide distribution of rate constants for step I in the h.e.r. at this metal. The a.c. results broadly indicate two forms of adsorbed H at polycrystalline Pt, and recent work (202) shows that the same type of behaviour arises at *single crystal* surfaces of Pt. The two types of adsorption may be associated with H atoms *on* and *in* the surface interstitially, as discussed by various workers (184, 203,204). The results from the a.c. method are more difficult

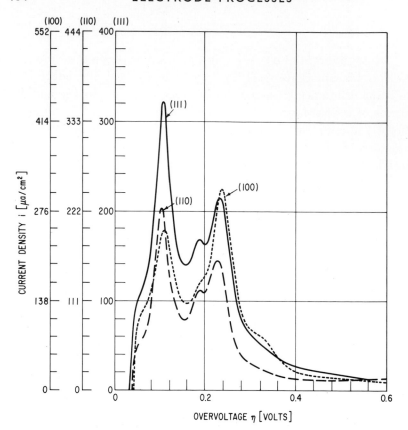

Fig. 29. Charging current peaks from the triangular-wave potentio-dynamic method for adsorbed hydrogen at single crystal faces 100, 110, and 111 at platinum. (After Will, 202.)

to interpret quantitatively than those from the d.c. method on account of the large frequency dependence of the capacity. This difficulty is not altogether eliminated in d.c. measurements, since the results can then be dependent on the rate ("rise time") at which the transient is taken (213). However, in d.c. measurements the behaviour can be analysed explicitly in terms of non-steady-state kinetics at constant i_T.

By measurements at various temperatures, the coverage of H at noble metals can be determined as a function of temperature (for a given H_2 pressure) and the heat of adsorption, ΔH_{ads},

TABLE 7–1

Thermodynamic Quantities* for Electrochemical Adsorption of Hydrogen at Pt, Ir and Rh (2.3 M H_2SO_4) (Strongly Bound Species)

Metal	ΔG_θ^0 Kcal. mole^{-1}		ΔS_θ^0 e.u.	ΔH_θ^0 Kcal. mole^{-1}
Platinum	$-10°C$	-7.3	-43	-18.5
	$70°C$	-4.1	-42	
Iridium	$0°C$	-7.0	-55	-22
	$70°C$	-3.6	-54	
Rhodium	$10°C$	-2.9	-55	-18.5
	$70°C$	$+0.6$	-56	

* Standard states, $\theta_H = 1$, $p_{H_2} = 1$ atm. (25°C).   Taken from ref. 191.

deduced.   Other thermodynamic quantities such as ΔS_{ads}^0 and ΔG_{ads}^0 can also be obtained.   Some data of Breiter are reproduced in Table 7–1 for several metals.

It will be noted that the presence of solvent water does not diminish the heats of adsorption of hydrogen (referred to $\frac{1}{2}H_2$) to values which are very much lower than those associated with adsorption from the gas phase.   Hence, theoretical discussions (144,184,185) of the role of H adsorption energy in determining the activation energy of the h.e.r., which were susceptible to the criticism that the energy of adsorption of H at electrodes in contact with solutions was unknown, are now validated in this respect.

Open-circuit e.m.f. decay curves also may be used to obtain information on the adsorption behaviour of intermediates through deductions of the electrochemical capacitance.   The principle of the method was first discussed by Butler and Armstrong (205) for the ionic double-layer capacity and developments have been made by various authors (206,207,208,209); the theoretical significance of the results obtained from the e.m.f. decay method have been critically examined by Lukovstev and Temerin (208) and Conway and Bourgault (168), particularly for the case of potential-dependent pseudocapacitance.   The calculations proceed as follows, e.g. for an anodic process.

Let the capacitance involved be C_η where C_η may be a function of η.   On interruption of a current i, the initial polarising current, the electrode process continues on open circuit through ion discharge across the double-layer capacity by the same mechanism as when steady current was passing, if a simple discharge step is occurring at a non-ideally polarisable electrode.   That is, for an anodic process,

$$\left(\frac{dq}{dt}\right)^0 = -C_\eta\left(\frac{d\eta}{dt}\right)^0 = i^0 = i_0 \exp\left[\frac{\eta^0}{b}\right] \qquad (213)$$

where the superscript zero indicates initial conditions and the negative sign is included since $d\eta/dt$ is negative for an anodic process (η positive).   If C_η has a constant value C, rearrangement of Equation 213 gives for any potential η at time t

$$\exp\left[-\frac{\eta}{b}\right]d\eta = -\frac{i_0}{C}dt \qquad (214)$$

at any time t.   Integration gives

$$-b\exp\left[-\frac{\eta}{b}\right] = -\frac{i_0 t}{C} + I = -\frac{i_0}{C}(t + J) \qquad (215)$$

where I and J are integration constants ($J = -IC/i_0$).
Taking logarithms yields

$$-\frac{\eta}{b} = \ln\frac{i_0}{Cb}(t + J) = \ln\frac{i_0}{Cb} + \ln(t + J) \qquad (216)$$

i.e.

$$-\frac{d\eta}{d[\ln(t + J)]} = b \qquad (217)$$

so that the e.m.f. decay slope is numerically the same as the Tafel slope assumed in Equation 213.   When $t = 0$, $\eta = \eta^0$ and $i = i^0$, so that, using Equation 215,

$$J = \frac{Cb}{i^0} \qquad (218)$$

Except at short times $J \ll t$, so that $d\eta/d(\ln t) = -b$; evaluation of J for known i^0 and b will give C.

If C is an adsorption pseudocapacitance, it may vary limitingly as $C_0 \exp [-\eta/b']$ or $C_0 \exp [\eta/b']$ for high and low anodic overpotentials, respectively, where C_0 is a constant.   Introduction into Equation 214 gives

$$\exp \left[-\frac{\eta}{b} \right] d\eta = -\frac{i_0}{C_0} \exp \left[\pm \frac{\eta}{b'} \right] dt \qquad (219)$$

respectively, for the two cases of variation of C with η stated above. Then

$$\exp \left[-\left(\frac{1}{b} \pm \frac{1}{b'} \right) \right] d\eta = -\frac{i_0}{C_0} dt \qquad (220)$$

and $d\eta/d[\ln (t + J)]$ is then given after integration by

$$\frac{d\eta}{d[\ln (t + J)]} = \frac{1}{1/b \pm 1/b'} \qquad (221)$$

and

$$J = \frac{C/i^0}{1/b \pm 1/b'} \qquad (222)$$

The e.m.f. decay slope will hence be greater or less than the Tafel slope depending on the sign of the argument in η in the relation of the capacity to potential.   For an anodic process, the e.m.f. decay slope will be numerically less than the Tafel slope when C_η is increasing with decreasing potential ($\theta > 0.5$), and vice versa when C_η is decreasing with decreasing potential ($\theta < 0.5$).   The e.m.f. decay method is hence valuable in giving the direction of capacity dependence on potential over a range of potentials (168).

The actual capacity as a complete function of potential can be calculated by a variation of the above method.   Quite generally, at all potentials (*cf.* Equation 213),

$$C \left(\frac{d\eta}{dt} \right)_\eta = i_0 \exp \left[\frac{\eta}{b} \right] = i_\eta \qquad (223)$$

and if the same Tafel parameters i_0 and b apply during e.m.f. decay as during polarisation

$$C = \frac{i_\eta}{(d\eta/dt)_\eta} \tag{224}$$

so that C_η can be obtained at all potentials, and integration of C w.r.t. η then can give the change of charge and associated coverage over the range of potentials through which the integration has been carried out (207). In a number of anodic processes, there is hysteresis between ascending and descending current-potential relations, and in the open-circuit decay the self-discharge current will generally be related to potential in a way analogous to that on the descending current-potential relation taken potentio-statically. In anhydrous systems, the hysteresis is much diminished (177), suggesting that it is associated with the formation of oxide films when water is present.

The original theory of e.m.f. decay (205,206) was developed on the basis of a constant double-layer capacity for an ion discharge process. In the case of systems exhibiting an adsorption pseudo-capacitance (as in the cases discussed above), the process continuing on open circuit cannot be quite identical with that in the steady state. For example, for the reactions I and II in the h.e.r. (p. 112), removal of the adsorbed H on open circuit with II the rate-determining step must proceed by the coupled mechanism

$$MH + H_3O^+ + e \rightarrow H_2$$
$$\left.\vphantom{\begin{array}{c}a\\b\end{array}}\right\rangle \text{ common potential}$$
$$MH + H_2O \rightarrow H_3O^+ + e$$

which is a kind of mixed cathodic and anodic process analogous to that in corrosion. It will be noted that an *ideal* polarised electrode cannot suffer decay of e.m.f. by either of the types of process described above since, by definition, charge transfer across the double-layer cannot occur.

A different approach for the study of open-circuit decay in terms of the double-layer capacity and the kinetics of the electrode process occurring was suggested by Delahay (210). The method, which is referred to as the "coulostatic" or "charge-step" method, involves acceptance of a controlled charge by the electrode from an external coulostatic circuit with subsequent decay of potential back to an equilibrium value. The rate of this decay is determined, as for the other cases discussed above, by the double-layer capacity and the electrode-kinetic parameters for the electrochemical process which allows leakage of charge across the double-layer. The method has been applied to fast charge-transfer processes (210) and has the advantage of allowing the determination of the

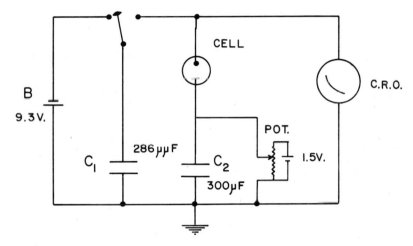

Fig. 30.   Circuit for coulostatic measurements.

differential double-layer capacity, even over ranges of potential in which a rapid electrochemical process can occur. Under the latter conditions, the a.c. bridge method is difficult to use because of the contribution of the capacitative part of the faradaic impedance to the measured total capacity.

For use of this method, a circuit such as that shown in Fig. 30 is used. A capacitor C_1 is charged up from the battery B and switched in to the electrode cell by the switch. The charge from C_1 is transferred very rapidly, changing the overpotential at the electrode; the decay of overpotential is then followed on an oscilloscope. A potentiometer is shunted by the capacitor C_2, and allows compensation of the cell voltage to be made.

An alternative method of studying consecutive reaction stages and associated intermediates in electrode reactions is that of "cyclic voltammetry." This procedure consists in subjecting the electrode to a repetitive "triangular" voltage-time sweep, usually by feeding a reference signal of this form into a potentiostat and observing the time-, and hence potential-dependent, current which passes during the voltage sweep by means of an oscilloscope. The currents which are measured are composite and will contain components due to non-faradaic, pseudo-faradaic (arising from charging or discharging adsorption capacitances associated with intermediates in the reactions) and faradaic currents passing during the voltage sweep. If any processes are diffusion-controlled,* further complications arise. The technique is thus a kind of polarographic sweep method, except that in most applications which have been made (212) the processes observed are not usually diffusion-controlled. The transient currents which pass during the sweep are determined in part by $C_{ads} \, d\eta/dt$, and it is the quantity $|d\eta/dt|$ taking periodically positive and negative constant values which can be varied in this technique from run to run. The transient currents which pass in various potential regions of the sweep may be integrated to give approximate estimates of the charge associated with the formation or removal of intermediates,† except at potentials where a net over-all reaction begins to be predominant. Since the adsorption pseudocapacitance varies with the rate at which it is measured, on account of non-equilibrium effects, the potential-sweep method can give capacitances associated with oxidation or reduction peaks which depend on the

---

* The development of this method was first made for diffusion-controlled reactions in polarography, and the theory was worked out by Sevčik (211). For most of the recent applications, however, his treatment will be inapplicable.

† This procedure and the differential galvanostatic method for the study of adsorbed intermediates in electrode reactions are analogous to the method of flash desorption used in the study of adsorption at the gas-solid interface, where the adsorbate is differentially desorbed as the temperature is increased in a controlled manner. Here the corresponding intensive variable is potential.

sweep rate (213).   The current peaks determined by $C_{ads}\,d\eta/dt$ will thus not necessarily be proportional to $d\eta/dt$ in sweeps taken at various rates.   Also, if, with increasing potential in a sweep, a potential region is passed through in which the capacitance has a maximum value (see Fig. 26), the transitory current-time relation will exhibit a maximum.   This will not generally be visually distinguishable from current maxima which arise for kinetically different reasons in passivation or inhibition processes.   In such cases, the current maximum is also observed in very slow potentiostatic scanning and is connected with the steady-state kinetics of the over-all faradaic process; in the other type of case, the current maximum arises from a pseudofaradaic process and is of a different origin.   Previously, little critical distinction has been made with regard to the effects that can arise in applications of this method. However, for an adsorption peak where the currents are pseudofaradaic, the $\int i\,dt$ area under the peak, proportional to the charge involved in forming or removing a layer of adsorbed intermediates, should be independent of sweep rate for reversible processes.

The method has the advantage of providing a rapid technique for observing the qualitative features of complex reactions, but it must be pointed out that rather little quantitative information can at present be deduced since the method lacks any firm theoretical foundation as applied to successive non-diffusion-controlled processes in the non-steady state.   It must be emphasised that the study of most electrochemical reactions requires complementary approaches by various methods, and that examination by the triangular-wave sweep method cannot give more than a superficial insight into the quantitative kinetics of the reactions which have been studied (212) by this approach.   From the point of view of electrochemical kinetics, the method is somewhat difficult to develop quantitatively for successive reactions, since the electrode process is in a condition neither of steady total current nor of steady state nor of steady potential (213).   A typical record of potentiostatic current-potential behaviour for oxide and H-adsorption at Pt, and for the oxidation of formate ions in aqueous solution is shown in Fig. 31a and b.

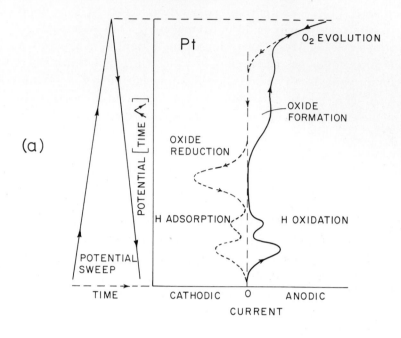

(a)

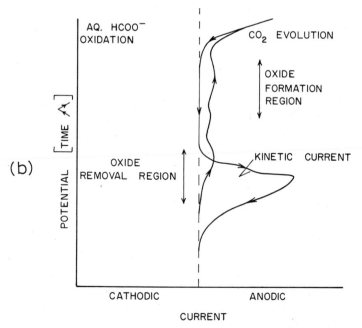

(b)

(ii) Deduction of Isotherms by the Electrical Methods.   The electrical methods discussed above, particularly the direct and differential charging procedures and the analysis of open-circuit decay rates, will give the capacity as a function of electrode potential or the pseudofaradaic charge, and hence coverage, as a function of potential.   Integration of the capacity-potential relationships will also give equivalent information on the pseudo-faradaic charge and coverage.   Experimental data obtained in this way can be compared with the form of electrochemical isotherms deduced theoretically on the basis of various assumptions (see Fig. 26c).   Alternatively, the capacity-potential profile can be interpreted directly.   It will be instructive to examine here the principle of the method involved, but it must be stated that hitherto few electrochemical reactions are known which exhibit pseudocapacitance behaviour of a sufficiently unambiguous kind for this method to be applied rigorously.

When $\theta = 0.5$, the quasi-equilibrium result for the maximum adsorption capacitance deduced for Langmuir adsorption (Equation 207) is

$$(C_L)_{\max} = \frac{k'F}{4RT} \tag{225}$$

For the more general Temkin case, in which the electrochemical free energy of activation is a function both of coverage and of potential, the effective maximum adsorption capacitance is given, for equilibrium conditions in the electrochemical radical-production step, by

$$C_m = \frac{k'F}{RT}\frac{1}{4+f} \tag{226}$$

Fig. 31.   Potentiostatic triangular-wave sweep curves for anodic charging and cathodic discharging (cyclic voltammetry): (a) oxide film and H formation and removal at Pt in aqueous solution; (b) formate oxidation in aqueous solution at Pt (schematic).

Thus the value of the "heterogeneity" parameter f could be calculated from the experimentally determined value of the maximum adsorption pseudocapacitance C_m.*

Equation 226 cannot be used directly, however, to evaluate the parameter f, since C_m is calculated theoretically per unit *real* surface area while it is measured experimentally per unit *apparent* surface area. Thus, Equation 226 can be used to calculate f only if the roughness factor (i.e. the ratio between the real and the apparent surface areas) is known from independent measurements.

An alternative method for the determination of f is as follows (178): From Fig. 25a it can be seen that the width of the C-ϕ_M profile at, for example, half the height of the maximum, is characteristic of f. Provided the C-ϕ_M profile is symmetrical, it can be shown that the adsorption pseudocapacitance has a value C which is a fraction γ of its maximum value ($\gamma = C/C_m$) at two values of the potential separated by a potential range $\Delta(\phi_M)$ characteristic of f.

Two values of the coverage exist for which $C = C_\gamma$ and are given by

$$\theta_\gamma = \tfrac{1}{2} \pm \left[\frac{1-\gamma}{4} \frac{4+f}{4+f(1-\gamma)}\right]^{1/2} \tag{227}$$

When $f = 0$, $\theta = \tfrac{1}{2} \pm \tfrac{1}{2}(1-\gamma)^{1/2}$. Correspondingly for $\Delta(\phi_M)$ between the two C_γ or ϕ_γ values,

$$\Delta(\phi_M) = \frac{2RT}{F} \ln \frac{1 + (1-\gamma)^{1/2}}{1 - (1-\gamma)^{1/2}} \tag{228}$$

Under Langmuir conditions, and more generally when $f \neq 0$,

$$\theta = \tfrac{1}{2} \pm a \tag{229}$$

and hence

$$\Delta(\phi_M) = \frac{2RT}{F} \ln \left(\frac{0.5 + a}{0.5 - a} + f\right) \tag{230}$$

* In order to obtain f, it is necessary to know the value of the constant k' in Equation 226. The geometry of the metal surface, the faradaic valency of the radicals adsorbed and their actual size are the main factors determining k', which can in most cases be estimated with an accuracy of 10%–30%.

where a in Equation 229 follows by comparison with Equation 227. The term a varies little with f, and the logarithmic term in a is almost constant, so that

$$\Delta(\phi_M) = p + qf \qquad (231)$$

where p and q are, to a good approximation, constants. Thus $\Delta(\phi_M)$ is almost linear in f (178). Hence f can be evaluated from the width of a symmetrical C-$\Delta(\phi_M)$ profile quite accurately. In practice, limitations arise from asymmetry which may be due to repulsive interaction effects, and when non-equilibrium is involved in the radical-producing step (see Chapter 6); the latter effects are, however, minimal for the formate decarboxylation reaction to which the above analysis was first applied (178) using e.m.f. decay data for deduction of the adsorption capacitance (see Equation 224).

The evaluation of f for non-equilibrium adsorption can only be carried out indirectly for certain favorable cases since both f and K_{NE} (= k_2/k_1; Equation 211) determine the capacitance behaviour. A numerical evaluation of the parameters f and K_{NE} can be obtained for certain reaction schemes, and the method has been discussed in detail in reference 190. However, attempts at quantitative applications for this case would be more uncertain than for the quasi-equilibrium case.

Deduction of heat and entropy quantities for electrochemical adsorption of intermediates at electrodes has already been discussed above. Provided relative coverage can be obtained reasonably precisely as a function of temperature, the deduction of the thermodynamic quantities for the adsorption process can be made with more certainty than the deduction of the Temkin parameter f from capacity profiles. Some independent indication of a quantity related to f, viz. $d(\Delta H_0)/d\theta$, can be obtained by deduction of heats of adsorption as a function of coverage (see Table 7–1). Since in the determination of heats and standard free energies of adsorption, only the total *charge* associated with the adsorbed intermediates under some standard conditions need be measured, this method is less susceptible to uncertainty than that based on the measurement of capacitance, e.g. by the a.c. method.

(iii) **Physicochemical Methods.** The electrical methods discussed above give results which can be quantitatively interpreted only in the case of simple reactions where one intermediate is likely to be adsorbed, e.g. in the h.e.r. or in chlorine evolution. For other reactions in which more than one species may be involved, e.g. OH, O, HO_2 in the o.e.r., N_3, N species in nitrogen evolution from azides, and R and RCOO species in the Kolbe reaction, the electrochemical methods cannot unambiguously provide a basis for the study of the intermediates since the chemical identity of the species giving rise to any capacitance which is measured may not always be clear. The role of oxides at surfaces of metals in organic oxidation reactions may sometimes be indicated by comparison of the electrochemical behaviour of the anode in the presence and absence of the organic substrate or in solutions containing no water (214). The possibility of using radio-carbon-labelled organic molecules for a study of the involvement of adsorbed radicals is a useful technique for better chemical identification of species adsorbed at the electrode, e.g. in the Kolbe reaction the C_1 and C_2 positions in acetic acid can be separately or alternatively labelled, and distinction between CH_3 and CH_3COO radical adsorption could be made as a function of potential (214,215).

If the adsorbed species appreciably cover the surface, the reflecting properties of the surface can be changed with respect to rotation of the polarisation of elliptically polarised light. Use of an ellipsometer to measure the polarisation of reflected light from electrode surfaces provides a new method for study of surface films involving precipitation of a solid product formed in electrode reactions. Recent applications have been made (216) to the study of films of calomel on mercury and oxides on platinum.

The possibility of using infra-red absorption techniques at dispersed electrode metals on silica, in order to follow production of adsorbed radicals at the surface, as has been done at the gas-solid interface, is attractive. However, most solvents which could be used would be strongly absorbing and provide too strong a background absorption for small changes of absorption due to electrochemically formed intermediates to be detected.   Similarly, direct electron-spin resonance studies at metal surfaces would be a powerful method of characterising adsorbed intermediates if the electrode metal did not interfere with the field in the r.f. resonant cavity of the instrument.   With regard to possible use of such a method, it must be borne in mind that most radicals which are formed in electrode reactions will be chemisorbed, and will then more or less lose their odd-electron free-radical character. The e.s.r. technique has, however, been extensively applied to the study of electrochemically produced radicals *in solution* (217), but this is of little interest with regard to characterisation of species which are adsorbed under steady-state conditions *on* the electrode surface.

In some reactions at large electrodes, the behaviour of adsorbed species can be inferred from observation of the rate of gas evolution from the surface as a function of potential on *open circuit*. The amount of gas evolved can be expressed in terms of diminution of coverage by the relevant chemical species or associated equivalent charge, and if this is known as a function of potential, an equivalent capacitance can be calculated.   An automatic technique for following open-circuit gas evolution was developed by Conway and Bourgault (218), who applied it to studies of the nickel-oxide electrode (168), at which open-circuit oxygen evolution occurs after polarisation.   Since several cubic centimeters of gas (say 5) are required for accurate measurement to 1 per cent, this is equivalent to about 100 coulombs of charge in the case of O_2.   For oxygen adsorbed as O, the charge required to cover 1 cm.^{2} of real area of the electrode will be about 250 μc.; hence the area required is of the order of 4×10^5 cm.^{2}.   With highly porous powder electrodes, this magnitude of area can be obtained with the order of 1 gram of material.   Hence the method is useful for porous battery and fuel-cell catalyst electrodes.   It does not, however, provide any precise knowledge of the chemical identity of the species on the surface.   If the real, electrochemically accessible area were known by another method, the faradaic valence of the ad-species could be calculated from the charge required to produce more or less full coverage. However, the real surface area accessible to one type of adsorbate test substance, e.g. Kr or N_2, may not be identical with that accessible to electrochemically formed intermediates, so that such comparisons can be misleading.

In some organic reactions, e.g. the Kolbe synthesis, the chemical nature of the radicals produced at the surface can be indicated by reactions which they undergo with suitable substrate substances. For example, the Kolbe electrolysis with acetates in the presence of various substrates leads to the production of acetylated, acetoxylated and methylated derivatives, suggesting that both $CH_3.CO^{\cdot}$ and $CH_3^{\cdot}$ as well as $CH_3.COO^{\cdot}$ radicals are produced. The latter will arise from discharge of the acetate ion at the surface and the methyl radical from heterogeneous decarboxylation of the acetoxyl radical; the evolved ethane produced in this reaction obviously can be produced by dimerisation of methyl radicals.

The dissociatively chemisorbed radicals which are probably involved as intermediates in fuel-cell oxidations of hydrocarbons have hitherto not been characterised. However, by analogy with the reactions which occur at the gas-solid interface in the absence of a liquid phase, it may be supposed that unsaturated hydrocarbons such as ethylene are initially adsorbed associatively or dissociatively as follows:

$$
\begin{array}{cc}
\mathrm{CH_2-CH_2} & \mathrm{H\quad H-C-C-H\quad H} \\
\mid\quad\mid & \mid\quad\diagup\mid\quad\mid\diagdown\quad\mid \\
\mathrm{M\quad M} & \mathrm{M\quad M\quad M\quad M\quad M\quad M}
\end{array}
$$

$$
\text{Associative Adsorption} \qquad \text{Dissociative}
$$

as indicated by infra-red absorption studies. Saturated hydrocarbons can be adsorbed only by the dissociative mechanism involving a degree of dehydrogenation and production of ethyl or ethylene radicals. It seems that the radicals involved as intermediates in hydrocarbon oxidations cannot be studied very advantageously by electrical methods alone, and complementary studies of the problem must be made by C^{14} radio-tracer methods (99,100) and gas chromatographic studies of intermediate products formed at various controlled potentials.   The fact that almost complete over-all oxidation of hydrocarbons to CO_2 can be achieved in fuel cells must not be taken to imply that more complex intermediates are not formed, but only that they are successively oxidised rather efficiently in the over-all reaction.

8
Applications to Selected Problems

Electrode processes may be conveniently divided into three classes as follows:

(a) The gas evolution reactions. These proceed usually by discharge of an ion in the solution or from a solvent molecule itself and in most cases involve two or more consecutive steps with adsorbed intermediates. In this class may also be included many organic reactions which, while not usually producing gaseous products, often proceed in several steps.

(b) The ionic redox reactions. These often proceed simply by electron transfer between the electrode metal and the redox electrolyte ion and in most cases do not involve adsorbed intermediates. The activation process is to be regarded as a thermal reorganisation of the solvation shell of the ion adsorbed in the double-layer, and the electron transfer occurs from the Fermi level of the metal across an energy barrier determined in part by the work function of the metal and the Volta p.d. at the interface.

(c) The phase-growth reactions (including phase dissolution). In this class of reactions, a phase is formed (or removed) or an existing phase is extended by successive acts of electron transfer and neutralisation (or ionisation), as in metal deposition. Alternatively, a different kind of phase can be formed, e.g. in anodic oxidations of metals at which films or layers of oxides or halides may be formed on the metal surface, which is itself attacked in the process.

Some aspects of these processes will be considered in the following sections of this chapter.

1. THE HYDROGEN EVOLUTION REACTION

Although a very large number of papers have been written on the electrochemistry of the h.e.r., no general agreement with regard to reaction mechanisms has been reached even in the case of the metal mercury for which the following steps in acid solutions

$$H_3O^+ + e + Hg \rightarrow Hg/H + H_2O \rightarrow H_2 \qquad\qquad I$$

or

$$2H_3O^+ + e \rightarrow H_2^+/Hg + 2H_2O \qquad\qquad Ia$$

with

$$H_2^+/Hg + e \rightarrow H_2 + Hg \qquad\qquad Ib$$

have variously been considered. It is actually unlikely that any final characterisation of mechanisms can be made in a general way, since the mechanism can depend specifically on the cathode metal under consideration, the solution composition and the pretreatment of the electrode surface. At some metals, the mechanism may even be different at different single crystal faces between which the electronic work functions can differ by as much as 1 e.v.   Studies of the h.e.r. have the advantage that only one type of intermediate, adsorbed H, is probably involved at most metals, although Horiuti and co-workers regard the H_2^+ ion as participating at Hg and Pt electrodes (186,188).   Also, the development of new phases during the electrolysis (e.g. as at some anodes) is not generally possible in the h.e.r. except at Pd and some of its alloys, and to a minor extent at Ni and Fe, where some permeation of atomic H into the metal occurs.

The three principal steps which may be involved were formulated on pp. 112, 114 as I, II, III for acid solutions, and steps corresponding to I and II can be written for alkaline solutions where the source of protons in discharge steps is H_2O and the conjugate base product is OH^-. Distinction between these steps as rate-controlling processes (including steps Ia and Ib proposed by Horiuti) has been discussed in many papers and six principal approaches have been made:

(a) Characterisation and interpretation of Tafel slopes.

(b) Characterisation of derivatives of the quantities η and $\ln i$ with respect to concentration, viz. $[\partial\eta/\partial(\ln c_{H^+})]_i$ and $\partial(\ln i)/\partial(\ln c_{H^+})_\eta$ and the related derivatives $[\partial(\ln i)/\partial(\ln c_{H^+})_{\phi_M, \psi_1}$ or $[\partial(\ln i)/\partial(\ln c_{H^+})]_{\eta, \psi_1}$, which are the reaction-order quantities.

(c) Characterisation of the coverage and related adsorption capacitance of the electrode.

(d) Determination of apparent activation energies from the temperature dependence of polarisation at constant current, or current at constant electrode potential (see p. 107).

(e) Examination of H/D/T isotope effects in relation to electrode metal and reaction mechanism.

(f) Miscellaneous experiments on solvent effects in the kinetics, effects of additives such as catalyst poisons or organic bases, irradiation of the electrode with u.v. light, etc.

A combined examination of Tafel slopes $[\partial\eta/\partial(\ln i)]_{c_{H^+}}$ and reaction-order quantities, as in (b) above, has led to some substantial clarification of the mechanism for several metals, e.g. Hg, Cu, Ni, Pt, Au, Pd, W studied by various workers. However, ambiguities may arise under some conditions. Thus, at appreciable coverages ($\theta_H \to 1$), step II leads to a Tafel slope of $2.3RT/\beta F$, which is the same as that for step I and Horiuti's mechanism Ia. In the case of the steps I and II under these conditions, the chemically significant reaction orders are also identical since, as $\theta_H \to 1$, θ_H will be independent of C_{H^+} (and potential), so that reaction II will be first-order in C_{H^+}. The reaction order of Ia is 2, however, so that it could be distinguished by this criterion. Distinction of I from II ($\theta_H \to 1$) can, however, be made in principle by open-circuit decay or galvanostatic discharge studies which should indicate an appreciable arrest due to adsorbed hydrogen in the case of reaction II proceeding at high-coverage conditions if the coverage at high cathodic potentials is greater than that at the reversible potential. Possible exceptions may arise if, at the reversible potential and at more cathodic polarisations, the hydrogen dissociation $H_2 \to 2\,MH$ is rapid and more or less at equilibrium with an equilibrium constant in favour of chemisorbed H.   This could lead to appreciable coverage by H even if step I were rate-determining, since the following desorption step $MH \to \frac{1}{2}H_2$ would be at quasi-equilibrium.   However, at the metals for which I is likely to be rate-determining, step III is not likely to be at equilibrium; this conclusion is based on the energy considerations given in Chapter 2, where it was shown that low energy of adsorption of H will tend to lead to a high activation energy for step I (144) and a low one for step II (184); analogously, those metals for which the energy of chemisorption of H is low usually have poor catalytic properties with respect to hydrogen molecule dissociation, the reverse of step III.

The theoretical characteristic kinetic derivatives for various reaction mechanisms are given in Table 8–1.

The case of Hg is of interest to consider further.   Most workers have regarded step I as rate-controlling in acid solutions, and this is well supported by the Tafel slope data $[b \doteqdot -2.3(2RT/F)]$ and the reaction order and related derivatives.   Lower Tafel slopes have been reported (219) at very low current densities, but this kind of behaviour may arise from contamination by platinum (220).   No significant coverage by entities such as adsorbed H or H_2^+ ions, which would give rise to adsorption pseudocapacitance, is indicated, so that steps such as II or Ia-Ib are usually not regarded as rate-determining (221) at Hg.   A further point of interest is that if step Ib were rate-controlling and step Ia were hence in quasi-equilibrium as supposed by Horiuti, the latter equilibrium would not be independent of double-layer configuration (148), since two charges are involved on one side of the reaction and one on the other (i.e., supposing that H_2^+ ions are not in equilibrium with H_2^+ in the bulk).   The result of this situation is that the derivative $[\partial \eta/\partial(\ln C_{H^+})]_{i,\psi_1}$ differs for steps I and Ib (if $\theta_{H_2^+}$ were > 0 and $\to 1$ as required to explain the Tafel slope of -0.12 v.), and step Ib is not indicated by the experimental value of this derivative.   These conclusions referring to the

TABLE 8-1

Kinetic Derivatives for Rate-Controlling Steps in the Hydrogen Evolution Reaction

Mechanism	Tafel Slopes				$\left[\dfrac{\partial \eta}{\partial(\ln C_{H_3O^+})}\right]_i$			
	Langmuir		Temkin		Langmuir		Temkin	
	$\theta \to 0$	$\theta \to 1$	Act.	Non-act.	$\theta \to 0$	$\theta \to 1$	Act.	Non-act.
Discharge								
Dil. soln.	$\dfrac{RT}{\beta F}$	—	—	—	0	—	—	—
Conc. soln.	$\dfrac{RT}{\beta F}$	—	—	—	$\dfrac{(1-\beta)RT}{F}$	—	—	—
Atom + ion								
Dil. soln.	$\dfrac{RT}{(1+\beta)F}$	$\dfrac{RT}{\beta F}$	$\dfrac{RT}{(\gamma+\beta)F}$	$\dfrac{RT}{(1+\beta)F}$	0	0	0	0
Conc. soln.	$\dfrac{RT}{(1+\beta)F}$	$\dfrac{RT}{\beta F}$	$\dfrac{RT}{(\gamma+\beta)F}$	$\dfrac{RT}{(1+\beta)F}$	$\dfrac{(1-\beta)RT}{(1+\beta)F}$	$\dfrac{(1-\beta)RT}{\beta F}$	$\dfrac{(1-\beta)RT}{(\gamma+\beta)F}$	$\dfrac{(1-\beta)RT}{(1+\beta)F}$
Atom + atom								
Dil. soln.	$\dfrac{RT}{2F}$	—	$\dfrac{RT}{2\gamma F}$	$\dfrac{RT}{2F}$	0	0	0	0
Conc. soln.	$\dfrac{RT}{2F}$	—	$\dfrac{RT}{2\gamma F}$	$\dfrac{RT}{2F}$	0	0	0	0
H_2^+ ion neutralisation								
Dil. soln.	$\dfrac{RT}{(1+\beta)F}$	$\dfrac{RT}{\beta F}$	$\dfrac{RT}{(\gamma+\beta)F}$	$\dfrac{RT}{(1+\beta)F}$	0	0	0	0
Conc. soln.	$\dfrac{RT}{(1+\beta)F}$	$\dfrac{RT}{\beta F}$	$\dfrac{RT}{(\gamma+\beta)F}$	$\dfrac{RT}{(1+\beta)F}$	$\dfrac{(1-\beta)RT}{(1+\beta)F}$	$-\dfrac{RT}{F}$	$\dfrac{(\gamma-\beta)RT}{(\gamma+\beta)F}$	$\dfrac{(1-\beta)RT}{(1+\beta)F}$

TABLE 8-1 (Continued)

Mechanism	$\left[\dfrac{\partial(\ln i)}{\partial(\ln C_{H_3O^+})}\right]_\eta$				$\left[\dfrac{\partial(\ln i)}{\partial(\ln C_{H_3O^+})}\right]_\phi$			
	Langmuir		Temkin		Langmuir		Temkin	
	$\theta \to 0$	$\theta \to 1$	Act.	Non-act.	$\theta \to 0$	$\theta \to 1$	Act.	Non-act.
Discharge								
Dil. soln.	0	—	—	—	β	—	—	—
Conc. soln.	$1-\beta$	—	—	—	1	—	—	—
Atom + ion								
Dil. soln.	0	0	0	0	$\dfrac{1+\beta}{2}$	β	$\beta+\gamma$	$\dfrac{1+\beta}{2}$
Conc. soln.	$1-\beta$	$1-\beta$	$1-\beta$	$1-\beta$	1	1	$1+\gamma$	$\dfrac{1+\beta}{2}$
Atom + atom								
Dil. soln.	0	0	0	0	2	0	2γ	2
Conc. soln.	0	0	0	0	2	0	2γ	2
H_2^+ ion neutralisation								
Dil. soln.	0	0	0	0	$\dfrac{1+\beta}{2}$	β	$\gamma+\beta$	$\dfrac{1+\beta}{2}$
Conc. soln.	$1-\beta$	$-\beta$	$\gamma-\beta$	$1-\beta$	0	0	2γ	$\dfrac{1+\beta}{2}$

mechanism at mercury probably also apply to other soft metals such as tin, lead and thallium.

The mechanism at platinum depends on the state of activation of the surface. With activated electrodes (repetitively anodised and cathodised, or platinised), a process occurs at low and intermediate current densities with a Tafel slope of $-2.3(RT/2F)$ indicating uniquely that step III is rate-controlling. At higher current densities, this process passes into a limiting current associated with $\theta_H \rightarrow 1$, followed by a further process with slope approximating $2.3(2RT/F)$ (222). This sequence of changes of Tafel slope is fairly unambiguously indicative of step III occurring with relative surface coverage by H approaching unity, followed by alternative desorption by the atom + ion process II, which will not be associated with a limiting current and can hence occur at an increasing rate with increasing overpotential.

The mechanism at the metals having intermediate catalytic and adsorptive behaviour is still the least well settled. The h.e.r. in acid solutions proceeds at these metals with various Tafel slopes from about 0.08 v. to 0.12 v., and at silver in acid solutions there is a change of slope from about 0.07–0.09 v. to 0.11–0.13 v., depending on pH. Few studies of H coverage at these metals have been made on account of the problem of anodic oxidation and dissolution of the metal below the reversible hydrogen potential. In alkaline solution at Ni, the coverage by H increases with increasing overvoltage as indicated from e.m.f. decay and discharging studies (198,207), and the Tafel slope is about 0.10 v. The discharge step I (in the form appropriate for alkaline solution) is probably the rate-controlling step (154), but the evidence is as yet conflicting rather than conclusive for this and related metals.

One of the earlier problems that linear Tafel relations could only apply at limitingly low $(\theta_H < 0.1)$ or high $(\theta_H > 0.9)$ coverage by adsorbed H may now be regarded as largely solved if the kinetics are treated for Temkin or induced heterogeneity conditions (113,171,172) at intermediate coverages by H. Linear

Tafel relations are then predictable over wider ranges of coverage (see Equations 179 through 189 and Table 8–1).

The relation of hydrogen evolution kinetics (e.g. the exchange currents) to the properties of the electrocatalyst metal has been largely rationalised in terms of the dependence of the activation energy on the free energy of adsorption of atomic hydrogen.   As has been shown above (Chapter 6, Sec. 8), there are no reasons for expecting a *direct* dependence of exchange currents for the h.e.r. at various metals on, for example, the electron work function, and the observed dependence arises indirectly through the relationship of the heat of adsorption of hydrogen to the electronic work function, as discussed by Conway *et al.* (182,183).

Complementary information on the kinetics of the h.e.r. can be obtained through the study of hydrogen/deuterium and hydrogen/tritium isotope effects.   Two types of effect may be distinguished. In aqueous solutions low in D content, the relative rates of H and D production can be characterised by the *separation factor S*, defined by

$$S = \frac{[C_H/C_D]_{gas}}{[C_H/C_D]_{soln}} \tag{232}$$

where the ratios involving C_H and C_D refer to the relative concentrations of H and D produced kinetically in the gas from the species in the solution.   The ratio $[C_H/C_D]_{gas}$ can be identified with the ratio of rates of production of H and D in the gas.   From solutions dilute in D with respect to H, the gaseous species produced in the electrolysis are principally H_2 and HD, and the dischargeable species in solution are mainly H_3O^+ and $H_2DO^!$ in acids, or H_2O and HOD in neutral or alkaline solutions.   The second quantity is the ratio R of exchange currents for the h.e.r. and deuterium evolution reaction from the respective pure H- and D-containing solutions, i.e. from H_2O and D_2O solutions.   It is to be noted that R and S, although related, are not identical quantities, since the properties of the dischargeable species D_3O^+ (or D_2O) giving rise to D in the isotopically pure solvents are not the same as in the H_2O solution case where the principal source of D is the H_2DO^+ (or HOD) species. In addition to the difference of identity of the D-containing species, in pure D_2O secondary solvent isotope effects can arise because the dischargeable ion D_3O^+ is solvated by D_2O, whereas H_3O^+ is solvated by H_2O. For the case of S measurements, however, both species H_3O^+ and H_2DO^+ are largely solvated by H_2O (in dilute D solutions), so that secondary solvent isotope effects are, to a first approximation, absent. In general, measurements of S will therefore tend to be more easily interpretable than those of R, but a statistical mechanical treatment allows a theoretical relation between R and S to be evaluated if appropriate partition functions for the H- and D-containing species are available (223,224).

Experimental S values for acid solutions have been previously divided into two groups (188), one with values of S in the range 6–7 for the transition and related metals, and the second with values of about 3, e.g. for mercury and other non-catalytic metals. However, this division is not so clear now that recent potential-dependence studies have been reported (225,226,227,301). In alkaline solutions, the S values are generally somewhat larger and the lowest values are about 5–6. Data are shown in Tables 8–2 and 8–3. The potential dependence of S values has been investigated at various current densities (226,228), and more recently (225,227) under potentiostatic conditions; the latter approach is desirable, since under controlled current conditions (226,228) time variation of electrode potential can occur and lead to spurious variations of S. At platinum and some other transition metals, the variation of S with potential is appreciable, and this effect probably arises on account of the variation with potential of the coverage of the metal by adsorbed H, and the associated change of energy of adsorption of H. Moreover, at platinum, the mechanism of the h.e.r. can also change and lead to variation of S from small values (ca. 3–4) to a larger value (ca. 7–8) at more cathodic potentials (227,229). At mercury, the variation of S with potential is small (223,230), but significant, and probably arises from electrostriction effects in the double-layer (see p. 38), and the effects of the double-layer field (which is about 10^7 v. cm.$^{-1}$ at appreciable

TABLE 8-2

Observed S and R Values at Ni, W, Fe and Hg Cathodes at 20°–25°C

Metal	Proton Source	H_3O^+ Value	H_3O^+ Reference	H_2O Value	H_2O Reference
Ni	S_D	7.0 6.7	228 188	4.5–6.5	225
	S_T	18.0 (average value)	301	24.5 (Raney-nickel) 4.1 (average value)	225 301
	R	3.0	302	—	—
Fe	S_D	—	—	7 (max. value)	225
	S_T	—	—	12.0 (max. value)	225
	R	3.0	302	—	—
W	S_D	6.0† (average value)	301	4.4† (average value)	301
	S_T	3.4*	302	—	—
	R	6.3†			
Hg	S_D	2.5–4 (aqueous) 4.0 (methanol)	225,227,230 227	—	—
	S_T	5.8 (average value) 3.8–5.1 (average value)	301 225	—	—
	R	2.0 (aqueous) 3.3 (methanol)	307 227	—	—

* Value for initial low Tafel slope region.
† Value for second (higher) Tafel slope region.

TABLE 8-3
Observed Isotope Effects at Pt Cathodes at Room Temperature

Proton Source	H₃O⁺			H₂O		
	Value	Reference	Comments	Value	Reference	Comments
S_D	5.3	228	15°C in HCl	7–7.8–5.8	225	KOH
	6.4	303,304	H_2SO_4			
	3.6–6.8–6.2	229	H_2SO_4			
	4.2–9.8–7	227	HCl (maximum)			
	4.4–2.8–4	227	$HClO_4$ (minimum)			
	8.3	225	Maximum value in H_2SO_4			
S_T	9.6	301	Average value	15.3	301	Average value in KOH
	21.5	225	Maximum value in H_2SO_4	15.3	225	Value at $\eta = 300$ mv in KOH
				17.5	225	Maximum value ($\eta = ?$) in KOH
				14	306	
R	2.0	302	R value corresponds to 30-mv Tafel slope region in HCl/DCl			
	1.5	302	R value for Pt-black in HCl/DCl for 30-mv Tafel slope region			
	1.9–2.5	305	Tafel region (?); H_2SO_4-HCl mixture			

potentials at the mercury-solution interface) on the OH force constant in the H_3O^+ ion or the H_2O molecule. Also with increasing electron density on the cathode, the bending frequency will tend to increase as in acid-base reactions.*

The principal difficulty of interpretation of the H/D isotope effects in electrochemical hydrogen evolution (as in other proton-transfer reactions) is in the assignment or calculation of fre-

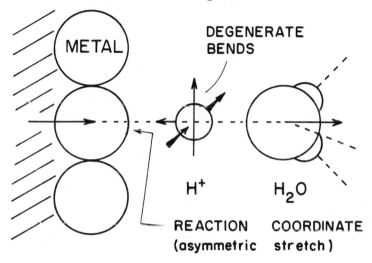

Fig. 32.   Activated complex for proton discharge at a metal, showing vibrational modes and reaction coordinate (schematic).

quencies of the activated complex (Fig. 32). In the proton-discharge step, the activated complex may conveniently be regarded as a species of the form*

$$(e_M)\ \text{M---H}^+\text{---}(OH_2)$$

where the $H^+.H_2O$ (oxonium ion) entity is treated as a pseudo-diatomic ion. For calculating S, this is a fair approximation since

---

* The activated complex is analogous to that in acid-base reactions in protonic media; in fact, in the discharge step in the h.e.r., the cathode acts like an anion of variable base strength, increasing with increasing η. Bending frequencies increase with base strength in some series of related bases acting as the proton acceptors in prototropic reactions.

the corresponding D-activated state is (e_M) M- - -D$^+$- - -(OH$_2$), and the OH$_2$ entity is hence the same in the two cases and solvation effects in excess H$_2$O will be identical. The calculation for R is more complex since the pseudodiatomic ions are then H$^+$.H$_2$O and D$^+$.D$_2$O, and changes in the frequencies of the non-dissociating OH and OD bonds as the activated complex is formed will not necessarily be identical.

In the calculation of S, the frequencies of the symmetrical stretching mode and the doubly degenerate bending mode in the activated complex for the discharge reaction (Fig. 31) may be estimated for the case of mercury (186,203), and adequate agreement with the experimental value of $S \doteq 3$ may be obtained. However, the uncertainties in the assignment of frequencies to the vibrational modes of the activated complex make diagnostic predictions of mechanism from calculated S values of limited value, particularly when more complex reactions such as the atom-ion desorption step are considered. Also, at solid metals, the state of the adsorbed H is uncertain, and surface interstitial two- or three-site intersections may arise (203) and lead to greater complexity in the interpretation. In general, however, the low values of S in acid solutions seem to correspond (188) to a rate-controlling proton-discharge step, and the higher values to the atom-ion desorption step or to discharge at surfaces appreciably covered by adsorbed H.

Proton tunneling effects have been considered in the h.e.r. (26,27) but experimentally are not indicated as being appreciable by low temperature measurements down to $-150°$C in alcoholic solutions e.g., as recently carried out by Conway and Salomon (162). The Tafel relation may also be deduced for a proton tunneling process as first shown by Christov (27) and the resulting slope is found to be dependent on H or D mass as shown by Conway (25); the slopes b depend on the barrier dimensions. Also, the frequency factor ratio for H and D discharge reactions is not anomalous (162), and the Tafel slopes are identical; for appreciable proton tunneling, calculations indicate they would differ by 25 to 30 per cent. The reaction probably proceeds by classical OH bond activation associated with electron tunneling to an activated state with charge reorganisation and approach of the resulting H atom to a stable adsorption configuration at the electrode.

2. THE OXYGEN EVOLUTION REACTION

The electrochemical evolution of oxygen requires at least three steps for a proper stoichiometric kinetic formulation, and several alternative reaction schemes may be proposed [see Chapter 6, Sec. 4 (iii)] e.g. from alkaline solution* in which OH^- is the source of O:

$$M + OH^- \rightarrow MOH + e \qquad\qquad IV$$
$$MOH + OH^- \rightarrow MO + H_2O + e \qquad\qquad V$$
$$2MO \rightarrow 2M + O_2 \qquad\qquad VI$$

or

$$M + OH^- \rightarrow MOH + e \qquad\qquad IV$$
$$2MOH \rightarrow MO + M + H_2O \qquad\qquad XII$$
$$2MO \rightarrow 2M + O_2 \qquad\qquad VI$$

Other more complex steps involving hydroperoxide species HO_2 can also be suggested (167). In these steps, the intermediate species have been written MO or MOH. However, depending on the nature of the metal anode, these species may be true adsorbed intermediates at the metal-solution interface, or they may represent the surface layer of an electrochemically formed oxide having a thickness normal to the surface many times that of a monolayer. In the latter case, the ad-species may be regarded as leading locally to a higher-valence state of the surface oxide which has grown by conversion of metal atoms to ions in an oxide lattice;† in the former case, the ad-species may form only up to an extent of one or two monolayers, e.g. as at Pt, and no bulk-phase type of oxide is formed. The distinction between adsorbed O-containing species and an oxide film is a tenuous one, but oxide layers must

---

* In acidic solutions the discharge step analogous to IV is

$$M + H_2O \rightarrow MOH + H^+ + e \qquad\qquad IVa$$

† Metal or oxygen ions may migrate depending on conditions. Distinction between these processes may be made in some cases by nuclear activation techniques.

generally be quite thick (e.g. > 1000 Å) before typical bulk properties are exhibited. At platinum and some related noble metals, the intermediates in the o.e.r. are best regarded as adsorbed oxygen species but different Pt:O ratios in the ad-layer have been reported (231,232) with increasing anode potential, which correspond formally to lower- and higher-valent two-dimensional platinum oxide surface states. However, this kind of information is obtained from electrode-charging or -discharging curves and is hence related to the electrochemical isotherm for adsorption of the O-species. It is hence dangerous to identify inflections in such charging curves with changes of degree of formal surface oxidation of the substrate electrode metal.

The reversibility of production of oxide intermediates at most noble metals hitherto studied is much less than that for corresponding production of adsorbed H cathodically. At platinum, this is clearly seen by the potentiostatic triangular potential-sweep method (p.161): in the anodic direction of polarisation, after removal of adsorbed H, there is a region (Fig. 31a) of low (double-layer) charging current which, at about $+0.7$ v. E_H, passes into a region of oxide ad-layer formation, and extends up to potentials at which free oxygen evolution is proceeding at an appreciable rate, i.e., greater than about 10^{-4} a. cm.$^{-2}$. The current for oxide-layer production remains fairly constant until greater currents can be passed by commencement of steady oxygen evolution, but at higher sweep rates some resolution into two overlapping charging regions (*cf.* the H case) is apparent. Upon reversal of the direction of the potentiostatic voltage sweep, it is seen (Fig. 31a) that the oxide is not reduced until potentials are reached which are relatively more cathodic than those required to form the oxide. A single sharper peak is observed in the cathodic potential sweep. The formation and reduction of the oxygen ad-species at platinum is thus highly irreversible. Similar conclusions follow from the galvanostatic anodic charging and cathodic discharging curves of Vetter and Berndt (233) at various pH's in aqueous solutions. By contrast, the anodic and cathodic potentiostatic charging currents observed for the removal and production of adsorbed H at platinum arise quantitatively over the same potential range, indicating reversibility of the electrochemical desorption and adsorption of H.

With increasing anodic potential, the coverage of MO and MOH species (reactions IV, V and XII, pp. 116, 183) will tend to increase, and beyond the reversible potential for oxygen production (by the over-all process $4OH^- \rightarrow O_2 + 2H_2O + 4e$) the current will (with increasing anode potential) increasingly pass by the over-all faradaic process for oxygen evolution, and relatively less by the pseudofaradaic process of formation of the layer of O-containing intermediate ad-species.   In the steady state, of course, the coverage by O, OH or other species reaches a constant value, and the rates of production and removal of the ad-species become equal.

Time variation of the current-potential relation for oxygen evolution at platinum and gold is extensive in some regions of potential where a steady coverage or thickness of oxide film is not reached rapidly.   However, provided measurements are taken at controlled times and a steady state is allowed to be approached, astonishingly reproducible current-potential behaviour can be obtained (234).   The Tafel slopes which are observed are 0.12 $[2.3(2RT/F)]$ for platinum in sulfuric acid solutions (235), 0.045 $[\frac{4}{5}(2.3RT/F)]$ at low current densities at gold in acid and alkaline solution (234) and a higher slope of $2.3(4RT/F)$ in alkaline solution at higher current densities.   At gold, the behaviour at the higher current densities is accounted for if thin and moderately conducting barrier-layer films are involved at the interface.   Part of the total metal-solution potential drop falls across this film and part in the ionic double-layer, across which the ion discharge takes place.   The latter process then occurs with an effective symmetry factor (referred to the total metal-solution potential difference), which is less than 0.5 and can be as low as 0.25–0.2, depending on the properties of the electrode metal and metal oxide film (234). Similar high Tafel slopes are observed in the Kolbe reaction (177). At the "valve" metals (Ta, Zr, Ti, Al), much thicker oxide films can be formed and a large potential difference can be maintained across the metal oxide layer, which is then effectively an insulator. The kinetics of the o.e.r. are thus intimately connected with the electrical and the electrochemical properties of the oxide film. At a number of substances (PbO_2, oxides of nickel and cobalt), oxygen evolution can occur at the interface of the bulk oxide and the solution; usually such oxides are electronically conducting or are good semiconductors. At the charged nickel oxide interface, oxygen evolution occurs with Tafel slopes of $2.3RT/2F$ to $2.3(\frac{2}{3})RT/F$ to $2.3RT/F$, depending on the conditions and preparation of the oxide, the pH and the temperature (168,176). All Tafel slopes at nickel oxide are less than $2.3RT/\beta F$ with $\beta = 0.5$, and hence are not determined by barrier-layer effects.

The oxygen-reversible potential (1.23-v. E_H) is more difficult to set up than that of hydrogen, but in pure solutions the theoretical value can be established at activated platinum (235), and the anodic and cathodic current-potential relations pass through the required potential. At the noble metals, care must be exercised in the interpretation of stationary potentials since the latter may be set up through redox reactions involving the oxides of the metal, or as mixed potentials (see below), rather than through true equilibrium in the oxygen electrode reactions

$$4OH^- \rightleftharpoons O_2 + 2H_2O + 4e \quad \text{or} \quad 2H_2O \rightleftharpoons O_2 + 4H^+ + 4e$$

in basic or acidic solutions, respectively. The potential for the latter reactions should, however, depend logarithmically on the oxygen pressure by $[P_{O_2}]^{1/4}$, and this requirement is an important thermodynamic criterion of true reversibility.

Under cathodic conditions at potentials negative to the reversible potential, the reversible over-all reactions shown above are rarely applicable except at the smallest current densities. The alternative reductions

$$O_2 + 2H^+ + 2e \rightarrow H_2O_2 \qquad \text{[acidic]} \qquad \text{XIIIa}$$

and

$$O_2 + H_2O + 2e \rightarrow HO_2^- + OH^- \quad \text{[alkaline]} \qquad \text{XIIIb}$$

tend to occur under acidic and basic conditions, respectively, the former more easily than the latter. Under most practical conditions, the oxygen electrode at platinum tends to set up a potential of *ca.* $+1.0 \pm 0.05$-v. E_H rather than the theoretical value of 1.23-v. E_H.   Frequently, this has been supposed to be due to the participation of reaction XIIIa or XIIIb, but this can hardly be maintained since on open circuit, before any net reduction of O_2 has occurred, the concentration of hydrogen peroxide must be vanishingly small, whereas in order to set up a mixed or alternative potential at *ca.* $+1.0$-v. E_H, an appreciable concentration of peroxide would be required.   It seems more probable that the mixed potential* which is set up is one between the process

$$\frac{n}{4}\,[O_2 + 4H^+ + 4e] \rightarrow \frac{n}{2}\,H_2O \qquad\qquad \text{XIV}$$

and an oxidation of a platinum oxide,†

$$PtO\left(x - \frac{n}{2}\right) + \frac{n}{2}\,H_2O \rightarrow PtO_x + nH^+ + ne \qquad \text{XV}$$

In the above, no attempt has been made to specify any particular stoichiometry to the surface Pt oxide species which might be involved.   Whether or not the true reversible potential for oxygen is effectively set up will depend on the exchange currents and Tafel slopes for processes XIV and XV; in general, the potential exhibited will tend towards that for the more reversible process, and will also depend on the separation in volts between the individual true reversible potentials for process XIV and a process such as XV.

3.   CORROSION AND PASSIVITY

(i) Phenomenology.   Although the phenomenon of corrosion has been known virtually since the preparation of the baser metals, and a very large amount of work has been published on the subject (for general texts, see 236,237), basic understanding of the mechanism and kinetics of corrosion has been slow in development.   This is because the corrosion process can be, to a large extent, specific for the metal concerned, and, for a given metal,

* Further discussion of the subject of mixed potentials will be given in Sec. 3 of this chapter, on passivity and corrosion.

† The author is indebted to Dr. J. P. Hoare for this suggestion, which arose in discussions.

depends on conditions of pH, solution composition, availability of oxygen, etc., which determine the nature of the corrosion product, the oxide, hydroxide or other salt of the metal which is formed in the oxidation process. The recognition that corrosion of metals by a liquid phase is a mixed, electrochemically controlled process of anodic oxidation of the metal and a simultaneously occurring cathodic process, is basic in the understanding of the subject and was first treated quantitatively from this point of view by Wagner and Traud (238).

Since no over-all transfer of electron charge into or out from the corroding metal is possible, the faradaic anodic process associated with metal dissolution or oxide formation must be balanced by a corresponding cathodic process to remove the electrons produced in the anodic process. The anodic and cathodic processes are therefore coupled and must proceed at the same net rate and at a common or so-called mixed potential ["*misch*-potential," first referred to in 1924 (239) with regard to amalgam decomposition]. For many years, incorrect ideas persisted that the surface of a corroding metal was composed of various regions at relatively positive or negative potentials, at which anodic and cathodic processes occurred. This is in fact not the case: the metal is an equipotential surface, but various local regions can exist at which cathodic and anodic types of reactions occur. The anodic reactions may be represented by

$$M \rightarrow M^{z+} + ze \qquad\qquad \text{XVI}$$

or

$$M + zH_2O \rightarrow M^{z+}(OH^-)_z + zH^+ \qquad\qquad \text{XVII}$$

or some corresponding oxide, depending on the metal and the pH. The cathodic reaction is either hydrogen evolution,

$$zH^+ + ze \rightarrow \frac{z}{2} H_2 \qquad\qquad \text{XVIII}$$

or oxygen reduction,

$$\frac{z}{4} O_2 + zH^+ + ze \rightarrow \frac{z}{2} H_2O \qquad\qquad \text{XIX}$$

or reduction of any other depolarising entity available.   Reaction XVI corresponds to dissolution of many base metals in acids,* where XVIII is the cathodic process in the absence of sufficient air for depolarisation by XIX.   The latter is, however, the predominant cathodic process under wet aerial corrosion conditions.

The properties and behaviour of the metal oxidation product is of basic importance in the nature and kinetics of the corrosion reaction.   For reactions of type XVI, the oxidation product is represented as a soluble ion M^{z+}, and this, once formed, usually offers no protective action; it simply remains in solution.   However, under most practical conditions of corrosion, the pH is not low, and hydrogen ions are consumed by reaction XVIII or XIX with a resulting rise of pH.   This usually has the effect of precipitating an insoluble salt or hydroxide or oxide of the metal. Often this is a gelatinous permeable material that offers no protective action against further oxidation.   In some cases, however, the rate of corrosion can be driven sufficiently fast by providing a rapid cathodic depolarisation process, e.g. in nitric acid, that the products of the metal oxidation passivate the metal with respect to further anodic attack, which then proceeds only very slowly. This is the case with Fe, Al and some other metals under special conditions.   Stainless steels already have a passivating oxide layer on their surface under most practical conditions, and the dissolution rate and passivity also depends on the electronic properties of the metal, e.g. the d-character (cf. 182,183,240) and paramagnetic susceptibility which can be controlled by alloy formation with appropriate elements (240).   In the case of zone-refined iron containing alloyed impurities, e.g. carbon or hydrogen, the kinetics of step XVI ($M^{z+} \equiv Fe^{++}$) with regard to i_0 are

---

* Dissolution to completely soluble species may occur also in alkaline solution for those base metals forming stable "metallate" ions, e.g. Zn, Pb, Al, or in complexing solutions; e.g. Cu will corrode in aqueous KCN with evolution of hydrogen, and the product is a soluble cuprocyanide ion, $Cu(CN)_4^{3-}$.   Thermodynamically, this is because the copper ion formed is stabilised by the interaction with the CN^- ligands so that Cu is a "baser" metal with respect to $Cu(CN)_4^{3-}$ ion formation than it is with respect to Cu^{++} ion formation in ordinary aqueous solutions.

unchanged. However, the hydrogen evolution rate (XVIII) is increased by an order of magnitude (241).

The nature of passivating films has been discussed for many years. In the case of iron, it appears to be a mixed oxide composed of γ-Fe_2O_3 and magnetite Fe_3O_4, and the thickness of the layer is initially some 10–100 Å. The necessity for formation of relatively thick films (i.e. > several Å) has been questioned by Kolotyrkin (242), who regards the initially passivating layer as probably less than a monolayer of some "oxide" or modified adsorbed solvent species. This conclusion was based on the examination of electrode capacitance. It should be noted that passivation is not restricted to anodic metal dissolution or oxidation processes, but also arises in the anodic oxidation of hydrogen (242) and a number of organic substances including

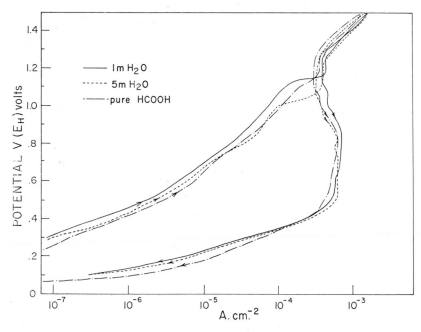

Fig. 33. Passivation limiting current in formate oxidation in anhydrous formic acid. (Upper region corresponds to steady CO_2 evolution.)

formic acid, formate, and hydrocarbons at the platinum electrode, where "oxide" or other ad-species inhibit the oxidation reactions under certain conditions (see Fig. 33) and in non-aqueous solvents.

(ii) pH-Potential Diagrams.   The type of oxidation products of the metal corrosion reaction and their passivating properties strongly depend on the conditions of pH and potential.   For a number of metals, the stability conditions (with respect to pH and electrode potentials) for various oxides, hydroxides, etc., have been mapped by Pourbaix (243).   A typical pH-potential map for the oxidation products of iron is shown in Fig. 34. Each line describes the conditions of some equilibrium between two species, e.g. Fe and Fe_3O_4, or Fe^{++} and $Fe(OH)_2^+$.   Horizontal lines refer to reactions involving electrons but not H^+ ions (i.e., the potentials are independent of pH), e.g., $Fe \rightarrow Fe^{++} + ze$ as shown in the family of lines indicated as 23 (Fig. 34); the attached numbers refer to the logarithm of the ferrous ion (activity) concentration.   Vertical lines refer to reactions involving hydrogen ions but not electrons (i.e., for acid-base reactions involving oxides, metal ions and hydroxides, which will be independent of potential, since valence changes and charge-transfer reactions are not involved); e.g., 2 refers to

$$Fe^{+++} + H_2O \rightarrow FeOH^{++} + H^+$$

Sloping lines refer to equilibria involving charge-transfer with hydrogen ions, e.g. the over-all process

$$3Fe + 4H_2O \rightarrow Fe_3O_4[2Fe^{+++} + Fe^{++} + 4O^{--}] + 8H^+ + 8e$$

The diagram may be divided into regions in which a particular species is predominant, and it is seen, for example (Fig. 34), that metallic iron is stable in the presence of water only when the potential is sufficiently depressed to the cathodic direction (this is the basis of providing "cathodic protection" by connecting a metal such as iron to a more base metal such as zinc, which by corroding itself provides a cathodic process at the "protected" metal, iron).   The potential-pH diagrams are constructed from a knowledge of the standard chemical potentials (free energies of

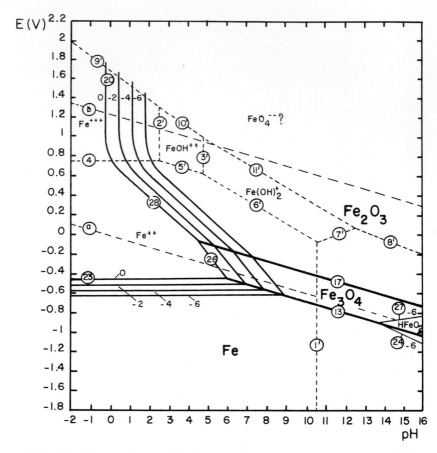

Fig. 34. Potential vs. pH diagram for oxidation of iron. (After Pourbaix, 243.)

formation) of the entities concerned. The relevant data are not always known, and this introduces uncertainty into some of the regions of stability represented by the diagrams, e.g. this difficulty arises with respect to data for ferric oxide, the solubility of which [as $Fe(OH)_3$] is variously represented by the solubility product $[Fe^{+++}][OH^-]^3$ equal to 10^{-36} or 10^{-42}; the latter figure was used as a basis for construction of Fig. 34 (243).

It is important to note that under equilibrium conditions solid products are not expected below a pH of 4 so that self-inhibition by films of such products will only occur in neutral or alkaline solutions.   In the case of low pH (nitric acid passivation) a higher oxide may be formed as a thin film, which provides the inhibition to further oxidative dissolution.

Kinetic factors may also enter into the consideration of which products are involved in the corrosion process.   Thus we may consider a situation in which an insoluble ferric oxide is produced from iron through the initial formation of ferrous ions, viz.,

$$Fe \rightarrow Fe^{2+} + 2e \nrightarrow Fe_2O_3$$

Although the oxide is the thermodynamically stable compound (under neutral pII conditions), it is possible that the first stage proceeds more rapidly than the second, so that ferrous ions and not oxide become effectively the immediate reaction products. Also, when gelatinous precipitates become the initial corrosion product, these can inhibit diffusion of simple metal ions and depolarisers from and to the surface and introduce complications.

(iii) **Current-Potential Diagrams for Corrosion.**   Kinetic representation of the corrosion process may be given by reference to the polarisation lines for the metal oxidation step, e.g. XVI in acid solutions, and for a simultaneously occurring cathodic process such as XVIII or XIX.   This is shown in Fig. 35, where E_M^0 is the reversible potential for process XVI and E_H^0 is that for example for XVIII;   corresponding exchange currents are $i_{0,M}$ for XVI, and two typical values $i_{0,H,1}$ and $i_{0,H,2}$ for XVIII.   The current-potential relations for XVI and XVIII are schematic;   they may be linear-logarithmic in potential-current density or linear-linear in these variables, or have some more complex form, e.g. see Fig. 36.   The metal oxidation reaction XVI coupled with the cathodic reaction XVIII will provide the driving free energy producing net reaction.   Reaction XVI will proceed at a rate determined by *both* the current-potential relation for itself and that for XVIII.   The potential for the metal will be raised anodically from its reversible value E_M^0 and that for the hydrogen production process will be depressed cathodically from E_H^0 until a crossing point for the current-potential relations is reached at which the anodic and cathodic processes are occurring at the same rate (referred to as the corrosion current and represented by i_c) and at a common or mixed potential E_m. The coordinates i_c, E_m of the intersection of polarisation lines can be calculated if the equations to the polarisation lines are experimentally determined, i.e., if the polarisation parameters are known. The E_m and i_c values (indicated as $E_{m,1}$ and $E_{m,2}$ and correspondingly, $i_{c,1}$ and $i_{c,2}$) will depend on the polarisation parameters defining the positions, slopes and shapes of the current-potential lines; two typical possible lines are shown for XVIII, from which it is clear that (a) the larger the i_0 value for the metal oxidation reaction the nearer will be the mixed poten-

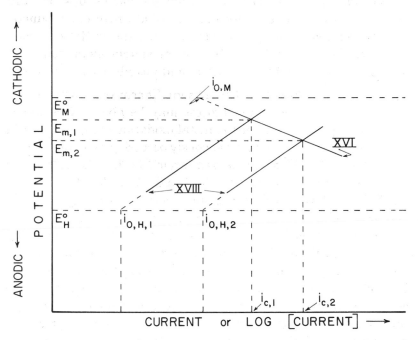

Fig. 35. Kinetic mixed-potential and corrosion-current diagram for a coupled corrosion reaction.

tial to E_{M}^{0} and the higher will be the i_c; (b) the higher the i_0 for the cathodic reaction, the more anodic is the E_m and the greater is the i_c for a given value of $i_{0,M}$; (c) for given $i_{0,M}$ and $i_{0,H}$ values the E_m and i_c values will depend on the slopes of the current-potential or log [current]–potential curves. Generally, the E_m will tend towards the E^0 value for the more reversible process, and the i_c will be determined by the kinetics of both processes (this is to be distinguished from the case of *consecutive* reactions in which the step with the smaller electrochemical rate constant is rate-controlling; here we are concerned with coupled reactions proceeding at the same electrochemical velocity). It is seen that when $i_{0,M}$ is very large, i.e., is larger than the rate at which XVIII would occur at the potential E_{M}^{0}, the rate of corrosion is simply limited by the rate at which XVIII occurs at the potential E_{M}^{0}. For this case, the corrosion current is effectively limited by the rate of only one step, i.e. the slower step XVIII. Correspondingly if $i_{0,H}$ is very large, the velocity of process XVI is that corresponding to the potential E_{H}^{0}, and i_c is then limited only by the rate of XVI at the potential E_{H}^{0}. In practice, on a solid metal, there will be a distribution of values of $i_{0,M}$ and $i_{0,H}$, depending on local exposure of various crystal faces of grains of the polycrystalline metal, so that there will be a distribution of i_c values. Also, the crystal faces with higher $i_{0,M}$ values or higher $i_{0,H}$ values will relatively tend to corrode faster. A further complicating factor is that diffusion control of metal ion removal from the surface may arise, and when XIX (the oxygen depolarisation) is the cathodic process, diffusion control of the reduction step may be rate-limiting, particularly at corrosion sites covered with solid oxidation products of the metal. Since the oxygen reduction reaction XIX will generally tend to occur over a different range of potentials from that for XVIII, the E_m values will be different from those arising when XVI and XVIII are coupled, and hence the type of oxidation products (see e.g. the potential-pH diagram, Fig. 34), may be different.

(iv) Potentiostatic Behaviour. It is possible to obtain more detailed information on the passivation behaviour of a dissolving metal by a potentiostatic technique (244) for the determination of the current-voltage curve. With increasing anodic polarisation at an attackable metal, the current at first increases in a linear* or logarithmic manner with increasing potential and, upon onset of passivation at a critical anodic current density for corrosion $i_{c,c}$, begins to decrease rapidly to a limiting current $i_{c,p}$ (Fig. 38). Usually this behaviour cannot be observed in controlled current experiments since, at the critical current density, the potential drifts up rapidly with increasing current until a new electrode process takes over which can pass more current with increasing applied voltage. This new process is generally a further oxidation of the oxide film or a "trans-passive" process of oxygen evolution, or solution decomposition in the general case, on the passivating oxide layer at the metal. The critical passivation currents usually depend on the composition of the metal, e.g. in steels, and also on the type of anion of the electrolyte.

In the potentiostatic method, after passivation conditions have been reached, the potential rises but the current remains small until again a trans-passive process can occur at high anodic potentials; such a process is usually anodic oxygen evolution. The passivation behaviour is shown schematically in Fig. 36 with regard to the current-potential behaviour observed under potentiostatic and galvanostatic conditions (Fig. 37), and in Fig. 38 with regard to the mixed-potential behaviour in a corrosion reaction. In the latter case, "active" corrosion conditions arise if the polarisation line for the cathodic process, e.g. XVIII intersects the anodic line, e.g. for XVI below the critical passivation current density $i_{c,c}$, and the mixed potential is $E_{m,a}$. If the

---

* This case arises quite generally from the Tafel equation (for an anodic reaction) in the form $i = i_0 e^{\chi \eta F/RT}$ when $\alpha \eta F \ll RT$ so that $\vec{i} = i_0(1 + \alpha \eta F/RT)$ for low polarisations. More precisely, under such conditions, the back reaction becomes significant, and the net current i_a for an anodic polarisation is $\vec{i} - \overleftarrow{i}$, the difference of individual forward and backward currents; the full current-potential relation is then a hyperbolic sine function of $\alpha \eta F/RT$, i.e.,

$$i_a = i_0(e^{\chi \eta F/RT} - e^{-(1-\alpha)\eta F/RT}) \doteq 2i_0 \sinh[\alpha \eta F/RT] \quad (\text{if } \alpha \doteq 1 - \alpha)$$

which becomes the Tafel relation for i_a when $\alpha \eta F/RT \gg 1$, and $i_a = i_0 \eta F/RT$ when $\alpha \eta F/RT \ll 1$.

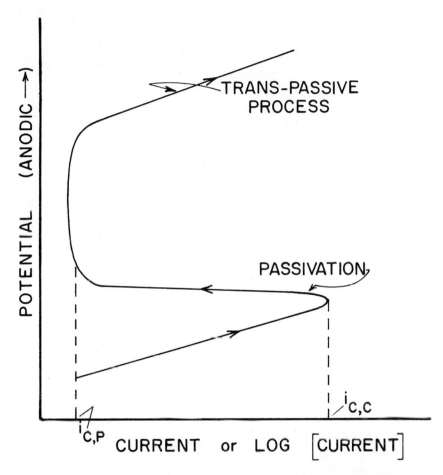

POTENTIAL   (ANODIC →)

TRANS-PASSIVE
PROCESS

PASSIVATION

$i_{c,c}$

$i_{c,p}$ CURRENT   or   LOG $\left[\text{CURRENT}\right]$

Fig. 36.   Current-potential curve for passivation as obtained by the potentiostatic method.

cathodic line intersects the current-potential relation for XVI above the passivation potential corresponding to $i_{c,c}$ and in the passivity region, only a small corrosion current $i_{c,p}$ will pass and the mixed potential $E_{m,p}$ will be much more anodic.   Since $i_{c,p} \ll i_c$, or $i_{c,c}$, the corrosion process will have been inhibited by the formation of the passive layer.   Usually highly anodic $E_{m,p}$ values corresponding to passivity are only found with Fe and Al in the presence of a strong oxidising agent such as nitric acid where the cathodic process is probably no longer XVIII or XIX but the reduction of nitric acid (XX; see Fig. 38). In some cases, passivation is attained by formation of a new higher oxide which is stable only at higher anodic potentials, e.g. at Ni. Also the conductivity and field in the surface layer will be important, and the onset of passivity may be associated with a critical increase of conductivity of the oxide layer (128,241).

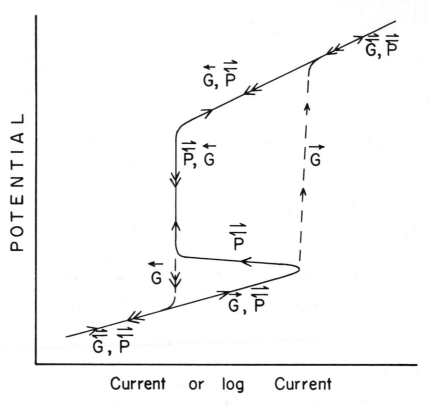

Fig. 37. Comparison of potentiostatic (*P*) and galvanostatic (*G*) current-potential relations when a passivation or transition region arises. Arrows indicate course of current-potential relations obtained by the two methods for ascending (→) and descending (←) potentials.

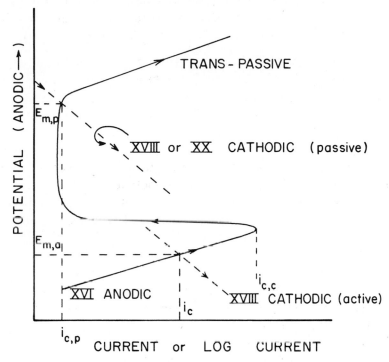

Fig. 38. Kinetic mixed-potential and corrosion-current diagram for a metal oxidation process occurring with passivation. Active corrosion and passive corrosion conditions are shown.

Corrosion type of "mixed-potential" behaviour is not limited to anodic processes of metal dissolution or oxidation, but can occur in general when an anodic process can be coupled with a cathodic one. An example was discussed in the previous section, where mixed potentials set up at the oxygen electrode were examined. Also, in the behaviour of the higher nickel oxide electrode, the electrode potential is normally greater than that of the reversible oxygen electrode, so that a self-discharge process can occur which involves reduction of the nickel oxide and evolution of oxygen. The latter reaction is the anodic partial process, and the reduction of the oxide is the cathodic process.　A mixed potential is set up (245), and the self-discharge current which passes internally is analogous to the corrosion currents discussed above.

(v) Inhibition of Corrosion.　Inhibition of corrosion is an important practical problem.　It can be achieved by any of three types of electrochemical approach, in addition to the gross method of painting the metal surface with a paint or tar: (a) cathodic protection by provision of a baser metal in contact with the metal to be protected, so that the latter is the cathodic element in a local cell and the baser metal is the one that corrodes; (b) anodic protection by driving the potential of the corroding metal into the passivation region (see Fig. 38); and (c) inhibiting the corrosion reaction by addition agents.　In the latter approach, either the metal dissolution reaction or the cathodic depolarisation (XVIII, XIX) is inhibited usually by organic substances, e.g. acridine, phenyl-acridine, quinoline derivatives as used in acid pickling, which are strongly adsorbed at the metal interface. Inorganic addition agents such as chromates, nitrites, pertechnetates are also effective, but it appears that these operate by facilitating the formation and stabilisation of protective passive films.　Conversely, some anions, e.g. Cl^-, have a marked effect in facilitating the active attack of metals, presumably by lowering the activation energy for removal, ionisation and hydration of a metal atom leaving the lattice to form a metal ion or complex ion. Another problem in which a critical balance of local anodic attack and protective passivation is required is that involved in the electrolytic machining of metals.　Here strong solutions of certain complex salts give good attack at the surface to be cut, but provide protective action at surfaces slightly removed from the counter electrode.　Good differential attack in certain directions of the "work" is then achieved.

(vi) Kinetic Origin of Passivation Effects.　Little attempt has been made previously to formulate even the principles of an electrochemical kinetic theory of passivation effects, which, as has been indicated above, are not restricted to corrosion processes nor to cases involving the existence of thick protective films such as form on the anodisable metals Al, Bi, Ta, Nb, Zn, Hf.   Similar passivation effects arise at Pt in most anodic oxidation reactions, including hydrogen ionisation.

It may be suggested that the effects can arise in two or three distinguishable ways: (a) modification of the available surface for the electrochemical reaction which is passivated by some entity P at a coverage θ_P.   This effect will modify the rate of the electrode process concerned by a factor $1 - \theta_P$; (b) modification of the electrochemical standard free energy of activation if the presence of P changes the energy of activation in a manner proportional to coverage through adsorption effects (*cf.* the Temkin isotherm and associated kinetic effects discussed in Chapter 6, Sec. 5 and Equations 178–183); (c) modification of the catalytic properties and local field at the electrode metal surface even by quite small surface coverages of P, as in heterogeneous catalyses which are sensitive to low surface coverages of poisons or self-inhibitors formed in the reaction involved.   This effect (c) is analogous to that considered under (b), but may be more specific and operate at lower surface coverages by the entity P (*cf.* 128).

Let a primary process

$$X \rightarrow X^+ + e \qquad\qquad \text{XXIa}$$

or

$$X^- \rightarrow XM + e \qquad\qquad \text{XXIb}$$

be considered (this could also be a cathodic process in the general case, but passivation effects are usually restricted to anodic reactions); X may be a metal, X^+ a resulting ion (not necessarily univalent) or X^- may be an organic or inorganic ion producing, for example, from X^- an adsorbed radical MX.   It is supposed now that beyond a certain potential, a new surface species P, e.g. an oxide or hydroxide, is formed anodically according to

$$M + H_2O \rightarrow MOH + H^+ + e \qquad\qquad \text{XXII}$$
$$(MOH \rightarrow O_2)$$

where M is the electrode metal and MOH may be formed in a

quasi-equilibrium manner [*cf.* Equations 173 and 183; Chapter 6, Sec. 4 (iii)] to an extent (coverage) dependent on potential.

Normally the rate of XXI would be written

$$i_{21} = F \frac{kT}{h} C_X \exp\left[-\frac{\Delta G_{21}^{0\ddagger} - \beta\phi_M F}{RT}\right] \tag{233}$$

in the absence of any inhibiting effects. However, if the latter arise through P ($\equiv$ OH in this example), Equation 233 will be

$$i_{21} = F \frac{kT}{h} C_X (1 - \theta_{OH})$$

$$\times \exp\left[-\frac{\Delta G_{21}^{0\ddagger} - \beta\phi_M F + (1-\beta)fRT\theta_{OH}}{RT}\right] \tag{234}$$

where the presence of OH modifies the free available surface and the activation energy for steps such as XXI. If XXII is in quasi-equilibrium (*cf.* Equation 183), then

$$f\theta = \frac{\phi_M F}{RT} + K_{22} \tag{235}$$

where for brevity K_{22} has been written as a constant involving the equilibrium constant for XXII and other factors including a concentration term. At low coverages by the supposed passivating species OH, Equation 234 will hold, and little effect of OH will be apparent unless other specific effects arise in $\Delta G_{21}^{0\ddagger}$. At intermediate coverage, the exponential term in $f\theta_{OH}$ will become predominant [it modifies $\Delta G_{21}^{0\ddagger}$ because of effects on the energy of adsorption of X at M (XXIa) or on account of effects on the energy necessary to remove X from the lattice and produce the ion X^- (XXIb); for example, this effect could arise if chemisorbed OH produces a local dipole double-layer field]. Under these intermediate coverage conditions if $\beta \doteq 1 - \beta$ ($\beta \doteq 0.5$), it is clear that a limiting passivation current will tend to be reached [$i_{21} \neq f(\phi_M)$]. As the coverage tends towards a larger value near unity (say $\theta_{OH} > 0.8$), the exponential terms in θ_{OH} will tend to become relatively constant but $1 - \theta_{OH}$ will then change (cf. Equation 173) according to

$$\frac{\theta_{OH}}{1 - \theta_{OH}} = K_{22}e^{\phi_M F/RT} \tag{236}$$

i.e.,

$$1 - \theta_{OH} \doteq \frac{1}{K_{22}}\, e^{-\phi_M F/RT} \tag{237}$$

if the coverage by products of XXI is relatively small compared with that by OH.   Equation 234 then has the limiting form,* for $\theta_{OH} \to 1$,

$$i_{21} = F\,\frac{kT}{h}\,C_X e^{-(1-\beta)f/RT}\, e^{-\phi_M F/RT} e^{-(\Delta G_{21}^{0\ddagger} - \beta\phi_M F)RT} \tag{238}$$

Hence i_{21} varies as $\exp[-(1-\beta)\phi_M F/RT]$, i.e., *decreases* after reaching a limiting value with the exponential in increasing anodic electrode potential.   This is the type of relationship required for the interpretation of passivation effects involving thin layers (242) up to a relative coverage approaching unity. The sharpness of the passivation current region will depend on the value of the Temkin parameter f.

Self-inhibition effects may also arise in some reactions, e.g. in the step $M.HCOO \cdot \to MH \cdot + MCO_2^-$ in formate oxidation, where the products of a reaction require two adsorption sites for each one involving the reacting intermediate.   Thus, typical passivation effects can still arise in the non-aqueous oxidation of formate under conditions where no "oxide" coverage can arise.

The current-potential relations which arise for an inhibited reaction of the type considered above are shown schematically in Fig. 39 for Langmuir and Temkin conditions of adsorption for the inhibiting species, e.g. OH.   The associated coverage and adsorption pseudocapacity on the same scale of electrode potentials is shown on the right-hand side of Fig. 39.

---

* Complete reversed current-potential curves can be calculated as $\theta_{OH} > 0$ and $\to 1$ with appropriate choice of the f value.

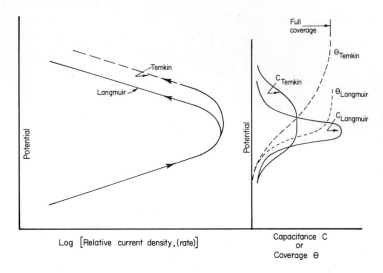

Fig. 39. Schematic current-potential curves for an inhibited oxidation process under Langmuir and Temkin conditions with associated coverage and capacity relations (*cf.* ref. 124) for the inhibiting species as a function of potential.

4. METAL DEPOSITION AND DISSOLUTION

The practical art of electrolytic metal plating has been known for many years, but until relatively recently the basic factors in its electrochemical kinetics have been little understood. The problems involved differ from those for most other electrode reactions in that a *new phase* (or extension of an existing phase) either is formed (deposition) or is removed (dissolution), and electrolytic crystal formation is the ultimate result of a discharge of ions from the solution. In general, there are two types of basic problem involved: (a) the detailed kinetics and energetic representation of the process of ion transfer, associated desolvation and neutralisation at the metal interface to produce an intermediate adsorbed metal atom or metal "ad-ion" of reduced effective net charge, and (b) the problem of incorporation of the deposited atomic entity into the growing lattice and the origin of the resulting morphology exhibited when a series of cooperative acts of incorporation of atoms into the lattice have occurred. One of the principal problems in this field still requiring much research is undoubtedly that of the relation of the microscopic kinetic steps which are involved, to the production of macroscopic structures observable as growth steps, facets, pyramids, blocks, cubes, etc. in the over-all electrocrystallisation, and how the formation of such structures characterising the metal plating depends on the solution composition, temperature, current density, presence of addition agents, etc.

(i) **Basic Kinetic Steps.** The following kinetic steps can be recognised, as treated by various authors (246,247,248,249):

(a) Ion discharge or ion transfer to form a neutral ad-atom (246) or partly charged "ad-ion," respectively, at a surface plane on the existing metal crystal (Fig. 40a).

(b) Migration of the ad-atom or ad-ion by surface diffusion (246,248,250,251) to a growing edge, at which further coordination with respect to other metal atoms is achieved with further loss of solvent molecules of hydration (Fig. 40a).

(c) Migration to a kink site (i.e. a corner in an edge or step), with further coordination by other metal atoms. (Figs. 40a and 40b.)

(d) Ion transfer direct to a kink or edge site (249) [instead of steps (b) and (c) following consecutively upon (a)], so that the surface diffusion step on crystal plane exposures would be absent. This type of process (d) is unlikely for both statistical and energetic reasons; thus, the regions exposed as edges and kinks are relatively small compared with exposures of surface planes, and detailed calculations (246) indicate unfavorable relative activation energies for such direct incorporation processes, e.g. as have been considered as the mechanism by Mott and Watts-Tobin (247) and Volmer (249).

In addition to steps (a)–(c) involving ion transfer and surface diffusion, there must be following steps (Fig. 40b) in which a typical deposited atom is built into the lattice structure, but the

(i)

Adion at plane surface

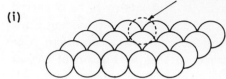

(ii)

Adion at edge

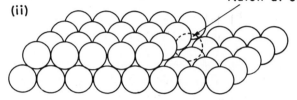

(iii)

Adion at kink

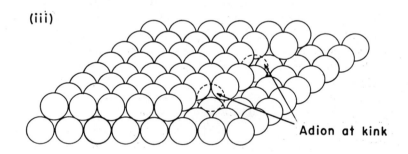

(iv)

Adion in surface vacancy

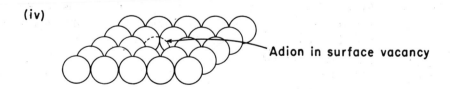

(a)

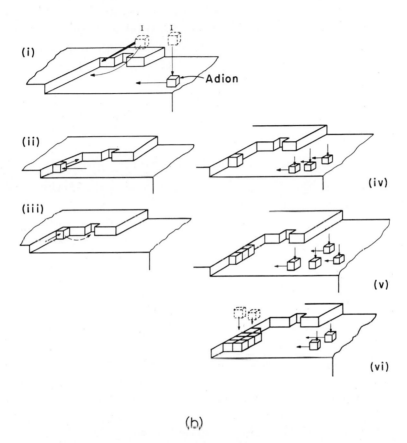

(b)

Fig. 40. Steps in metal electrodeposition. (a) Sites on a metal surface for transfer of metal ions in a cathodic process. (b) Successive steps in lattice building: (i) alternative ion-transfer steps to various sites for ion I; (ii) and (iii) surface diffusion steps; (iv), (v) and (vi) incorporation of transferred atoms into lattice by successive following transfer and diffusion steps.

atom does not itself participate in any further transfer or translational processes except in a passive way in so far as other deposited or transferred atoms are built around it. The kink site represents a site of special significance in crystal growth, for the particle having arrived at such a site need undergo no further translational processes in order to become a typical crystal atom (since other atoms build around it), and the energy of an atom at a kink site is the same as that for a bulk site inside the crystal lattice. This is seen as follows: for an hexagonal lattice of coordination number $C.N.$ the energy for complete removal or sublimation of a particle U_{sub} is

$$U_{\text{sub}} = \tfrac{1}{2}(C.N.)U_{11} \tag{239}$$

where U_{11} is the average nearest-neighbour bond energy. The factor $\tfrac{1}{2}$ arises since, in a lattice problem, U_{sub} is calculated from the sum of all nearest-neighbour interactions between identical particles, and this will give twice the total energy unless the result is multiplied by 0.5, since a particle *1* interacting with *1** is counted the same as *1** interacting with *1*. Alternatively, complete removal of a particle from the bulk can be regarded as involving a gain of energy $(C.N.)U_{11}$ with production of a lattice hole. Upon closing up the hole, an energy $-\tfrac{1}{2}(C.N.)U_{11}$ is lost, so that the total energy gained is $\tfrac{1}{2}(C.N.)U_{11}$. At the kink site, by definition, the local coordination number is only half that for a particle in the bulk. Condensation of a particle at such a site will involve a loss of energy equal to that involved in forming $\tfrac{1}{2}(C.N.)$ bonds; if these have each an energy of U_{11}, the energy of condensation of the sublimed particle at the kink site is equal in magnitude, but opposite in sign, to the energy of sublimation. The kink site position is thus energetically analogous to a bulk site situation, but the $C.N.$ is half that for the typical bulk situation. Hence a kink site is often called the half-crystal position. It will be noted that a particle can be removed from a kink site position without forming a hole as would be required for removal from the bulk.

While the ion-transfer and surface-diffusion steps can be

treated by the methods of consecutive electrochemical kinetics, the steps of crystal lattice development which occur after the particle has arrived at the half-crystal configuration cannot be investigated by purely electrochemical methods, and resort must be made to optical metallographic methods to investigate the morphology and micromorphology of developing crystal forms.

(ii) **Distinction Between Kinetic Steps.** The treatment of the kinetics from an *a priori* theoretical standpoint (246) has indicated that direct ion transfer to plane surface sites is the most likely rate-determining initial process, followed by surface diffusion, which may be rate-controlling in some cases near the reversible potential for the deposition. Other more direct and experimental indications are desirable and have been provided by two approaches, (a) the study of d.c. charging transients and (b) the study of the kinetics of metal deposition on solid and liquid surfaces.

From d.c. charging transients, the rate of rise of potential in a galvanostatic charging experiment can be obtained. If i_F is the faradaic (ion transfer) current density, and i_c that for any non-faradaic charging process, then the total (constant) current for the transient is given by

$$i = i_c + i_F = C \frac{d\eta}{dt} + i_0[e^{-\alpha\eta F/RT} - e^{(1-\alpha)\eta F/RT}] \quad (240)$$

where C is the double-layer capacitance, η is the overpotential for metal deposition at time t after switching on the constant charging current, and α is a transfer coefficient. If $\alpha\eta F/RT \ll 1$ (i.e., near the reversible potential), it may be shown (248) that

$$\eta_t = \eta_\infty(1 - e^{-t/\tau_1}) \quad (241)$$

where η_∞ is the steady-state overpotential after long times. τ_1 is a transition time defined by

$$\tau_1 = \frac{RTC}{zFi_0} \quad (242)$$

and z is the relevant faradaic valence change in the deposition ($\alpha = \beta z$). Equation 241 gives a rise time τ_1 which has been calculated (248) on the assumption that the transient is determined only by the kinetics of the ion-transfer step (Equation 241). Surface diffusion of product atoms or ad-ions to growth sites (edges, etc.) may be involved, but is not regarded as being rate-determining in the above derivation; the surface concentration of ad-atom species is approximately that at equilibrium, i.e. the concentration corresponding to electrochemical equilibrium between growth sites, surface ad-ions and ions in the solution when the electrode is at its metal-metal ion reversible potential. However, if the surface-diffusion step were rate-controlling, the surface concentration of ad-species will build up beyond the equilibrium concentration in a cathodic transient and be less in an anodic dissolution transient.

If the surface concentration of ad-ions is small, the faradaic current at time t is

$$i_{F,t} = i_0 \left[e^{-\alpha \eta F/RT} - \frac{C_{\eta,t}}{C_0} e^{(1-\alpha)\eta F/RT} \right] \tag{243}$$

where $C_{\eta,t}$ is the ad-ion concentration at η and time t, and C_0 is the equilibrium value. For low values of η ($\alpha \eta F/RT < 1$)

$$-\eta_t = \frac{RT}{zF} \frac{i}{i_0} + \frac{RT}{zF} \frac{C_{\eta,t} - C_0}{C_0} \tag{244}$$

The surface concentration $C_{\eta,t}$ must be related to time t; approximately (248),

$$\frac{dC}{dt} = \frac{i_F}{zF} - v \tag{245}$$

where v is the average flux of diffusing ad-ions from their point of deposition to growth edges, where they become incorporated into the lattice. Near equilibrium,

$$v = v_0 \left(\frac{C_{\eta,t}}{C_0} - 1 \right) \tag{246}$$

which corresponds to the concentration of ad-ions close to a growth edge being regarded as equal to the equilibrium value.

By substituting this relation into Equation 238 and integrating, we have

$$\frac{C_{\eta,t} - C_0}{C_0} = \frac{i_F}{zFv_0}\left(1 - e^{-t/\tau_2}\right) \tag{247}$$

where τ_2 is another transition time given by

$$\tau_2 = \frac{C_0}{v_0} \tag{248}$$

With the equation (Equation 237) for η_t, Equation 240 leads, with τ_2, to

$$-\eta_t = \frac{RT}{zF}\left[\frac{i_F}{i_0} + \frac{i_F}{v_0zF}\left(1 - e^{-v_0t/c_0}\right)\right] \tag{249}$$

Then for times t such that $\tau_1 < t < \tau_2$

$$-\eta_t = \frac{RT}{zF}\left[\frac{i_F}{i_0} + \frac{i_F}{C_0zF}t\right] \tag{250}$$

and

$$\frac{d\eta_t}{dt} = \frac{RT}{z^2F^2}\frac{i_F}{C_0} \tag{251}$$

Since $i_F\,dt$ is an element of charge passed in time t, the quantity $z^2F^2C_0/RT$ is a pseudocapacitance (see Equation 205) associated with the ad-ion intermediates formed in the discharge step. The experimental result which is of significance with regard to Equations 241, 242 and 248, 250 is that in the transients found for silver deposition, for example (248), the potential η_t takes 10–100 times longer to reach the "steady value" than would be expected if the ion-transfer step with rise time τ_1 were rate-determining. This delay is associated with change of concentration of the ad-ions which must occur to accommodate an increasing charge-transfer rate with increasing cathodic potential in the transient, and provides evidence for the role of surface-diffusion processes near the reversible potential. At higher cathodic potentials, the kinetics are determined at some metals by the ion-transfer rate only. In general, the indications of surface-diffusion control from transients, and near the reversible potential, may not apply to steady-state polarisation, particularly at higher potentials (*cf.* 251). The above treatment also allows some estimate of the surface ad-ion concentration C_0 on silver-(248) at the equilibrium potential. The result depends on surface preparation, but the order of magnitude of C_0 is from 10×10^{-11} to 100×10^{-11} moles cm.$^{-2}$ (a monolayer would correspond to *ca.* 1.7×10^{-9} moles cm.$^{-2}$ on an ideally flat surface).

The second indication of the role of ad-ions and surface diffusion in the kinetics is given by studies of the kinetics of metal deposition on solid and liquid surfaces, e.g. with Ga (252), at which growth sites such as edges or kinks cannot exist when the metal is in the liquid state. Under various conditions of polarisation, the rise time is somewhat longer for the solid surface than for the liquid, as expected [but the quantitative difference is small (252)]; also, the Tafel line is concave, which can also be shown to arise from a tendency for a limiting current to be reached on account of surface-diffusion control at the solid metal (no surface diffusion, of course, is necessary when the metal ion can be transferred directly into the liquid Ga phase).

The interpretation of the current-potential and time relations must also take into account the possibility of the dependence of the "activity" or electrochemical availability of dislocations as a function of overpotential (251); the step spacing l can then be dependent on this potential. At high overpotentials, the normal electrodeposition ion-transfer rate equation applies; but at low and very low overpotentials, the rate laws involve linear with exponential and square terms in η, respectively. With increasing potential, a transition from a rate expression involving the square of η to one involving the exponential function is expected. The above considerations imply a variation of step spacing with time, and hence potential, in a transient, and this effect complicates the interpretation of transients. An increase in the number of growth sites associated with decreasing l values can give rise to a current minimum in potentiostatic current-time transients, or to a potential maximum in galvanostatic transients. The latter effect (called "superpolarisation") has been observed at Ag and Zn, but decreases with better solution purification.

(iii) **Surface Nucleation.**   Two-dimensional surface nucleation, i.e. formation of incipient edges or steps on a plane surface by

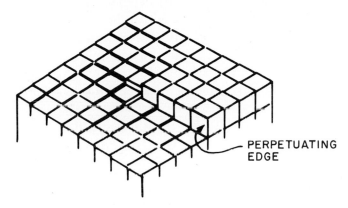

PERPETUATING
EDGE

Fig. 41.   Screw dislocation.

aggregation of ad-ions, is another kinetic process which must be considered (253, 254). It formed an important basis of earlier theories (253, 254) of metal deposition, but its necessity is now regarded as less, since it has been realised in more recent years that a real metal surface, on account of its defect nature (e.g. the presence of edges, screw dislocations which present a perpetuating edge; see Fig. 41), presents a distribution of growth sites to which ad-ions can diffuse and build up the lattice. Nucleation provides new sites for building by aggregation of the ad-species. While at low growth rates near the reversible potential, the intrinsic defects can provide sufficient growth sites, nucleation is more probable at higher current densities, where the growth rate must accommodate the current and where, under some conditions, the surface concentration of ad-ions can increase with potential if the surface diffusion is rate-limiting. A detailed treatment of the nucleation problem is given in ref. 255.

(iv) Local Distribution of Current Density. The theory of deposition involving a process of surface diffusion to growth sites leads to the conclusion that there is a linear concentration gradient between a growth step and a region in the middle of a crystal plane (256). At the crystal-growth step, the exchange of ad-ions and atoms in the lattice at the step can be very rapid, and the local ad-ion concentration approaches that for equilibrium as discussed above. However, near the centre regions of crystal planes, the ad-ion concentration will tend to be higher and the local anodic partial current density near equilibrium will therefore tend to be greater than that nearer edges. The net current producing ad-ions will be least in these regions, since the cathodic partial current over the area between growth steps will be independent of the ad-ion distribution unless the coverage by ad-ions becomes appreciable, as it may at high current densities. There can hence arise a microscopic inhomogeneity of current density across a crystal plane.

(v) Relation to Morphology of Electrolytic Crystal Deposits. The considerations reviewed briefly above can be extended to provide a qualitative explanation of some aspects of development of macroscopic crystal forms in electrodeposition.

For example, on a crystal face on which are exposed microscopic (e.g. monatomic or small) growth edges, these edges will tend to continue to grow outward, eventually overlapping each other until a new crystal plane of lower index is formed (Fig. 42). Growth on such a plane could occur only by two-dimensional nucleation of a new edge system unless dislocations appeared or were propagated in the edge growth. On a polycrystalline surface, certain faces of a given single crystal grain may grow faster than others because of differences in microscopic kinetic parameters at crystal surfaces of different indices. Such differences can arise on account of differences of binding energy

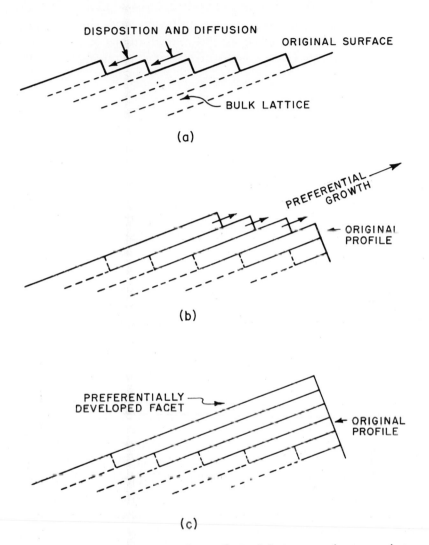

Fig. 42.   Successive stages in preferential step or edge growth to produce a facet or face of different index.

of ad-atoms at the various exposed surfaces, differences of the energy of activation for surface diffusion and differences of energy of adsorption of the solvent and of anions of the electrolyte; the absolute electrochemical rate of ion transfer can differ

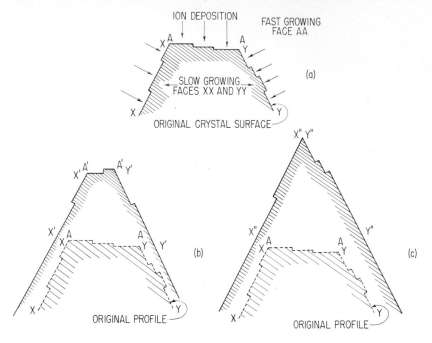

Fig. 43. Preferential growth of crystal faces in relation to morphology of electrodeposit.

also from one face to another if the potentials of zero charge are different (e.g., depending on the work functions of different faces). The result of differential rates of growth of adjacent crystal faces is that one type of face tends to become eclipsed by another; in fact, the *slower*-growing faces tend to be preserved at the expense of the *faster*-growing ones, as shown schematically in Fig. 43.

With screw dislocations (Fig. 41), an edge is automatically provided, and by the nature of this kind of dislocation it is seen that, as growth occurs from the exposed edge, it can continue in a spiral fashion without the edge growing out and disappearing (as would be the case with simple step edges on a plane surface).

The types of morphology which electrodeposits exhibit are varied and depend for a given metal on the anions of the electrolyte, the nature of the cation (whether it is a simple aquo-cation or a Werner complex ion), the current density and the presence of addition agents. Also pulsing of the current (251) has marked effects on the type of growth of electrodeposits. With regard to general morphology of deposits, deposition of copper, for example, from $CuSO_4$ in $1N$ H_2SO_4 (255) gives a pyramidal growth form at current densities up to 5×10^{-3} a. cm.$^{-2}$, but from 5×10^{-3} to 15×10^{-3} a. cm.$^{-2}$ layers are formed exhibiting smooth-faced cubic structures. At higher current densities (ca. 25×10^{-2}), fine crystallites appear. Below 0.05 N H_2SO_4 only pyramids and fine crystallites appear. Correspondingly, dendrite growth at various metals, in the form of long, thin, treelike crystals, appears at a critical current density near to the limiting diffusion current for the metal deposition, and the rate of growth is associated with the dendrite tip radius and penetration of the growing needle-like crystal through the diffusion layer with associated spherical diffusion kinetics occurring in preference to those for diffusion to a plane. This type of growth is susceptible to a quantitative treatment, the first of its kind for a particular morphology that has been given (257).

The growth of pyramids appears to be connected with the laying down of successive stepped layers of diminishing lateral extension; the inclination of the faces, which are often not smooth, depends on current density, e.g. for Cu deposition (258), and arises on account of varying ratio of the step height to extension, e.g. as reported for Pb, Ag and Cd (259). Similarly, macrostep formation appears to arise from bunching of growing microsteps (cf. Fig. 42). Detailed treatments of these morphological problems are given in references 251, 260 and 261, and early kinetic studies are given in references 262 and 263.

The macroscopic morphology of electrodeposits is markedly dependent on the type of ion from which the metal arises and particularly on the presence of organic additives. Usually these tend to produce a bright or more level deposit compared with that produced in the absence of addition agents. Unsaturated organic molecules often containing nitrogen and/or sulfur are found to be effective. Often both cationic and anionic addition agents are used which operate synergetically, presumably by mutual enhancement of adsorption. Most electrodeposition additives not only affect the microscopic kinetics of the consecutive steps, but become physically built into the lattice, often without radical chemical change (as indicated by subsequent dissolution of the metal and examination of the organic substances returned to solution). Detection of occluded additive compounds can be directly achieved by radio-labelling and autoradiography. The occlusion suggests that part of the activity of these compounds may arise by the production of defects at the growing surface as well as from effects on the kinetics of the ion-discharge and surface-diffusion steps on account of adsorption at the interface at which these processes are occurring.

5.   IONIC REDOX REACTIONS

(i) Energetics. A number of electrode reactions involve an oxidation or reduction of a conjugate redox pair. Two well-known examples are the Fe^{++}/Fe^{+++} aq. couple (264) and the quinone (Q)/hydroquinone (H_2Q) couple (264). The single electrode reactions are

$$Fe^{++}_{aq} \rightarrow Fe^{+++}_{aq} + e_M$$

and

$$H_2Q \rightarrow Q + 2H^+ + 2e_M$$

Similar redox reactions arise with the hypovanadous/vanadous couple

$$V^{++}_{aq} \rightarrow V^{+++}_{aq} + e_M$$

studied by Joshi et al. (163). In these reactions, the electrode participates in the redox reaction only as a source or sink of electrons and is thus involved rather less specifically than in the case of reactions in which adsorbed intermediates are formed. The energetic quantities which determine the standard free energy ΔG^0_R of the single half-cell reaction such as that between Fe^{++} and Fe^{+++} are readily seen by reference to the cycle:

$$
\begin{array}{ccc}
Fe^{++}_{(gas)} & \xrightarrow{I} & Fe^{+++}_{(gas)} + e_{(gas)} \\[4pt]
\Big\uparrow {\scriptstyle -\Delta G^0_{s,Fe^{++}}} & & \Big\uparrow {\scriptstyle -\Delta G^0_{s,Fe^{+++}}} \ \Big\uparrow {\scriptstyle \Phi_{e,M}} \\[4pt]
Fe^{++}_{(aq)} & \underset{\Delta G^0_R}{\rightleftharpoons} & Fe^{+++}_{(aq)} + e_M
\end{array}
\qquad (252)
$$

where ΔG^0_s terms are the standard free energies of solvation of Fe^{++} and Fe^{+++} ions, I is the third ionisation potential of Fe and $\Phi_{e,M}$ is the electron work function of the metal M (e.g. Pt) at which the redox equilibrium is set up. From Cycle 252, the standard free energy for the half-cell reaction is then

$$\Delta G^0_R = I + \Delta G^0_{s,Fe^{+++}} - \Phi_{e,M} - \Delta G^0_{s,Fe^{++}}$$

when the Volta potential $\Delta \varphi_M$ between electrode and solution is zero. Usually the thermodynamics of such reactions must be examined in conjunction with that of the standard hydrogen half-cell reaction, so that the standard potential of an over-all cell reaction such as

$$Fe^{++}_{(aq)} + H^+_{(aq)} \rightarrow Fe^{+++}_{(aq)} + \tfrac{1}{2}H_2$$

is derived from suitable e.m.f. measurements and may be discussed in terms of energetics of the over-all reaction according to the principles discussed in Chapter 2, Sec. 3(ii). Ionic redox reactions may also, of course, occur homogeneously, e.g. between Fe^{++} and Fe^{+++} in solution and between other mixed types of ions, e.g., between ferrous and stannic ions. These cases will be considered only in so far as some of the factors determining their rates are related to those involved in determining the velocity of the corresponding heterogeneous redox reactions.

(ii) **Kinetic Aspects.** A representation of the course of electro-chemical redox reactions has been given by Randles (264, 265)

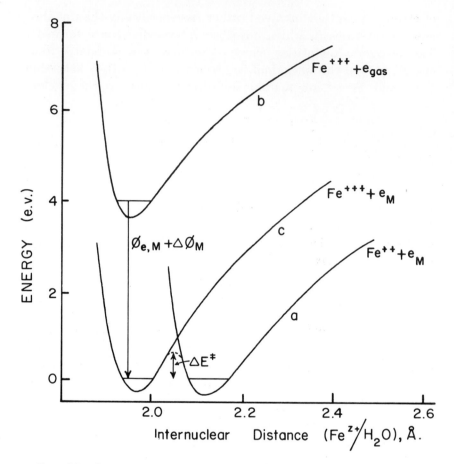

Fig. 44. Potential-energy diagram for an electrochemical redox reaction (Fe^{++}/Fe^{+++}). (After Randles, 264, 265, Fig. I.)

in terms of potential energy diagrams (Fig. 44). The structural change which is involved in the reactant(s) in a redox reaction as the activated complex is approached and product(s) is formed is different from that in, say, the proton-discharge event in the h.e.r., in which a chemical bond is stretched and broken in the activation step. In the ionic redox type of reaction, some rearrangement of the solvation shell of the ions occurs as the thermal activation process. The energy changes are shown in

Fig. 44 (265), where the axis of abscissae represents the mean distances between the centres of the ions and their respective hydrate shells in solution.   Curve a is for the $Fe_{(aq)}^{++}$ ions, curve b that for the state $Fe_{(aq)}^{+++} + e_{(gas)}$ and c that for $Fe_{(aq)}^{+++} + e_M$, the final state in the oxidation reaction.   The heat change in the over-all half-cell reaction $Fe_{(aq)}^{++} \rightarrow Fe_{(aq)}^{+++} + e_M$ is zero when $\Phi_{e,M} + \Delta\phi_M$ is 4.1 e.v., which is approximately the energy change in the reaction $Fe_{(aq)}^{++} \rightarrow Fe_{(aq)}^{+++} + e_{(gas)}$.   The region near the crossing point of curves a and c defines the activated state, and the height above the zero-point level for the initial state defines the approximate activation energy.   Changes of metal-solution p.d. affect the state $Fe_{(aq)}^{+++} + e_M$ by changing the distribution of electrons with regard to their energy in the metal.

The theory of Randles does not examine the detailed nature of the activation process nor that of the electron-transfer process. Two types of approach to this problem have been considered, and are closely related to corresponding problems arising in the kinetics of analogous homogeneous ionic redox reactions.   In the first, electron transfer from the reduced species to the oxidised species is considered as occurring with subsequent reorganisation of the hydration shell configuration (i.e. change of average number of hydration water molecules electrostatically and chemically bound by the ion in its reduced form, change in possible orientation of these water molecules and change in dielectric polarisation of the remainder of the solvent beyond the hydration shell region); in the second, discussed by Hush (266), increments of charge are regarded formally as passing in the homogeneous reaction from the reduced to the oxidised ion as the activated complex configuration is approached (or vice versa for the reverse direction of reaction), until the whole equivalent of charge is passed, eventually giving the final-state ion; in this theory, the activated complex is, statistically, an entity partway between $Fe_{(aq)}^{++}$ and $Fe_{(aq)}^{+++}$ both in effective charge and configuration of the solvation shell.

In the third type of approach, a thermal reorganisation of the solvation shell is regarded as first occurring, and when a suitable configuration is reached for which an electronic energy level in the ion is at the same energy as one in the metal (at the Fermi level, i.e. at the energy level corresponding to that of the highest occupied electron energy states), electron tunneling occurs (270) as a rapid process producing the conjugate ion but one having an unstable solvation configuration for its charge (140). The configuration then relaxes to that of the final-state ion in its equilibrium solvation state. The third kind of process mentioned above may be related to the Franck-Condon principle, which expresses the condition that in molecular spectral transitions from one electronic eigenstate to another, the electron transitions are much more rapid than the motions of the nuclei corresponding to molecular vibrations. Because of the usually different equilibrium internuclear separations in ground and electronically excited states, the electronic transition usually results in a simultaneously induced vibrational excitation. In the present case, the analogy arises because the solvent reorganisation about the ion undergoing reaction will tend to be a relatively slow process compared with the electron transition by tunneling. The latter kind of process is sometimes referred to (269; but see 268) as "non-adiabatic," i.e., when the electron is so fast that motions of nuclei (the ion and hydrate water molecules) cannot keep up with it. The corresponding term "adiabatic" (268) refers to the condition that a system will remain in a given energy eigenstate when changes (e.g. internuclear separations) are made in the configuration of the system at a vanishingly slow rate (the choice of these terms is, however, unfortunate and usually confusing (269)).

The details of the activation process have been considered above in terms of analogies to the homogeneous ion redox case; however, they apply in essentially the same manner to an oxidation-reduction reaction at an electrode (181, 266). Solvent reorganisation in the double-layer region must be regarded as arising, and when a suitable configuration is reached, transfer of the electron to or from the metal (instead of to or from the conjugate redox ion) occurs, producing the product ion in an "excited" solvation configuration (140). Analogous considerations were suggested for the activation and neutralisation processes in the discharge step of the h.e.r. (Chapter 4). The first type of step in which electron transfer precedes solvent reorganisation is usually regarded as improbable (140, 266, 267, 268, 269), and an "adiabatic" (268) type of process is preferred (269).

An equivalent representation to that given by Randles for the redox type of reaction is shown in Fig. 45, based on the considerations of Gurney (270) and Butler (271). The two states of the ion ($Fe_{(aq)}^{++}$ and $Fe_{(aq)}^{+++}$) in solution, with associated solvation energies U_s, are represented by potential energy functions for their hydration by II and III in Fig. 45 respectively. In the dehydrated state at the right-hand side of these curves (infinite separation between the ions and their corresponding hydration shells and excess solvent), the energies for curves II and III differ by the negative of the ionisation energy, i.e., for $Fe_{(gas)}^{+++} + e \rightarrow$ $Fe_{(gas)}^{++}$. Electrons are available in the metal at a highest level $\Phi_{e,M} + \Delta\phi_M$ (if $\Delta\phi_M$ is the metal solution p.d. as shown). Electron transfer can occur from an occupied level in the metal to a vacant level in the ion in its oxidised form* (and vice versa). Usually there will be a distribution of quantised energy states in the metal (closely spaced) and in the ions (270) (more widely spaced in energy†) between which the electron transfer can occur, and this must be allowed for in calculations of the electrochemical rate constant by integrating over these states (140, 270; see following section).

(iii) Redox Behaviour at Semiconductors. In a metal, the availability of electrons for a cathodic process or electron "holes" (electron-deficient states) for an anodic process is not a limiting factor in the kinetics, and the electron "activity" is not normally included in kinetic-rate expressions. At semiconductors, however, the number of "free electrons" per atom is much less than that arising as a delocalised system of valence electron orbitals

---

* A similar treatment was made by Gurney for proton discharge in the h.e.r., but it neglected H adsorption energy and hence gave incorrect predictions (cf. p. 182).

† However, coupling of vibrational, librational and rotational motions in the liquid phase produces virtually a continuous energy distribution for the ion.

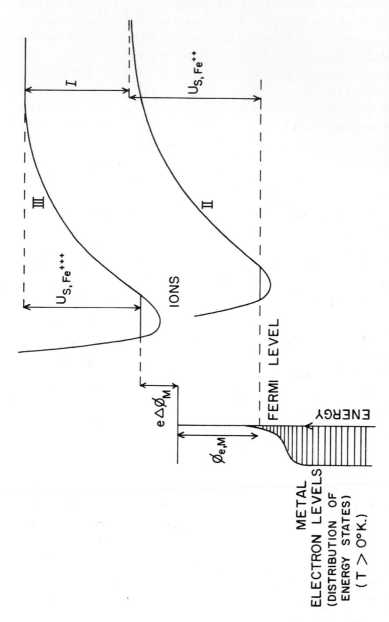

Fig. 45. Potential-energy diagram for an electrochemical redox reaction in relation to electron energy levels in the metal. (After Gurney, 270 and Butler, 271.)

in metals.   Splitting of a system of valence electron states for N separated atoms into a series of closely spaced levels in a band, as the atoms are brought together into a lattice, depends on the energy of the states involved and the interatomic spacing of the N particles in the lattice.   In a metal, a system of delocalised orbitals arises with a series of closely spaced but not identical energy states, a requirement which arises on account of the necessity that the Pauli exclusion principle applies to all the zN electron states if each atom contributes z valence electrons (e.g., z would be 2 for Mg, 3 for Al).   For zN states in N *separated* atoms the Pauli principle applies only to the electron states in *each* atom irrespective of the $N - 1$ others with which no interaction is assumed to occur if the separations are sufficiently large ($> ca.$ 10 Å).

In an insulator, all electron states in bands (corresponding to valence electron shells in the isolated atoms) are filled and an applied field cannot establish preferential mobility of electrons downfield unless sufficient energy is supplied, e.g. by photo-excitation, to excite an electron from the filled band to the next available empty band.   In a semiconductor, the highest energy of the filled band is relatively close to the lowest energy level of the next empty band (or new levels can be created near to the filled band by addition of impurities as in the so-called *extrinsic* semiconductors) so that an electron can be thermally excited to a small extent (*intrinsic* semiconductors) into this next available band, depending on the gap in energy between the top (in terms of energy of states involved) of the filled band and the lowest level available in the higher-energy empty band.   The excited electron occupying the higher-energy band provides a negative-charge carrier while the vacant electron state which is left in the previously fully occupied band (valence band) provides a "positive hole" capable of participating in conduction in a way similar to that in which the excited electron can now contribute to the conduction in the higher-energy band (conduction band).

The special properties which semiconductors can exhibit as electrodes will be connected with the fact that there are a limited number of electron and hole states available and that a distribution of them can be set up near the surface of a semiconductor in a way similar to the distribution of cations or anions near a charged interface in aqueous solution. More closely, the analogy to formation of electrons (e) and holes (p) in a thermal equilibrium in the semiconductor is the ionisation of water to produce protons and hydroxyl ions; thus,

$$ep \rightleftharpoons e + p$$

is analogous to

$$H_2O \rightleftharpoons OH^- + H^+$$

Here "ep" represents a combined electron and hole, i.e. an occupied state prior to excitation of e to the higher unoccupied band, leaving a positive hole p in the previously filled band.

In electrode processes, semiconductors thus present some properties of special interest and are also involved in a more practical way as oxides in some passivating oxide films, in the barrier layer at the valve metals (Ta, Zr, Nb, etc.), and as the films formed in the o.e.r. at most metals.

Both electron-transfer redox reactions and the anodic dissolution of the semiconductor itself, in the case of Ge, have been extensively studied. The first rigorous work with single crystal materials was carried out by Brittain and Garrett (272). These authors found different current-voltage behaviour at Ge anodes, depending on whether the electrodes were n-type or p-type germanium (i.e., whether the condition of the germanium was such as to provide negative ("n") electron-charge carriers or positive hole ("p") carriers by doping with electro-positive or electro-negative impurities, respectively; the pure germanium is both n- and p-type, i.e., it is an intrinsic semiconductor but can be doped to give predominantly n or p-type properties). At n-type electrodes, the current does not rise exponentially with electrode potential (Tafel relation) but reaches a limiting value after a short rise, while at p-type electrodes normal current-voltage behaviour is observed. Illumination increases the limiting current, so that it is concluded that the supply of holes (electron-accepting states for the anodic reaction) to the surface region of the electrode surface is the rate-limiting process in this region of the current-potential relation.   The difference of the behaviour of n- and p-type germanium electrodes is illustrated in Fig. 46 from work of Beck and Gerischer (273).

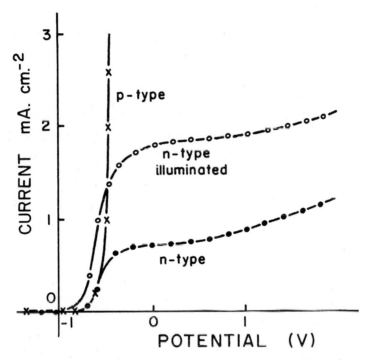

Fig. 46.   Anodic dissolution kinetics at n- and p-type germanium. (After Beck and Gerischer, 273.)

Similar effects arise with redox reactions involving other species e.g. Ce^{4+}/Ce^{3+}.   In this case (274), the rate of cathodic reduction of ceric ions is limited at n-type electrodes and is also increased by illumination.   The anodic process of Ge dissolution continues to occur, and the measured current is the difference of the anodic dissolution current and the reduction current of the oxidant ions Ce^{4+}.   However, the dissolution current is greater than that in the absence of oxidant ions, and this leads to the conclusion that the reduction of Ce^{4+} ions provides holes to the surface (by removing electrons according to $Ce^{4+} + e[Ge] \rightarrow Ce^{3+}$), which are then available for dissolution of the Ge (formally $\frac{1}{4}Ge \rightarrow \frac{1}{4}Ge^{4+} + e$), a process which hence proceeds at a faster rate, since its velocity is now no longer limited (in the limiting-current region of the current-voltage curve) entirely by the rate of diffusion of holes to the surface. The co-process of Ce^{4+} reduction thus acts as a hole injection mechanism. A number of other redox reactions have been studied at semiconductors and proceed by electron transfer to or from either the valence band (e.g., in the case of the Ce^{4+}/Ce^{3+} reaction) or the conduction band (e.g., with $H^+/\frac{1}{2}H_2$, $C_2O_4^{--}/CO_2$).

Gurney's type of treatment (270) can be extended to semiconductor electrodes (140), and the rate of the electron transfer reaction is related to the integrated product of concentration of occupied electron energy levels in one species and the concentration of unoccupied states in the other. In a semiconductor, the occupied states are n and the unoccupied states p and can be varied by depletion or injection (see above) at the surface or by changing the composition of the semiconductor. Because of the double-layer-like distribution of p and n states near the surface region of a semiconductor electrode, the condition of the surface region of the semiconductor is of great importance in semiconductor electrode kinetics.

The electron-transfer current i_c for a cathodic process may be written in terms of the distribution of occupied and unoccupied energy states as

$$i_c \propto C_{\text{ox}} \int_{-\infty}^{\infty} \nu(E)[D_{\text{occ}}(E)][W_{\text{ox}}(E)]\,dE \qquad (253)$$

and for an anodic process

$$i_a \propto C_{\text{red}} \int_{-\infty}^{\infty} \nu(E)[D_{\text{emp}}(E)][W_{\text{red}}(E)]\,dE \qquad (254)$$

where $D(E)$ are distribution functions for the densities of the indicated *occupied* or *empty* states as a function of energy E and $W(E)$ are corresponding functions for the distributions of electronic energy levels in the indicated *oxidant* or *reductant* species; $\nu(E)$ is a factor which represents the permeability of the energy barrier to electrons as a function of E, and

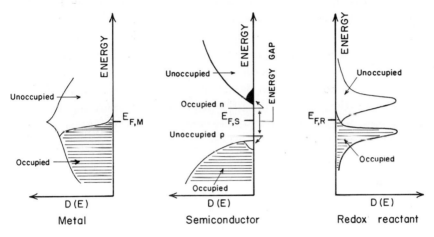

Fig. 47. Electron energy distribution functions for a metal, a semiconductor and a redox reactant (schematic; based on ref. 273).

includes the frequency with which electrons of given energies approach the barrier in a favorable direction for reaction. The distributions involved may be compared by reference to Fig. 47, which shows schematically the density of electron energy states as a function of energy E, for a metal, a semiconductor and the redox reactant. The Fermi levels $E_{F,M}$ for the metal and $E_{F,S}$ for the semiconductor are shown; in the latter case, the E_F occurs in the energy gap between occupied levels and the next higher band of states (unoccupied). A small region at the top of the occupied band and the bottom of the unoccupied band corresponds to population by positive holes (p) and electrons (n), respectively. On the right-hand side, corresponding energy distribution profiles are shown for occupied and unoccupied levels in the redox reactant (these correspond to occupied and unoccupied electron shells in the hydrated ions). An equivalent "Fermi level" $E_{F,R}$ can be indicated for the redox reactant, as shown, at the highest occupied electron energy state in the ion.

The energy levels which are available for supply or withdrawal of electrons in a cathodic or anodic reaction, respectively, are only those in the equal small regions shown in Fig. 47 in the almost completely occupied and the almost completely unoccupied bands, between which there is an appreciable energy gap. Hence electron transfer at semiconductors can occur only between the reactant and electron levels in the allowed bands. In a metal, the distribution function products corresponding to the above equations for i_a and i_c are the most important factors which control the preferential energy region for electron transfer, which

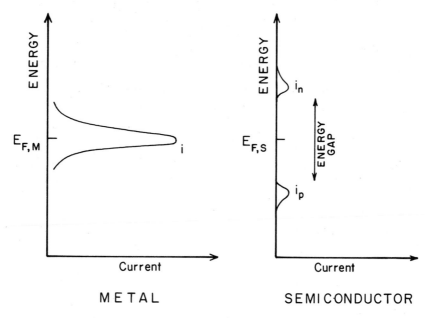

Fig. 48. Comparison of current distribution for an electron-transfer reaction as a function of electron energy for a metal and semiconductor (schematic).

is next to the Fermi level at a metallic electrode. In the semi-conductor case, this region does not normally contain any energy levels if $E_{F,s}$ is in the energy gap. Hence the rates of electron-transfer reactions between a redox reactant and the semi-conductor at equilibrium are very much smaller than corresponding rates for the same reactants at a metal, since the distribution function products are finite at a semiconductor only for regions of energy which would correspond to negligible contributions to the exchange current at a metal. This situation is illustrated in Fig. 48, where the distributions of current contributions as a function of energy are shown for a metal with a maximum i at the Fermi level, and for a semiconductor where two, much smaller, current contributions i_p and i_n arise at energies where p and n states are available. These current contributions correspond to the smaller regions of state occupancy or vacancy shown in the previous figure (semiconductor distribution of energy states).

(iv) Redox Reactions at the Dropping Mercury Cathode. Most rapid redox reactions can be studied at the dropping mercury electrode by polarographic techniques. If the reactions concerned are reversible, no direct information about the kinetics is obtainable and the rate of the electrode reaction (usually a reduction) is determined by the rate of diffusion of the redox reactant O to the mercury drop when the reactant is a molecule; when the reactant is an ion, the process is also entirely diffusion-controlled, provided the transference number of the reacting ion is small compared with that of other ions in solution, a situation that can be achieved by operating in excess of an electrochemically inactive electrolyte.

At a plane electrode of area A, the rate of diffusion dq/dt of substance O toward the electrode along a normal coordinate x is given by Fick's first law as

$$\frac{dq}{dt} = DA \frac{dc}{dx}$$

where D is the diffusion constant of O in cm.^{2} sec.$^{-1}$. In a solution in which convective or mechanical stirring is occurring, dc/dx is approximately constant within a boundary region 0.01–0.05 cm. out from the electrode. Hence dc/dx may approximately be written $(c_b - c_e)/\delta$ where δ is the boundary-layer thickness and c_b and c_e are the concentrations of O in the bulk and at the electrode respectively in g. mole cm^{-3}. If O is reduced in a z-electron over-all reduction, $O + ze \rightarrow R$, the diffusion current i_d is

$$i_d = zF \frac{dq}{dt} = zF \frac{DA(c_b - c_e)}{\delta}$$

which has a limiting maximum value $i_{d,l}$ given by

$$i_{d,l} = zF \frac{DAc_b}{\delta}$$

when $c_e \rightarrow 0$ as the oxidant is used up at the electrode by the reduction at a rate just equal to its maximum rate of arrival by diffusion determined by the maximum concentration gradient (assumed linear) c_b/δ. If O is a cation having a transference number t_+, and $t_+ \neq 0$, the current is determined both by diffusion and by electrolytic migration (field-assisted diffusion), and the relation given in Chapter 1 then follows, viz.,

$$i_d = zF \frac{DA(c_b - c_e)}{\delta t_-}$$

where $t_- = 1 - t_+$.

At the polarographically controlled dropping mercury electrode, the electrode potential is gradually changed in a linear manner with time, and currents pass accordingly as the electrode potential approaches and passes the various reversible electrode potentials for the ionic species in the solution. For simple metal ions in solution, the reduced product R is the metal atom in solution in Hg, i.e. a dilute amalgam, so that the reversible potentials are not those characteristic of the pure metals corresponding to the ions. The potentials are more noble on account of the loss of free energy of the metal upon dissolution in the Hg as amalgam; for example, the electrode potential of Na is about a volt less electropositive than that of metallic sodium with respect to unit-activity Na^+ ion in aqueous solution.

As higher cathodic potentials are reached, and the reversible potential for $O + ze \rightarrow R$ is exceeded, the cathodic current for such a reaction increases until it is limited by the maximum diffusion rate of O which gives $i_{d,l}$ for the species O. This limiting current is proportional to the concentration of O which gives the method its value as a quantitative analytical tool. Also the half-wave potential (see below) is characteristic of the reduction occurring. If any other reductions can occur at higher potentials, e.g., for other reducible species present in solution, a second or third current region will appear as the potential is further raised, and the corresponding limiting currents and half-wave potentials will be characteristic of the concentrations and electrochemical nature of these species (Fig. 49).

The equation to the polarographic current-potential relation may be obtained as follows, if the reduction is reversible. (Oxidations of most substances at mercury are not usually possible on account of the non-noble character of the electrode metal. However, they may be studied analogously at a rotating Pt-wire electrode, but in this case the results may be complicated by the formation of adsorbed oxide species at Pt.)

The diffusion-controlled reduction current for O may be written

$$i_d = k_O(c_b^O - c_e^O)$$

where k_O is a combined constant characteristic of O. Also, under limiting conditions,

$$i_{d,l} = k_O c_b^O$$

whence

$$c_e^O = \frac{i_{d,l} - i_d}{k_O}$$

Also, the reduction produces reduction products R at the electrode which diffuse away into the solution or into the electrode, depending on the nature of R (e.g., R may be a metal in Hg

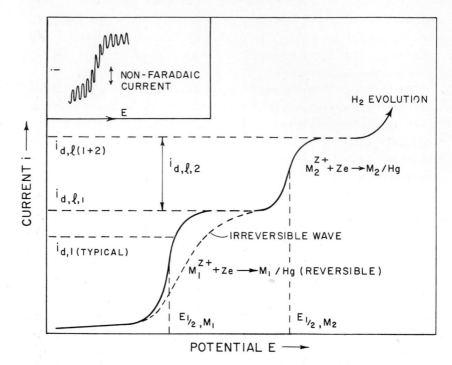

Fig. 49. Polarographic current-potential curves for reduction of two ions M_1^{z+} and M_2^{z+} at Hg. Diffusion current i_d and limiting currents $i_{d,l}$ as shown. *Inset:* non-faradaic charging currents as drops form and grow.

or a reduced organic substance, e.g. hydroquinone). Then,

$$i_d = k_R c_e^R \quad \text{or} \quad c_e^R = \frac{i_d}{k_R}$$

and $c_b^R = 0$ at the beginning of the reduction experiment. Applying the Nernst equation to the O/R equilibrium gives

$$E = E^0 + \frac{RT}{zF} \ln \frac{a_O}{a_R}$$

$$= E^0 + \frac{RT}{zF} \ln \frac{(i_{d,l} - i_d)/k_O}{i_d/k_R}$$

$+$ any activity coefficient ratio terms

Then

$$E = E^0 + \frac{RT}{zF} \ln \frac{i_{d,l} - i_d}{i_d} + \text{constant}$$

When $i_d = \frac{1}{2} i_{d,l}$, the logarithmic term is unity and E is referred to as the half-wave potential $E_{1/2}$ and also corresponds to equal concentrations of O and R species at the electrode.

Also, a plot of the electrode potential E *vs.* $\ln\left[(i_{d,l} - i_d)/i_d\right]$ is seen to give a linear relation of slope RT/zF which can hence characterise the valence change (number of electrons) in the reduction step and indicate whether the reaction is effectively a reversible one (the definition of a "reversible" reaction is of course a quantitative matter, depending on the magnitude of the exchange current; all reactions are ultimately irreversible if the net currents passed exceed i_0 by a factor greater than about 3).

When irreversibility occurs in the reduction, the above relation does not hold and E must be increased relatively more than in the case of the reversible reaction as i is increased towards $i_{d,l}$, as shown in Fig. 49. The slope is then not simply RT/zF.

The actual appearance of the current-potential relation for a diffusion-controlled reaction at the dropping mercury electrode differs from that shown in Fig. 49 by the periodic influence of the non-faradaic double-layer charging current (see inset to Fig. 49), which arises as each drop is produced and as it grows, since with increasing area of the drop with time, the double-layer capacity is increasing and requires a charging current to maintain a given potential. This type of effect does not of course arise in anodic polarography at the rotating platinum electrode, except that the double-layer capacity can depend on electrode potential.

The diffusion process at the dropping mercury electrode is a more complex problem to treat than that at a stationary plane electrode, since the mercury drop is expanding, which (a) increases its area and (b) gradually brings its surface outward towards the reactant diffusing in the solution toward it. The exact solution to this problem has, however, been given in the well-known Ilkovič equation, and analogous problems have been treated by

MacGillavry and Rideal (11), Rosebrugh and Lash-Miller (11) and Sand (12). The result for i_d is

$$i_d = 7.082 \times 10^4 z m^{2/3} t^{1/6} D^{1/2} c_b^O$$

for the instantaneous current for the z electron reduction at time t elapsed during the drop life calculated for 25°C, where i_d is in amperes, m the rate of flow of mercury is in g. sec.$^{-1}$, t is in sec., D in cm.^{2} sec.$^{-1}$ and c_b^O in mole cm.$^{-3}$.

In irreversible reductions, when the process is virtually diffusion-controlled at the plateau of a wave, the current is proportional to $t^{1/6}$ and to the square root of the head of mercury which determines the flow rate m. In the lower region, the current is mainly kinetically limited and depends on the area of the electrode, and is hence independent of head. In a reversible wave, the current is dependent on the square root of the head at any point along the wave.

6.   RAPID ELECTROCHEMICAL REACTIONS

Most of the redox reactions of the type referred to in the previous section are relatively fast in so far as they have exchange currents in the range 10^{-2}–10 a. cm.$^{-2}$. The limit of applicability of d.c. steady-state measurements at stationary electrodes is about 10^{-2} a. cm.$^{-2}$ if errors due to ohmic and diffusional effects (concentration polarisation and the approach to a limiting, diffusion-controlled current) are not to be unreasonably large. At a rotating disc electrode (275), diffusion limitation can be diminished in a controllable manner on account of the inverse dependence of the diffusion-layer thickness, which determines the concentration gradient of reacting ions at the surface (see Chapter 1) on the square root of rotation frequency of the disc electrode. Fast reactions also occur in a number of metal deposition processes, e.g., involving discharge of base metal ions at mercury and at the parent solid metals. Only deposition of some of the transition metals, e.g. Ni, are sufficiently slow to be studied by d.c. methods.

Most rapid electrochemical reactions are influenced by diffusional effects, which must be either extrapolated out or allowed for by a proper hydrodynamic treatment of the rate of mass transfer of reactant molecules or ions to the electrode surface.

When the current is determined only by rate of diffusion of the reactant to the surface, and the faradaic process at the electrode occurs virtually immediately as any diffusing particle arrives at the interfacial region, conditions are as in reversible d.c. polarography. Under such conditions, however, the kinetics of the over-all diffusion-controlled process give no information on the kinetics of the rapid faradaic process at the interface, and the current-potential curve is determined only by the half-wave potential $E_{1/2}$ and the concentration of the electrochemically reducible (or oxidisable) species in solution.

Transient methods based on the observation of the time-dependent current when a potentiostatically controlled voltage is applied to an electrode, or of the time-dependent potential when a galvanostatic current pulse i is applied, may also be used to obtain kinetic information. If the rate of the electrode reaction is controlled by diffusion alone, it can be shown that the product $i\tau^{1/2}$ is constant, where τ is a transition time determined by the relation

$$E = E_{1/2} + \frac{RT}{zF} \ln \frac{\tau^{1/2} - t^{1/2}}{t^{1/2}} \qquad (255)$$

which gives the potential E in terms of the polarographic half-wave potential $E_{1/2}$ for the process involving a z electron transfer and the time t during the transient (when $t = \tau/4$, E is the half-wave potential). The transition time τ will depend on the current density i passing according to

$$\tau^{1/2} = \frac{\pi^{1/2} z F D^{1/2} c}{2i} \qquad (256)$$

where D is the diffusion constant of the reactant at bulk concentration c. The product $i\tau^{1/2}$ is obviously constant for the case considered. If a first-order reaction precedes the electrochemical step, the kinetics are more complex (276) and $i\tau^{1/2}$ is no longer constant but decreases linearly with the magnitude of the constant current passing, a condition that provides a criterion for the participation of a pre-electrochemical reaction step. Physically, this effect arises because, at higher currents, the electrochemically reacting material is more quickly exhausted from the region near the electrode, and the quicker the transient is made (τ being then smaller) with increasing current, the less time is there for formation of the electrochemically reducible product of the pre-electrochemical reaction. The method can be applied to obtain rate constants in terms of transition times determined at various currents (277). Analogous determinations of rate constants can be made by the potentiostatic and coulostatic methods (210). Determinations of rate constants for dissociation of complex ions can also be made, the following reaction being electrochemical reduction of the resulting simple ion.

For processes which involve only a rapid electrochemical step, the a.c. impedance method may be used. This is most suitable for measurements at the mercury drop electrode, where frequency variation for the double-layer capacity is negligible. The principle of the method is that the electrode reaction presents an over-all complex impedance Z to an applied a.c. signal and this impedance can be regarded as made up of an ohmic solution resistance R_s, a diffusional impedance Z_D (involving diffusional resistance R_D and capacitance C_D contributions); a double-layer capacitance C_{dl} and a faradaic resistance R_F. It is the latter which is determined by the electrode kinetics of the electrochemical process studied, and which it is the purpose of the a.c. method to deduce from measurements of Z (determined as a series or parallel combination of a resistance and a capacitance in an a.c. bridge, or by phase-angle measurements). Usually most simple ionic redox reactions do not involve an adsorption pseudocapacitance such as arises in the gas evolution reactions and some metal deposition processes at solid metals. The detailed theory of the a.c. method will not be given here, but is treated in references 278, 279 and 280 and reviewed in reference 152. The diffusional resistance and capacitance elements are inversely related to the frequency of the a.c. signal and arise on account of the relationship between concentration polarisation set up by the current and the magnitude of that current as a function of time under alternating conditions. The concentration polarisation and the current are not in phase, and this behaviour can be represented by a series or parallel combination of a diffusional resistance and a diffusional capacitance. For a parallel equivalent circuit,

$$R_{D,\mathrm{p}} = \frac{RT}{(zF)^2}\left(\frac{2}{D\omega}\right)^{1/2}\frac{1}{c} \tag{257}$$

and

$$C_{D,\mathrm{p}} = \frac{(zF)^2}{RT}\left(\frac{D}{2\omega}\right)^{1/2}\frac{1}{c} \tag{258}$$

where c is the concentration of electrochemical reactant and ω the frequency; for a series circuit,

$$R_{D,\mathrm{s}} = \tfrac{1}{2}R_{D,\mathrm{p}}; \quad C_{D,\mathrm{s}} = 2C_{D,\mathrm{p}} \tag{259}$$

After the solution resistance component R_S has been measured in a separate experiment, the resistance associated with the electrode reaction R_E can be found as

$$R_E = R_F + R_{D,\mathrm{s}} = R_F + \tfrac{1}{2}R_{D,\mathrm{p}} \tag{260}$$

$$= \frac{RT}{zFi_0} + \frac{RT}{(zF)^2}\frac{1}{c}\left(\frac{1}{2D\omega}\right)^{1/2} \tag{261}$$

where c is the concentration of electrochemically active reactant. The resistance R_E can be measured as a $f(\omega)$, and by extrapolation to $(1/\omega)^{1/2} = 0$ $(\omega \to \infty)$, R_F can be found as

$$R_F = \frac{RT}{zFi_0} \tag{262}$$

since the diffusional component R_D goes to zero as $\omega \to \infty$. Hence i_0 can be evaluated. The term R_F as a function of i_0 is obtained for low (cathodic) overpotential η, i.e., for conditions near equilibrium, as

$$i = i_0 \left\{ \exp\left[-\frac{\alpha\eta zF}{RT} \right] - \exp\left[\frac{(1-\alpha)\eta zF}{RT} \right] \right\} \qquad (263)$$

by making the approximation $|\alpha\eta F|/RT \ll 1$ so that

$$i \doteq i_0 \left[-\frac{\eta zF}{RT} \right] \qquad (264)$$

The ohmic equivalent resistance R_F is defined by $-d\eta/di$, i.e. RT/zFi_0. Hence determination of R_F gives the exchange current i_0. In practice, the method depends on satisfactory frequency independence of the double-layer capacitance and lack of complications from adsorption pseudocapacitance; it is usually satisfactory for reactions with i_0 values up to 1 a. cm.$^{-2}$. Generally, as above, the current-density-overpotential relationship is linearised as an approximation for a.c. impedance behaviour near the reversible potential of an electrode process, and is assumed to be symmetrical about this potential. In reality, i-η curves are usually to some extent asymmetric about the reversible potential, and a rectification of the faradaic current results. The effect was first investigated by Doss and Agarwal (281) in 1950 and has been treated by Delahay (282) and others since that time. The method consists in studying the extent either of voltage rectification at controlled mean current equal to zero, or of current rectification at controlled mean potential, e.g. at the equilibrium potential, and can lead to the determination of rate constants for very fast reactions since the limits of the method are determined by the upper limit of frequency that can be used, which is about 50–100 Mc. sec.$^{-1}$.

7. ORGANIC ELECTRODE PROCESSES

A discussion of electrode processes would not be complete without reference to the field of organic electrochemistry, which, while not developed so quantitatively in its theoretical aspects as the inorganic electrochemistry of redox reactions, gas evolution reactions and metal deposition, constituted a large body of the electrochemistry that had been developed by the end of the nineteenth century. Faraday had already observed the electrolysis of organic acids such as acetic, later to be studied by Kolbe; many aromatic substitutions had been achieved by anodic electrolysis of benzene and derivatives in halide and *pseudo*halide salt solutions by the turn of the last century.

(i) **Mechanisms.*** Organic reductions can be regarded as proceeding in one of the following general ways:

(a) Electron transfer and proton transfer. Here the organic oxidant O may be reduced to a radical ion O^- by direct electron transfer or by a two-electron reduction to O^{--}, followed by proton transfer from the solvent if the latter is hydroxylic or if it contains H^+ ions. The electron and proton transfer may go in consecutive steps, two of which are usually necessary if the product is not to be a free radical. An example of this type of reaction is the reduction of dibromoethane and dibromobutane (283) at Hg which yield ethylene and butylene, respectively, by the mechanisms

$$R\ CH\ (Br).CH(Br)R\ +\ 2e\ \rightarrow\ R\ CH{=}CHR\ +\ 2Br^-$$

If H atoms (see below) were the reductive agents, the hydrocarbons ethane and butane would tend to be produced unless H atom abstraction also occurs. In aprotic solvents, however, relatively stable radical ions can be produced by the electron transfer mechanism particularly in the case of aromatic oxidants.

(b) Electrochemical hydrogenation. Here the electron-transfer step involves production of adsorbed atomic hydrogen at the electrode surface, followed by a heterogeneous reaction with the oxidant. This type of reaction would be expected to predominate at those metals at which hydrogen chemisorption occurs and the H-coverage is appreciable, e.g., at the noble transition metals.

* See table in Appendix, p. 283.

Organic oxidations may proceed similarly:

(a) By electron withdrawal to form a carbonium ion radical which reacts in hydroxylic solvents by uptake of an OH^- ion. In the halogenation and *pseudo*halogenation (e.g. in KCN and KCNS electrolytes) of aromatic substances, it is unknown whether an electron-withdrawal step occurs first, followed by reaction with the X^- (halide) ion or whether the molecule reacts with adsorbed X or X_2 molecules at the interface (produced in a prior electrochemical step) by discharge of X^- at the electrode [see (b)].

(b) By electrochemical catalysed oxidation involving reaction with metal oxide species produced in a prior electrochemical step. This is probably the mechanism of some electrochemical oxidations in aqueous solution at Pt. However, specific chemisorption of the organic reductant at the electrode metal in addition to its reaction with oxide ad-species is probably necessary.

The necessity for control of electrode potential in organic electrode reactions is a factor which has only relatively recently been appreciated. Apart from determining the coverage of some electrodes by adsorbed H- or O-containing species, potential will also be most important in determining the adsorption of the organic reactant itself as was discussed in Chapters 3, 4 and 5. The adsorption will depend on the electrode potential in relation to that of zero charge.* This factor has not been widely appreciated in work on organic electrochemical reactions. Often the effects of electrode potential are highly specific. In the reduction of nitrobenzene, various steps are possible and their occurrence is sensitive to the electrode potential, e.g.,

$$C_6H_5NO_2 \xrightarrow{2e} C_6H_5NO \xrightarrow{2e} C_6H_5NH.OH \xrightarrow{2e} C_6H_5NH_2$$

Similarly, in the reduction of *p*-aminoacetophenone at the mercury cathode, either the hydrol or the pinacol results,

---

* In the case of polar molecules, the potential or field will not only determine the surface excess but also cause orientation of the whole molecule or of its functional groups. Hence specific and stereospecific effects can arise with changing potential.

depending on the potential (284):

$$p\text{-}NH_2.C_6H_4.CO.CH_3 \xrightarrow[-1.1v]{2e} p\text{-}NH_2.C_6H_4(OH).CH_3$$

or

$$p\text{-}NH_2.C_6H_4.CO.CH_3 \xrightarrow[-1.5v]{2e} [p\text{-}NH_2.C_6H_4.\overset{\displaystyle OH}{\underset{\displaystyle CH_3}{C}}]_2$$

Such types of reactions probably depend sensitively on the electrochemical adsorption characteristics of both the reactant and the immediate product, e.g., whether it is desorbed rapidly or not at the electrode potential used for the reduction. Hardly any experimental studies have yet been made with regard to such effects, e.g., relating the type of reaction to potential and to electrochemical adsorption of reactants and products by electrocapillary measurements at Hg.

Most organic reactions at electrodes are highly specific with regard to the nature and preparation of the electrode surface. This arises partly on account of the dependence of mechanism on the H- and O-adsorption characteristics of the electrode, i.e., whether the reaction can proceed by a type (a) or a type (b) mechanism, and partly on the adsorption characteristics of the electrode for the reactant and product adsorption. The use of alloys allows the electrode properties to be varied in a more controllable manner and reaction yields of certain products to be specifically improved; e.g., 12% Fe in Ni improves the reduction of nitrobenzene in alkaline alcoholic solution from 58% to 72%, while the yield of pinacol in the reduction of acetone is much improved if Pb-Sn or Pb-Cu alloy electrodes are used.

Many reactions which have been studied involve large organic molecules, but it is entirely premature to speculate about the detailed kinetics of the reactions involved. Nevertheless, controlled potential electrolysis at electrocatalyst surfaces of different constitutions offers much scope for performing certain organic preparations in a manner in which an additional control of conditions is available over that normally involved in homogeneous reactions, where solvent, chemical potential of reactants and temperature are the variables. Even the mechanisms of apparently relatively simple organic reactions, e.g. the oxidation of formic acid and the formate ion, the Kolbe electrosynthesis (177, see below), are not well understood.

A number of organic reductions can be carried out at dissolving Zn (the Clemmensen method) and at amalgams on open circuit. These reactions proceed by corrosion-type mechanisms; in fact the organic reduction process is the conjugate cathodic reaction to the anodic metal dissolution reaction. The conditions are effectively potentiostatic.

The potentials which are set up will be determined by the kinetics of both the reduction and the metal dissolution and are in fact mixed potentials as discussed in the section on corrosion and passivity (p. 187). The type of base metal used in such reductions will tend to have specific effects on the course of the reaction since (a) the adsorption of any intermediates formed will depend on the nature of the metal used, e.g., as in the Clemmensen reduction of ketones at zinc; (b) the type of mechanism will depend on the co-adsorption of H; and (c) the mixed potential at which the reduction proceeds will depend on the *kinetics* of the metal dissolution process and that of the organic reduction, and will influence the adsorption of reactants and products.

(ii) **The Kolbe Reaction.** The Kolbe reaction (285,286,287) is one of the few organic reactions that have been examined in any detail with regard to the electrode kinetics, and then only recently from a point of view which could lead to diagnosis of electrochemical rate-controlling mechanisms. Since this reaction is of considerable interest both in electrochemistry and synthetic organic chemistry (287), some discussion of the details of the problem of its mechanism will be given.

The classical work of Kolbe (285) constituted the first detailed study of the anodic reaction involving principally aliphatic carboxylic acids RCOOH and their anions RCOO$^-$, where it was shown that electrolysis of an aqueous solution of an alkali metal carboxylate, led to the production of carbon dioxide and the hydrocarbon R_2.

Various detailed studies have been made in order to establish the optimum conditions for the formation of ethane from acetate in aqueous and non-aqueous solvents. In aqueous solutions, the nature of the anode is of great importance, and appreciable coupling* occurs only with smooth platinum or iridium anodes. The reaction is also favoured by using high current density ($>10^{-2}$ a. cm.$^{-2}$), a high carboxylate concentration (>1 M) in an acidic medium and relatively low temperatures ($<50°C$). In non-aqueous solvents, conditions for optimum yields are less critical. Low current densities promote the formation of olefins and paraffins (CH_4 in the acetate case) possessing only half the number of carbon atoms required for the coupled product. Another side reaction frequently encountered, particularly in alkaline solutions, is the formation of alcohols (Hofer-Moest reaction), favored by the presence of such inorganic salts as perchlorates, bicarbonates and persulfates and at electrodes other than Pt; e.g., it occurs with a good yield of alcohols at Au. Little is known, however, about the formation of alcohols in the electrolysis of carboxylic acids.

Experimentally, it has been observed that there are three important limitations in the choice of reactants for synthetic applications. The three types of structure which suppress the Kolbe reaction are (a) α-β or β-γ unsaturation in the reactant acid; (b) α-alkyl substituents and cycloalkyl structures; and (c) aromatic groups (ArCOOH). Electrolysis of compounds possessing these structures usually results in oxygen evolution as the major reaction with the production of numerous degradation (oxidation) products. The inhibitory effects of unsaturation, α-substituents and cycloalkyl residues, are diminished when these functions are removed to other positions in the acid molecule. However, recent investigations have shown that the Kolbe reaction with α-substituted acids is no longer adversely affected if the solvent is changed from an aqueous to a non-aqueous

---

* Somewhat analogous *cathodic* coupling occurs in the electrolysis of quaternary ammonium salts.

medium, which suggests that side oxidations by MOH entities are more facile with these structures. Similarly, with aromatic acids, if the phenyl ring is removed further than the β-position, electrolysis will give the expected Kolbe dimer. When the aromatic ring is vicinal to the COOH group, as in benzoic acid, benzene is the main product rather than the expected diphenyl.

Studies in non-aqueous solvents have been undertaken by numerous investigators, and the most comprehensive early work was that by Glasstone and Hickling (286), using ethylene glycol as the solvent. The results show that current efficiencies for the production of the coupled product were similar in aqueous and in non-aqueous solvents, but only appreciable (*ca.* 90%) at the highest current densities in the absence of foreign ions. The experimental conditions used in the earlier work cannot, however, be considered ideal in relation to modern techniques available for the investigation of electrode processes.

Measurements of electrode potentials over a range of current densities have been carried out by several investigators (286,288) for the acetate case and for higher homologues, and plots of anode potential versus log current-density show in all cases breaks in the curves, corresponding to a sudden increase in the anode potential at a particular current density. Analysis of products over the current-density range has shown that in acidic solutions (286,288) the major product at low current densities was oxygen together with a variety of oxidative degradation products. As a critical current density and associated potential is approached, the yields of carbon dioxide and the Kolbe product begin to become appreciable, while the rate of production of oxygen decreases. At, and above, the critical current density, the major products were the Kolbe hydrocarbons with only traces of oxygen.

The potential at which the Kolbe electrosynthesis occurs in aqueous solution presents a seemingly (286) anomalous situation. Oxygen evolution in aqueous acid solutions normally occurs significantly (*ca.* 10^{-4} a. cm.$^{-2}$) at a much lower potential (*ca.* 1.7 v., but the reversible potential is at 1.23 v. E_{H}, under standard conditions) than that required for the Kolbe reaction

(2.1–2.2 v.), yet in the presence of dischargeable carboxylates, the Kolbe reaction occurs preferentially at higher potentials with suppression of oxygen evolution. The role of oxygen evolution has received rather little attention; qualitatively, all that can at present be said is that when the Hofer-Moest reaction is occurring (basic solutions) at the anode, oxygen is one of the major products,* but when the Kolbe reaction occurs, little, if any, oxygen is present in the mixture of reaction products.

In a theory proposed by Glasstone and Hickling (286), it was suggested that hydroxyl radicals (arising from the anodic discharge of OH^- ions, which normally lead to oxygen evolution) combine to form hydrogen peroxide, which then reacts with the acetate ion to form either peracetic acid or acetate radicals, eventually yielding the Kolbe product.

The suggestion has also been made (289,290) that acetate ions are preferentially adsorbed at the anode, so that water molecules cannot approach the surface to be discharged to give O_2. However, it is difficult to envisage this in terms of double-layer theory, especially when, at potentials below the critical potential for the Kolbe reaction, oxygen evolution can already proceed with facility.

(iii) **Proposed Mechanisms.** Numerous theories have been proposed for the mechanism of the Kolbe electrosynthesis, and three have received serious consideration.

An acyl peroxide theory was proposed by Schall (291) and subsequently developed by Fichter (292). Initially, Fichter

---

* From a chemical kinetic point of view, this situation is actually not unexpected. When the electrochemical rate constants for the competing reactions of carboxylate ion discharge, oxygen evolution and radical coupling are such that the oxygen evolution rate and the corresponding rate of production of oxidising radicals (e.g. OH or O, which are involved in that reaction) are appreciable, any simultaneously discharged $RCOO^-$ ions will be subject to oxidation by the intermediates involved in the oxygen-producing reaction, so that the normal coupling reaction will be inhibited. Thus, Hofer-Moest products will be expected as a direct result of the kinetic situation which allows, under certain conditions, significant competitive rates of oxygen evolution from OH^- in aqueous media. Under these conditions, surface oxide coverage can be significant as shown by Conway and Vijh (214).

postulated that "active oxygen" liberated at the anode oxidized the carboxylic acid anion, which then decomposed through an acyl peroxide intermediate, to give the characteristic Kolbe products. Subsequently, he proposed (more acceptably) that the primary step was the discharge of the carboxylic acid anion. The resulting discharged ions were then regarded as forming a diacyl peroxide intermediate [cf. Glasstone and Hickling (286)], which then decomposed with the formation of the characteristic Kolbe products, or by hydrolysis to give side products, a reaction which would predominate in alkaline media to give alcohols.

Fichter (292) regarded the similarity of products obtained by electrolysis and by thermal decomposition of the corresponding diacyl peroxides as proof of his peroxide mechanism. Diacyl peroxides are, however, known to decompose relatively slowly when present in solution at low concentrations, and easily detectable amounts should be present but are not found.

Further, it is known that aliphatic acyloxy radicals, resulting from the decomposition of diacyl peroxides in solution, lose CO_2 rapidly to give alkyl radicals. Hence, it is rather unlikely and inconsistent with other known radical reactions in solution and the gas phase that two acyloxy radicals would first *combine* to form the peroxide intermediate, which then decomposed via the same acyloxy radical again to give alkyl radicals and CO_2. A heterogeneous direct first-order decomposition of the acyloxy radicals formed from the discharge of the carboxylate anions seems much more probable.

Goldschmidt et al. (293) made a study of the products of electrolysis of propionates in anhydrous propionic acid and compared them with the products of decomposition of dipropionyl peroxide. The parallelism between products of the Kolbe reaction and those of the decomposition of the corresponding diacyl peroxides, Goldschmidt points out, suggests rather that the two processes have common paths (i.e., the decomposition and electrolysis reactions proceed through a free-radical intermediate) than that diacyl peroxides are directly involved in the Kolbe reaction. This viewpoint seems the most satisfactory one in regard to the problem of the validity of the "peroxide" mechanism in the Kolbe reaction.

A mechanism based on formation of hydrogen peroxide was proposed by Glasstone and Hickling (286) and involves the assumption that hydrogen peroxide formed by the anodic discharge of hydroxyl ions initiates the decomposition of the carboxylate ion. Numerous criticisms have been raised against this mechanism of the role of oxygen in the reaction, the most serious being that the addition of concentrated hydrogen peroxide to acetate solutions produces only trace amounts of hydrocarbon; furthermore, attempts to detect even trace amounts of hydrogen peroxide during and following electrolysis have not been successful.

The hydrogen peroxide theory also requires that hydroxyl ions or water molecules be present and hence is applicable to only aqueous solutions. However, the kinetics of the Kolbe reaction in non-aqueous media are electrochemically quite similar to those for the reaction in aqueous solution.

Glasstone and Hickling attached great importance to the fact that the Kolbe reaction occurs at potentials much higher than that required for oxygen evolution, and attributed this to formation of radicals from H_2O_2. However, it is necessary only to assume that, under conditions existing when the Kolbe reaction is occurring, the discharge of carboxylate ions is kinetically favored compared with that of hydroxyl ions (or water) in the oxygen evolution reaction, because of inhibition effects in the latter reaction probably arising from absorbed carboxylate radicals (see below).

A theory based on the discharge of carboxylate ions to form free radicals was originally proposed by Crum-Brown, Walker and co-workers (294). This was one of the earliest proposals of mechanism and still seems the most satisfactory; the reaction can be written

$$RCOO^- \rightarrow RCOO\cdot + e$$
$$RCOO\cdot \rightarrow R\cdot + CO_2$$
$$R\cdot + R\cdot \rightarrow RR$$

At the time this scheme was proposed, it was not possible to provide electrochemical criteria indicating which step may be rate-determining or what current-potential behaviour would be associated with each step. Such an analysis has been given recently by Conway and Dzieciuch (177).

Additional evidence favouring the above free radical mechanism has been obtained by Wilson and Lippincott (295) from a kinetic study of the reaction, using a variable-frequency square-wave current (*cf.* the rotating-sector technique for photolysis reactions). The authors have argued that if the reaction follows first-order kinetics, the current efficiency (or yield) should be independent of frequency (since the yield will not depend on the number of radicals produced per cycle, but on the total number produced per unit time). However, if the reaction is second-order, the yield will be frequency-dependent, being higher at lower frequencies. On this basis, kinetic expressions were derived, assuming that the radicals formed at the electrode can react to form products by a series of consecutive reactions, only one of which is rate-determining, and that this step is either first- or second-order.

The formation of ethane in the electrolysis of acetates in both aqueous and glacial acetic acid was shown to be frequency-independent, and hence to follow first-order kinetics. This suggests that the mechanism is the same in both solvents and is strong evidence against the hydrogen peroxide theory postulated by Glasstone and Hickling (286). With the same kinetic treatment, the acyl peroxide theory requires that the reaction be second-order in the concentration of radicals produced at the electrode. On the basis of this theory, the data of Wilson and Lippincott (295) would indicate that the slow step is the first-order decomposition of acetoxyl radicals. Tafel slopes (177) were not, however, considered.

A detailed study of the kinetics of the Kolbe reaction carried out with aqueous and trifluoroacetic acid (TFA) solutions of potassium trifluoroacetate at platinum was made by Conway and Dzieciuch (177), who theoretically and experimentally examined the current-potential behaviour and the role of adsorbed

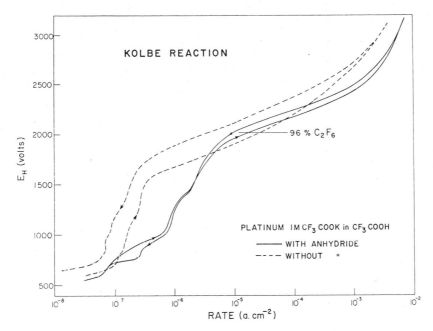

Fig. 50. Potentiostatic current-potential curve for the Kolbe reaction with CF_3COO^- In CF_3COOH in the presence of traces of water and in completely anhydrous conditions (with $CF_3CO.O.CO.CF_3$ present).

intermediates by galvanostatic discharging and open-circuit decay analysis. The trifluoro acid was chosen in order to minimise side oxidation reactions, which can occur more easily with the methyl function in acetic acid. The Tafel slopes are from $(2.3)4RT/F$ to $(2.3)6RT/F$ at Pt, and probably arise from electron transfer across a thin anodic film of adsorbed carboxylate radicals. The Tafel slopes were deduced for the steps shown above, and it is clear that the high Tafel slope $[>(2.3)2RT/F]$ can arise with a discharge step only by participation of some anodic film, since the apparent value of the symmetry factor β is as low as 0.25–0.17. Recent potentiostatic experiments with Vijh (296) serve to define the transition from low- to high-potential behaviour in detail at platinum and gold, and a sharp transition region is observed in both non-aqueous and aqueous solutions (Fig. 50). The degree of "structure" in this region is sensitive to the amount of water present in solution (including the presence of traces of water in the "non-aqueous" TFA solutions), and the extent of hysteresis in the transition region is dependent on the presence of water presumably due to oxide film formation. Analogous effects are found in formate oxidation. Complete removal of water can be achieved in TFA by addition of traces of the TFA anhydride, which reacts with water to form more TFA. These are the best conditions for examining the Kolbe kinetics free from complications associated with oxide films. Arrests are still found in galvanostatic transients from high potentials in the most anhydrous solutions and presumably are associated with discharged adsorbed carboxylate species. The arrests are much larger when water is present, and co-adsorption of O-containing entities is then probably involved.

8. ANODIC FILM GROWTH AND KINETICS AT OXIDE FILM ELECTRODES

The study of electrochemical oxidation on the surface of film-covered electrodes has received rather little attention, although oxygen evolution studies have usually been conducted under such conditions, since metal oxide or adsorbed O formation usually precedes oxygen evolution. Also, oxide films having semiconducting properties arise in corrosion. Generally, electrode kinetic studies are conducted on initially bare metals; hence care must be taken to remove any films that may be present; alternatively, anodic reactions (other than the film-growth process itself) are normally investigated in such a manner as to minimize film growth. It is clear, however, that the presence of a film may markedly influence the oxidation process occurring at the surface (a) by affecting the energetics of the reaction at the double-layer; (b) by imposing a barrier to charge transfer through the film; and (c) by affecting the adsorption of products of ion discharge steps at the surface of the electrode.

The kinetics of anodic film growth have only relatively recently been extensively and quantitatively investigated, and experimental data are limited to only a few metals (297).   Most of the detailed studies have been limited to the "valve metals" Zr, Ta, Al, and more recently Nb and Bi; practically useful capacitative films of ZrO_2 or Ta_2O_5 and other oxides are obtained.

Several theories have been proposed according to which the formation current density should be dependent exponentially or linearly on the electric field across the oxide.   The kinetics of growth of thin films have been discussed in detail by Mott and Cabrera (298), primarily with regard to the formation of oxide films by chemical reaction with oxygen ("tarnishing reaction"), but the kinetic principles have been subsequently applied to anodically formed films.   The essential difference between anodic film growth and the tarnishing reaction is that in anodic oxidation only ions need cross the film for growth to occur, whilst in tarnishing reactions both ions and electrons must move across the film.   In anodic film-growth reactions, ionic transport is usually rate-determining for thick films (297), but in steady-state anodic reactions proceeding on the film, electron transport through the film is then necessary and in some cases can, in part (see below), determine the rate of the surface electrochemical reaction.   The anodic metal oxidation process is also more convenient for investigation than the gas-solid oxidation reaction, as the rate of film growth can be controlled by controlling the current through the oxide or, indirectly, the field across the oxide.   The film thickness can be followed by observation of the interference colours (thick films) or by ellipsometry (thin films).

Theories of film growth which have been proposed all assume the oxide to be of stoichiometric composition and to contain mobile metal ions, whose motions are unimpeded by other mobile ions, and which are in thermal equilibrium with the oxide lattice.   The energy diagram normally used to represent the situation is shown in Fig. 51 and applies in principle to any oxidation process involving the formation of a film, regardless of the detailed mechanism of oxidation and of whether the process occurs under "high-field" or "low-field" conditions—the field referring to the electrostatic field across the barrier-layer oxide film. In Fig. 51 is represented the potential energy of a mobile metal ion as it leaves the metal and passes into and through the oxide, in the absence of an external field. The point marked A represents the position of an ion in the metal, and the point B represents an interstitial site; ϕ is the activation energy which must be surmounted to move the ion from the metal to an

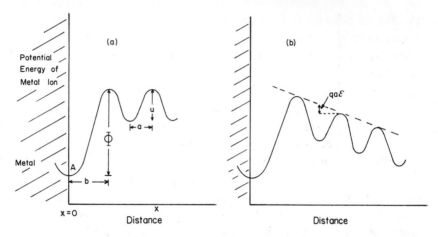

Fig. 51. Potential barrier for ion transfer at the metal-oxide interface and for field-assisted ion transfer in the oxide film.

interstitial site, and U is the energy required to move the metal ion between interstitial sites. The presence of a field lowers the barrier by an amount $qa\mathscr{E}$ (see Fig. 51 and compare Fig. 18), where $\mathscr{E}$ is the field, q the charge on the ion and a the "half-jump" distance. This representation is similar to that used in the absolute-rate theory of electronic or ionic conductance.

The total ionic current density at a point x in the oxide (see Fig. 51) is assumed to be given by

$$i = 2avn \exp\left[-\frac{U - qa\mathscr{E}}{kT}\right] - 2avn \exp\left[-\frac{U + qa\mathscr{E}}{kT}\right] \quad (265)$$

$$= 4avn \exp\left[-\frac{U}{kT}\right] \sinh\frac{qa\mathscr{E}}{kT} \quad (266)$$

where a is the half-jump distance for the ions ($2a =$ distance between interstitial sites), v the vibration frequency of ions at x, n the concentration of ions at x, U the activation energy for motion between interstitial sites, q the charge on the mobile ion, $\mathscr{E}$ the electric field at x, k the Boltzmann constant and T the absolute temperature. Equation 266 may be compared with that in the footnote on p. 196.

The first term in Equation 265 refers to ions moving in a direction down the field, and the second to ions moving against the field. For low fields or thick films ($qa\mathscr{E} \ll kT$), the following approximation can be made:

$$\sinh \frac{qa\mathscr{E}}{kT} \doteqdot \frac{qa\mathscr{E}}{kT}$$

hence Equation 266 can be written

$$i = \frac{4a^2 nvq\mathscr{E}}{kT} \exp\left[-\frac{U}{kT}\right] \tag{267}$$

which corresponds to ohmic* behaviour.

In the high-field approximation, applicable to thin films, it is assumed that the reverse current can be neglected, so that Equation 265 can be written

$$i = 2avn \exp\left[-\frac{U - qa\mathscr{E}}{kT}\right] \tag{268}$$

giving non-ohmic behaviour.

In the original treatment by Mott and Cabrera (298) for low fields, they assumed that (a) regions of space charge at the two interfaces can be neglected and (b) the rate of growth is controlled by the rate of diffusion of metal ions across the oxide layer. For these conditions, the rate of growth can be written

$$\frac{dx}{dt} = \frac{4a^2 nvqV\Omega}{kTx} \exp\left[-\frac{U}{kT}\right] \tag{269}$$

* It is of interest to note that, of course, Ohm's law is a special case of activation-controlled transport of charge carriers near equilibrium.

where V is the potential across a film of thickness x ($\mathscr{E} = V/x$), and Ω the volume of oxide per metal ion; or

$$\frac{dx}{dt} = \frac{k_p}{x} \qquad (270)$$

where

$$k_p = \frac{4a^2 nvqV\Omega}{kT} \exp\left[-\frac{U}{kT}\right] \qquad (271)$$

Integration of Equation 270 gives

$$x^2 = 2k_p t + C \qquad (272)$$

i.e. a parabolic equation for the rate of oxidation in terms of film thickness x.

In the case of thin films, i.e., with the high-field conditions applying, Mott and Cabrera assumed (a) that the rate-determining step was the initial transfer of ions from the metal to the oxide over the barrier of height ϕ, at which there is a surface concentration of ions, and (b) that space charge effects were negligible, so that the electric field was constant. In this high-field approximation they assumed that every metal ion escaping from the metal would be swept through the oxide by the high field, so that conduction through the oxide would not be an activated process. On the basis of this model, the density of current across the film is given by

$$i = N_s v_s q \exp\left[-\frac{\phi - qb\mathscr{E}}{kT}\right] \qquad (273)$$

where N_s is the number of ions per square centimeter of metal surface at the metal-oxide interface, v_s their vibrational frequency normal to the barrier and b the half-jump distance for this process.

The Tafel slope for the ion-transfer process at the metal-film barrier is given by differentiating Equation 273, so that

$$\frac{d\mathscr{E}}{d(\ln i)} = \frac{kT}{bq} \qquad (274)$$

giving a slope which is proportional to the absolute temperature; this result is to be expected when a single barrier determines the rate,* and when no limit is placed on the concentration of ions in the initial state of the barrier-transfer step at the metal-oxide interface.

The rate of oxidation can be written from Equation 273:

$$\frac{dx}{dt} = N_s \nu_s \Omega \exp\left[-\frac{\phi - bq\mathscr{E}}{kT}\right] \qquad (275)$$

where x is the thickness of the film at time t and Ω the volume of oxide per metal ion.

Equation 275 can be written

$$\frac{dx}{dt} = u \exp\left[\frac{x_1}{x}\right] \qquad (276)$$

where $x_1 = qbV/kT$ and $u = N_s \nu_s \Omega \exp\left[-\phi/kT\right]$.

Equation 276 leads to the conclusion that for a constant potential V_1 below a critical temperature, a "limiting" film thickness is predicted, i.e., when the film-growth rate corresponds (arbitrarily) to less than one layer of atoms added in ca. 10^5 sec.

An approximate integration of Equation 276 for $x \ll x_1$ gives

$$\frac{x_1}{x} = \ln \frac{x_1 u}{x_L{}^2} - \ln (t + C) \qquad (277)$$

where C is a constant of integration, x_L the limiting thickness and x the film thickness at time t.

Rewriting Equation 277 in the form

$$\frac{x_1}{x} = A - \ln (t + C); \quad A = \ln \frac{x_1 u}{x_L{}^2} \qquad (278)$$

---

* The Tafel equation for an activation-controlled electrode process is analogous, and the associated logarithmic current-potential slope is, of course, of the same form as that given in Equation 274. Accordingly, the slopes involved in film-growth processes, defined by Equation 274, are also referred to as "Tafel slopes."

gives an inverse logarithmic relationship between time and film thickness in the growth process. The Mott-Cabrera theory for the electrolytic oxidation case was tested by Vermilyea (299) for high-field (i.e. thin-film) conditions. The experimental "Tafel" slopes were found to be temperature-independent, contrary to the Mott-Cabrera theory (sometimes referred to as the "Tafel-slope anomaly"). From Equation 273

$$\ln i = \ln (N_s \nu_s q) - \frac{\phi}{kT} + \frac{bq\mathscr{E}}{kT} \qquad (279)$$

which predicts that the field $\mathscr{E}$ is a linear function of the absolute temperature T with a slope dependent on $\ln i$, whereas Vermilyea found that the field is a linear function of the reciprocal temperature $1/T$, with associated kinetic slope independent of $\ln i$, but with an intercept dependent on $\ln i$, a result also subsequently observed by Young (297).

Vermilyea (299) rejected the existence of any space-charge effects and postulated the creation of vacancies (or interstitial ions); the diffusion of such ions to the metal-oxide interface and the migration of mobile metal ions to the oxide-solution interface, involves a dual barrier which can determine the rate. This view was rejected by Dewald (297), who subsequently put forward a theory to account for the Tafel slope anomaly. The treatment is developed on the same kinetic basis as that in the theory of Mott and Cabrera, but allows for dual control by diffusion barriers for ion transfer both into, and through, the oxide; also, space-charge effects are introduced on the assumption that the space charge is due entirely to metal ions in transit, which are assumed to be stoichiometric "excess" ions (i.e., either interstitials or substitutionals).

Dewald (297) has shown that the field at any point x in the oxide is given by

$$\mathscr{E} = \mathscr{E}_0 + \frac{1}{\beta} \ln (1 + \beta \gamma n_0 x) \qquad (280)$$

where $\beta = aq/kT$, $\gamma = 4\pi q/\epsilon$, ϵ is the dielectric constant of the oxide and n_0 the number of ions per cubic centimeter at $x = 0$.

This equation represents the fact that the field at any point x is composed of two parts, a surface charge contribution $\mathscr{E}_0$ and a space-charge term. The surface charge contribution is given by

$$\mathscr{E}_0 = \frac{kT}{bq} \ln \frac{i_0}{m_s v_s q} + \frac{U}{bq} \tag{281}$$

and

$$n_0 = \frac{(m_s v_s)^{a/b}}{2av} i_0^{\,1-a/b} \exp \left[\frac{U - a\phi/b}{kT} \right] \tag{282}$$

where m_s and v_s are the surface density of metal ions and their vibration frequency, respectively, i_0 the current across the film-electrolyte interface and v the vibration frequency of the ion in an interstitial position.

The average field $\bar{\mathscr{E}}$, which is experimentally accessible, is obtained by evaluating

$$\bar{\mathscr{E}} = \frac{V}{x} = \frac{1}{x} \int_0^x \mathscr{E} \, dx \tag{283}$$

where V is the voltage drop across a film of thickness x. Substituting Equation 280 into 283 for $\mathscr{E}$ and integrating gives

$$\bar{\mathscr{E}} = \mathscr{E}_0 + \frac{1}{\beta}\left[\left(1 + \frac{1}{\delta}\right) \ln (1 + \delta) - 1\right] \tag{284}$$

where

$$\delta = \beta \gamma n_0 x = \left[\frac{2\pi q^2}{v \epsilon k T} (m_s v_s)^{a/b}\right] \exp \left[\frac{U - a\phi/b}{kT}\right] xi^{1-a/b} \tag{285}$$

Equation 284 gives the dependence of the average field on three variables, current density (through $\mathscr{E}_0$ and n_0), thickness of the film x and temperature (through $\mathscr{E}_0$, β and δ). The second term in Equation 284 is the space-charge contribution to the average field.

The dimensionless quantity δ determines the importance of a space charge. If δ is much less than 1, the space charge is negligible and the equation reduces to that obtained by Mott and Cabrera. However, if δ is of the order of 1 or larger, space-charge effects are important and the rate of oxidation is determined entirely by the bulk properties of the film. Expanding the $\ln (1 + \delta)$ term in Equation 284 gives

$$\ln (1 + \delta) = \delta - \frac{\delta^2}{2} + \cdots$$

for small δ, or

$$\ln (1 + \delta) = \ln \delta + \ln \left(1 + \frac{1}{\delta}\right)$$

$$= \ln \delta + \frac{1}{\delta} - \frac{1}{2\delta^2} + \cdots$$

for large δ. Neglecting second- and higher-order terms, the two limiting cases are given by

$$\bar{\mathscr{E}} \doteq \mathscr{E}_0 = \frac{kT}{bq} \ln \frac{i}{m_s v_s} + \frac{\phi}{bq} \qquad (286)$$

when $\delta \ll 1$, and

$$\bar{\mathscr{E}} \doteq \frac{kT}{aq} \left(\ln \frac{2\pi q^2}{\epsilon v k T}\right) xi + \frac{U}{aq} \qquad (287)$$

when $\delta \gg 1$.

For both high and low values of δ, the field is logarithmic in current density, and in both cases the Tafel slope $[d\mathscr{E}/d(\ln i)]_T$ is proportional to the absolute temperature. For low values of δ the Tafel slope is given by kT/bq, while for high values of δ it is given by kT/aq.

Dewald's formulation has been based on the behaviour of thin films formed at constant current; hence, in the steady state, the concentration of mobile ions in the film is assumed to be constant. If the current is suddenly changed to a higher value, it is frequently observed that the potential "overshoots," that is, the potential passes through a maximum and then sometimes a minimum before approaching a final steady-state condition. Such behaviour is also observed in decarboxylation reactions probably on account of co-adsorbed oxygen species at the anode (177). The essential reason for this behaviour is that the variation of the concentration of charge carriers lags behind the variation of the field when the current is suddenly changed, that is, the concentration of mobile ions changes relatively slowly during the rapid change of potential. The subsequent approach to the steady state beyond the minimum, then, corresponds to normal film growth, i.e. a readjustment of the thickness to the new potential and corresponding field.

The effects of surface films on surface-oxidation kinetics have been discussed (300) for two cases using a dual-barrier model. In the first case, it was assumed that in the steady state, two potential-dependent reactions are occurring at equal rates, one corresponding to migration of charge carriers across a p.d. ΔV_f across the film and the other to an electrochemical oxidation reaction at the oxide surface across a p.d. ΔV_s. If the over-all rate equation is expressed as usual in terms of the *total* metal-solution p.d. ΔV_t ($= \Delta V_f + \Delta V_s$),*

$$i = i_0 \exp \left[\frac{\alpha V_t F}{RT} \right] \tag{288}$$

then the transfer coefficient α in this equation is given by

$$\alpha = \frac{\alpha_f \alpha_s}{\alpha_f + \alpha_s} \tag{289}$$

where α_f and α_s are the transfer coefficients for the charge-carrier transport and surface-oxidation reactions, respectively. Hence the Tafel slope is given by

$$\frac{dV_t}{d(\ln i)} = \frac{RT}{F} \frac{\alpha_f + \alpha_s}{\alpha_s \alpha_f} \tag{290}$$

The second case is that which arises when one of the reactions is essentially at equilibrium. If the process involving transfer of

---

* Gohr and Lange (308) were the first, it appears, to recognise the kinetic importance of the inhomogeneous field in the metal-film–ionic-double-layer region at film-covered electrodes. This viewpoint was subsequently developed, as above, by Meyer (300). The change of local field at the electrode surface when even a fraction of a monolayer of oxide species is present may be an important factor in the onset of passivation.

charge carriers in the film (as in a normal metal) is essentially at equilibrium, then the normal rate expression for the surface reaction will hold, giving a Tafel slope:

$$\frac{dV_t}{d(\ln i)} = \frac{dV_s}{d(\ln i)} = \frac{RT}{\alpha_s F} \tag{291}$$

It is therefore possible, on the basis of the dual-barrier model, to account for fractional and high values of the Tafel slopes without resorting to unusual adsorption isotherms or improbable values on the surface-charge-transfer symmetry factor when only the reaction at the surface double-layer is considered, as has sometimes been the case previously. Such high Tafel slopes are often encountered in anodic electrode processes, where films are often formed.

The postulate of two types of barrier seems quite reasonable on film-covered electrodes, but conclusive direct experimental data is lacking to support this model. MacDonald and Conway (234) have given indirect evidence in support of the dual-barrier process in oxygen-evolution kinetics at gold electrodes by relating Tafel behaviour and open-circuit e.m.f. decay kinetics. The mechanism of charge transfer through these films is still speculative, as little is known concerning the structure and semiconducting properties of these films.

9. STOICHIOMETRIC NUMBERS*

(i) Introduction. The concept of stoichiometric number ν was first proposed by Horiuti and co-workers (309). It was defined for any constituent step in a reaction sequence (not necessarily electrochemical) as the number of times that step has to occur for every complete act of the over-all reaction. Determination of ν has formed an important part of the work on criteria of mechanisms of consecutive reactions, e.g. as in the h.e.r. A detailed discussion, in terms of general equations for an

---

* The Author is indebted to Dr. E. Gileadi for discussions on this subject in 1962, and for some original contributions to this problem recorded in this section.

electrode reaction, was given by Parsons (310) and reviewed by Bockris (152). This treatment will be used as a brief basis for introduction and its limitations pointed out.

A general reaction of the form

$$xX + bB^z + ne \rightarrow wW + cC^{(bz-n)/c} \tag{292}$$

is considered. The rate-determining step corresponding to it is represented (152) by

$$\frac{xX}{\nu} + \frac{bB^z}{\nu} + \frac{ne}{\nu} \rightarrow \frac{wW}{\nu} + \frac{cC^{(bz-n)c}}{\nu} \tag{293}$$

where ν is the stoichiometric number for the rate-determining step ("r.d.s.") as defined above; i.e., reaction 293 must proceed ν times for 292, the over-all reaction, to occur once. The relation (see Chapter 2, Equation 5)

$$\bar{\mu}^0 = \mu^0 + zF\phi \tag{294}$$

is then used to separate formally between the chemical (μ^0) and the electrical ($zF\phi$) parts of the standard electrochemical potential $\bar{\mu}^0$ of each of the species taking part in the reaction. The difference between the electrical part of $\bar{\mu}^0$ for the activated state and that for the initial state is then calculated, assuming that the former lies somewhere between that for the initial and final states (see Chapter 6), so that

$$(\bar{\mu}_{A^\ddagger}^0 - \mu_{A^\ddagger}^0) - \bar{\mu}_P^0 = [(\bar{\mu}_Q^0 - \mu_Q^0) - (\bar{\mu}_P^0 - \mu_P^0)] \tag{295}$$

where P and Q refer to states just before and just after the r.d.s., respectively, and $A^\ddagger$ is the activated state. With this, the rate constants for the forward and reverse reactions are given by

$$\vec{k} = \frac{kT}{h} \exp\left[-\frac{\overrightarrow{\Delta G_1^\ddagger} + (1 - \beta)p + \beta q + (\beta n/\nu)\,\Delta\phi\, F}{RT} \right] \tag{296}$$

and

$$\overleftarrow{k} = \frac{kT}{h} \exp\left[-\frac{\overleftarrow{\Delta G_1^\ddagger} + (1 - \beta)p + \beta q - \{(1 - \beta)n/\nu\}\,\Delta\phi\, F}{RT} \right] \tag{297}$$

where p and q represent the change in the electrical part of the standard electrochemical potential in going from the initial state to state P and from state Q to the final state, respectively. The partial currents in the forward and reverse directions are given by

$$\vec{i} = \frac{n}{\nu} F\vec{k}_1 a_X^{x'} a_B^{b'} \tag{298}$$

and

$$\overleftarrow{i} = \frac{n}{\nu} F\overleftarrow{k}_2 a_W^{w'} a_C^{c'} \tag{299}$$

where x′,b′ and w′,c′ are the numbers of molecules or ions needed to form the activated complex in the r.d.s. from reactants and from products, respectively. It is next assumed that, at potentials removed from the potential of zero charge, one can write

$$(1 - \beta)p + \beta q = \Gamma + \gamma \frac{n \Delta\phi F}{\nu} \tag{300}$$

where Γ is a function of composition alone, and γ is independent of composition. By combining Equations 296, 298 and 300, defining $\phi = \phi_r + \eta$ and writing $\vec{i} = \overleftarrow{i} = i_0$ at $\eta = 0$, the equation

$$i_c = \vec{i} - \overleftarrow{i} = i_0\left\{\exp\left[-\frac{(\beta + \gamma)nF}{\nu RT}\right] - \exp\left[\frac{(1 - \beta - \gamma)nF}{\nu RT}\right]\right\} \tag{301}$$

is obtained (152).

At low overpotentials, the exponentials can be expanded and all terms in η^2 and higher powers of η neglected. This leads to

$$\nu = -\frac{nFi_0}{RT}\left(\frac{\partial\eta}{\partial i_c}\right)_{\eta\to 0} \tag{302}$$

from which ν can be derived if data for the η-i relation are available at low current densities.

An additional parameter, λ, has been defined (311)* as the

---

* It is to be noted that in the discussion of Bockris and Potter (311), regarding the relation of λ and β to the Tafel slope, the significance of β was taken as different from that normally accepted, i.e., β in their paper is not simply a charge-transfer symmetry factor.

number of electrons gained (or lost) by the electrode in the completion of one act of the r.d.s. It was termed the electron number and is related to the stoichiometric number through the simple equation

$$\lambda = \frac{n}{\nu} \tag{303}$$

(ii) Limitations of the Derivation of Parsons. *a. The Value of γ.* The expression derived in the previous section (Equation 302) for the stoichiometric number is correct if there is no change in mechanism in the potential range investigated, as low current densities are approached, and the reaction which is r.d. at high overpotentials (i.e., over the linear portion of the Tafel plot, from which i_0 is obtained by extrapolation) is also r.d. at the reversible potential (*cf.* below). The method by which this equation is obtained is, however, not self-consistent, and it happens to lead to the correct result because of fortuitous cancellation of ill-defined terms.

In the present section we shall discuss the difficulties arising from Parsons's treatment, and in the following section a more satisfactory treatment, which considers the rates of reactions close to equilibrium, will be given, following a derivation by Makrides (312).

The problems inherent in Parsons's treatment are best illustrated by comparing the conclusions arrived at for different mechanisms for the h.e.r. For example, the two mechanisms commonly assumed for hydrogen evolution* may be considered:

	Path A		*Path B*
I	$e + H^+ + M \rightarrow MH$	I	$e + H^+ + M \rightarrow MH$
II	$2MH \rightarrow H_2 + 2M$	III	$e + MH + H^+ \rightarrow M + H_2$

---

* The actual source of protons is immaterial for the present discussion. H^+ stands for a hydrated proton or a water molecule. In the latter case the rest of the equation will have to be modified, but the same arguments will still apply.

If the reaction occurs through Path A, and step II is r.d., we obtain*

$$b = \frac{RT}{F} \frac{\nu}{(\beta + \gamma)n} = \frac{RT}{F} \cdot \tfrac{1}{2} \qquad (304)$$

also $\nu = 1$ and $n = 2$, hence $\beta + \gamma = 1$. Similarly, if the h.e.r. occurs through Path B, and again the second reaction is r.d., then

$$b = \frac{RT}{F} \frac{\nu}{(\beta + \gamma)n} = \frac{RT}{F} \frac{1}{1 + \beta} \qquad (305)$$

hence, as before $(\beta + \gamma)2 = 1 + \beta$. Now the rate of reaction II depends on potential in an indirect manner, because of the variation of coverage with potential. Reaction I is then assumed to be in quasi-equilibrium and the coverage is hence a function of total p.d. across the metal-solution interphase, and is independent of the form of the energy barrier. Hence we must assume $\beta = 1$ in Equation 304 and therefore $\gamma = 0$. Considering now Path B, it is usually assumed that $\beta \doteq 0.5$ for a charge-transfer process; hence, from Equation 305, $\gamma = 0.25$. From the definition of γ (Equation 300), however, it must have the *same value* in Equations 304 and 305, since the same reaction is involved. A similar kind of inconsistency is apparent if Path B is operative with reaction I r.d. Then

$$b = \frac{RT}{F} \frac{\nu}{(\beta + \gamma)n} = \frac{RT}{F} \frac{1}{\beta} \qquad (306)$$

and since $\nu = 1$ in this case,

$$2(\gamma + \beta) = \beta \quad \text{and} \quad \gamma = -\frac{\beta}{2} \doteq -0.25$$

is obtained.

A negative value for γ corresponds to a charge transfer in the *anodic* direction during a cathodic reaction, or vice versa, which is obviously inconsistent with the mechanism assumed. As pointed out above, the values assumed for β and γ in Equation 301 do not affect the values of ν obtained from Equation 302 since

---

* It is assumed here, and throughout this discussion, that $1 - \theta \doteq 1$ and that variation of the heat of adsorption with coverage can be neglected.

the term $\beta + \gamma$ cancels out when the difference between the forward and the reverse current is calculated at sufficiently low overpotentials.

b. The Relation Between λ and v. Some problems of general interest arise from considering Path B for the h.e.r. with reaction I rate-determining. It is evident that reaction I occurs only once for each act of the over-all reaction, and hence $v = 1$. On the other hand, λ, the number of electrons gained (or lost) by the electrode for every act of the r.d.s. is also unity. Since, for the h.e.r., $n = 2$, Equation 303 is not valid in this case, that is, $n/v \neq \lambda$. It was apparently realised by Parsons (310) that this mechanism presented a special problem, as he pointed out that the relationship $b' = b/v$ where b and b' are as defined by Equations 292 and 298, respectively, does not hold in this case. Nevertheless, it appears erroneous to assume that Equation 303 (*viz.*, $n/v = \lambda$) is applicable generally for any mechanism. Another interesting mechanism to consider is the anodic oxidation of ammonia in alkaline solutions. It was shown recently (313) that this reaction probably proceeds through the following steps involving adsorbed radicals:

$$NH_3 + OH^- \rightarrow NH_2 + H_2O + e \qquad \text{(A)}$$

$$NH_2 + OH^- \rightarrow NH + H_2O + e \qquad \text{(B)}$$

$$NH + OH^- \rightarrow N + H_2O + e \qquad \text{(C)}$$

$$2N \rightarrow N_2 \qquad \text{(D)}$$

It is clear that $v = 2$ for the first three steps and $v = 1$ for the fourth step, while λ takes the values 1, 2, 3 and 6 for these steps. From the stoichiometry of the over-all reaction, $n = 6$; hence the relation $n/v = \lambda$ is valid in this case if step C or D is r.d., but is invalid if step A or B is r.d. It may be concluded that Equation 303 is applicable only if charge transfer occurs before or in the r.d.s.

Equation 302 is often written

$$\lambda = -\frac{RT}{Fi_0}\left(\frac{\partial i_c}{\partial \eta}\right)_{\eta \to 0} \qquad \text{(302a)}$$

This is misleading, however, since Equation 302 is generally valid, while Equation 302a can be used only if Equation 303 is applicable.

The assumption that Equation 303 is generally valid has also led to some confusion regarding the relations between the rate constant of the r.d.s. and the over-all forward current density $\vec{i}$. This should be written

$$\vec{i} = \frac{n}{\nu} F k_1 \prod_i a_i \tag{307}$$

where k_1 is the electrochemical rate constant of the r.d.s. in the forward direction.

c. Rates of Reactions Close to Equilibrium. In this section will be outlined in a slightly modified form a derivation given by Makrides (312) following concepts first put forward by ·Prigogine (314) and developed further by Manes, Hofer and Waller (315).

The net forward rate v_i of a single step (which may constitute a complete stoichiometric reaction or be a consecutive step in it) is given (314) by

$$v_i = \frac{v_i^e}{RT} A_i \tag{308}$$

where v_i^e is the rate of the ith step in either direction at equilibrium and A_i is the "affinity" of the same step, defined as

$$A_i = - \sum_i a_i \mu_i \tag{309}$$

where a_i are the coefficients in the relevant stoichiometric equation and μ_i the chemical potentials of the species i involved. When a reaction proceeds through several consecutive steps, the total affinity will be equal to the sum of the affinities of the elementary steps, i.e., $A = \sum_i A_i$. In the steady state, all steps must occur at the same rate, hence

$$v_i^e A_i = \text{constant*} \tag{310}$$

* Equation 310 can be used to justify the quasi-equilibrium assumption. If v_i^e for a particular step is very large, the corresponding value of A_i will be very small and approach zero; hence this step will approach a state of equilibrium.

The net forward rate of the over-all reaction can be written as

$$v = z \, \frac{v^e}{RT} \, A \tag{311}$$

If the reaction is to proceed at a net forward rate v, it must have a total affinity A, distributed among all consecutive steps according to Equation 310. The parameter z in Equation 311 may be regarded as that fraction of the total affinity which is involved in promoting the net forward rate of the over-all reaction.

If a r.d.s. exists at equilibrium, $A_i \doteq 0$ may be written for all steps except the r.d.s., and hence (315)

$$A = A_{\text{r.d.}} \tag{312}$$

Substituting into Equation 308, and bearing in mind that

$$\frac{v_{\text{r.d.}}}{v^e_{\text{r.d.}}} = \frac{v}{v^e}, \tag{313}$$

the relation

$$v = \frac{1}{\nu} \frac{v^e}{RT} \, A \tag{314}$$

is obtained. The parameter z is seen to be equal to the reciprocal of the stoichiometric number.

(α) A Case When None of the Steps is R.D. at Equilibrium. Here a general reaction of the form

$$A + B \rightarrow C \tag{i}$$

$$C + B \rightarrow D \tag{ii}$$

may be considered, e.g. step II in the h.e.r. (*cf.* 316) where B is H_3O^+. Let

$$\gamma' = \frac{v^e_{\text{i}}}{v^e_{\text{ii}}} = \frac{A_{\text{ii}}}{A_{\text{i}}} \tag{315}$$

Let a "rate-controlling step" (r.c.s.) be defined as the step occurring in the coupled reaction at the lowest rate at equilibrium, i.e., step (ii) will be r.c. if $\gamma' \gg 1$ and it will be r.d. if $\gamma \gg 1$.

The net forward rates of the two steps in the reaction given above can be written as

$$v_i = \frac{v_i^e}{RT} A_i; \qquad v_{ii} = \frac{v_{ii}^e}{RT} A_{ii} \qquad (316)$$

also

$$A = A_i + A_{ii} = A_i(1 + \gamma') = A_{ii}\left(1 + \frac{1}{\gamma'}\right) \qquad (317)$$

Substituting Equation 317 in 316 gives

$$v_i = \frac{v_i^e}{RT} A \frac{1}{1 + \gamma'} \; ; \qquad v_{ii} = \frac{v_{ii}^e}{RT} A \frac{1}{1 + 1/\gamma'} \qquad (318)$$

Under steady-state conditions

$$v_i = v_{ii} = v \qquad (319)$$

If $\gamma' > 1$, step (ii) is r.c. and

$$v_{ii}^e = v^e \qquad (320)$$

hence

$$\frac{v_{ii}}{v_{ii}^e} = \frac{v}{v^e} \qquad (321)$$

and substituting into the second equation of 318 yields

$$v = \frac{1}{1 + 1/\gamma'} \frac{v^e}{RT} A \qquad (322)$$

which, by comparison with Equation 314, leads to

$$\nu = 1 + \frac{1}{\gamma'} \qquad (323)$$

In a similar manner, if $\gamma' < 1$, step (i) will be r.c. and

$$v_i^e = v^e \qquad (324)$$

and

$$\frac{v_i}{v_i^e} = \frac{v}{v^e} \qquad (325)$$

Substitution into the first equation of 318 then gives

$$v = \frac{1}{1 + \gamma'} \frac{v^e}{RT} A \tag{326}$$

and hence

$$\nu = 1 + \gamma' \tag{327}$$

Equations 323 and 327 are applicable whether a r.d.s. does or does not exist at equilibrium. The former relation is to be used for $\gamma' \geqslant 1$ and the latter for $\gamma \leqslant 1$.

Makrides (312) has pointed out that $\nu \to 1$ when γ' is very large or very small, and a plot of ν *vs.* γ' should pass through a maximum of $\nu = 2$ at $\gamma' = 1$. However, in a later paper (317), the variation of ν with γ' was discussed for the h.e.r. proceeding through the electrochemical desorption mechanism I, II, and it was maintained that the stoichiometric number should attain very high values if the discharge step were r.d. ($\gamma' \ll 1$). Frumkin (318), on the other hand, considered the same mechanism and arrived at the conclusion that ν should become very large as the electrochemical step becomes r.d. ($\gamma' \gg 1$). The equation obtained by Makrides for the stoichiometric number is similar in form to Equation 323 above (*cf.* Equation 25 in ref. 317). It is to be noted that if this equation is used indiscriminately for all possible values of γ', the conclusions reached by Makrides (317) would follow. Similarly, if Equation 327 is used for all values of γ', the conclusions reached by Frumkin (318) would follow.

It is to be concluded therefore that the stoichiometric number, for example, for the h.e.r. proceeding through electrochemical desorption (or for any similar pathway in other reactions), will be numerically equal to unity if either step is r.d. and will tend to go through a flat maximum of $\nu = 2$ if the exchange currents for the two steps are comparable or equal.

(β) APPLICATION OF THE GENERAL PRINCIPLES TO PROCESSES INVOLVING CHARGE TRANSFER. If an electrochemical process is considered, Equation 308 and succeeding relations have to be modified by introducing *electrochemical* affinities and *electrochemical* potentials instead of the purely "chemical" quantities.

Equation 309 is then to be written

$$\bar{A}_i = -\sum_i a_i \bar{\mu}_i \qquad (309a)$$

and also

$$-\sum_i a_i \bar{\mu}_i = -\sum_i a_i(\bar{\mu}_i - \bar{\mu}_{0,i}) = nF\eta \qquad (328)$$

where $\bar{\mu}_{0,i}$ is the electrochemical potential of the ith species at equilibrium and hence $\sum_i a_i \bar{\mu}_{0,i} = 0$. The electrochemical affinity is therefore given simply by

$$\bar{A} = nF\eta \qquad (329)$$

and substituting this into Equation 314, with

$$\frac{i}{i_0} = \frac{v}{v^e} \qquad (330)$$

leads to

$$i = \frac{nFi_0}{vRT}\eta \qquad (331)$$

from which the basic relation 302 is obtained.

(iii) **Conclusions.** It has been shown that, while the treatments of Parsons and Makrides lead to the same final equation (Equation 302) for the stoichiometric number, the latter derivation is to be preferred, since it avoids the parameter γ, which in Parsons's treatment has to be assigned numerical values which are not physically sound for certain mechanisms. In addition, Makrides's treatment is applicable to any ratio of the exchange current densities of the various steps, while Parsons's treatment presumes that i_0 corresponding to one of the steps is much smaller than that of all others.

The conclusion of Makrides that v can assume very large values when the h.e.r. proceeds through r.d. discharge, followed by electrochemical desorption, and the contention of Frumkin that v becomes large for the same mechanism with the second step r.d., are correct only for special cases.

9
Electrochemical Field Effects at the Gas-Metal Interface

A number of aspects of field effects at the gas-metal interface are closely related to those involved in electrode processes at the solution-metal interface, e.g. with regard to ionisation and electron tunneling. In concluding this volume, a brief discussion of these effects will accordingly be given.

Although electron emission from wires under the influence of high fields was recognised many years ago and electron work-function patterns of emitting surfaces had been photographed, the *field-emission* and *field-ion* microscopes, which enable the movements of adsorbed atoms to be seen directly, are relatively new developments (39). Special applications to adsorption problems have been made very recently, including the experimental evaluation of the adsorbent-adsorbate potential-energy function by studies of desorption in fields.

I. APPARATUS

The field-emission microscope consists essentially of a fine etched tungsten tip surrounded by an electron-excited fluorescent material on a screen, between which a high field is set up having an intensity at the tip of several volts per Å, in vacuo. This situation in the low-pressure gas phase near the electrode tip is thus analogous to that at a polarised electrode in solution, where fields of the order of magnitude 0.3–1 v. per Å are locally involved.

In the operation of the apparatus, a field is applied which causes electron transfer from (or to) the tip to (or from) the anodic screen. The pattern seen is then an electron emission flux distribution which is related to the geometry of surface atoms at the tip, to the presence of ad-species and to the distribution of values of the electron exit work function at the tip.

Field ionisation is the converse of the above process and consists of ionisation of residual or accommodated (adsorbed) gas molecules by electron tunneling from the gas to the tip (now the anode). Much greater resolution of the surface structure is seen under field ionisation than under field electron emission and information of much greater theoretical interest is also obtained by means of the former technique.

2. FIELD EMISSION OF ELECTRONS

In thermionic and photo-emission, electrons are given sufficient energy to overcome the potential barrier for their exit at the interface of the metal. In field emission, the barrier is deformed so strongly by an applied field that electron leakage by tunneling *through* the barrier can occur. This is shown diagrammatically in Figs. 52a and 52b. The first of these figures shows the situation for a simple difference of potential Φ_e (= 4.5 v. typically) for the electron inside and outside the metal (with zero k.e.) and the effect of the field (e.g. 3×10^7 v. cm.$^{-1}$) at the interface; Φ has the significance of a work function.

In Fig. 52b the image potential* of the electron has been represented and leads to a smearing out of the potential function. Application of the field then gives a barrier of the shape shown—a shape that obviously depends on the intensity of the field.

_____

* The validity of applying the image potential relationship to an electron at short distances from metal interfaces has been examined by Bardeen (36), Seitz (37) and Sachs and Dexter (38).

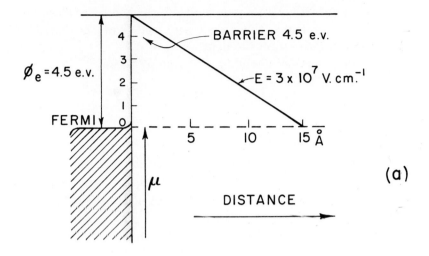

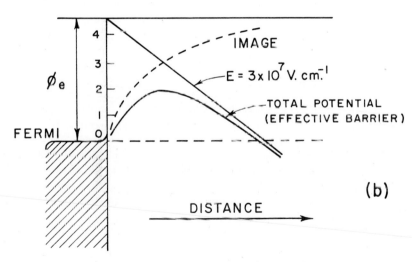

Fig. 52.   (a) Barrier for electron emission in a field.   (b) Barrier for electron emission in a field with electron image potential considered.   (After Gomer, 39.)

The tunneling probability then depends on the energy of electron states in the metal and the height and width of the barrier, which itself will depend on the field.

For a field $\mathscr{E}$, the permeability P is found* to be

$$P \doteqdot \exp\left[-\frac{(8\pi^2 m/h^2)^{1/2}(\Phi + \mu - \mu_x)^{3/2}}{e\mathscr{E}}\right] \tag{332}$$

where Φ is the work function, μ the height of the Fermi level, μ_x the kinetic energy of the electron at a position x in the barrier.

The influence of the image potential correction is not serious and is equivalent to reduction of the actual applied field to an effective value 10–20 per cent less.

In semiconductors (see Chapter 8), the applied field not only affects the energy of the electron outside the metal but will change the charge distribution and electrostatic potential profile normal to the interface *inside* the bulk of the material.

Anisotropic field emission will occur for most metals where Φ depends on the index of the crystal face exposed. This is the reason for the characteristic form of the emission pictures from tungsten "hemispherical" tips.

3. APPLICATIONS TO ADSORPTION

Various applications to problems of gas adsorption have been made and may be summarised briefly as follows:

(a) Direct "observation" of ad-species can be made and mobility of atoms on surfaces viewed (e.g. O on W). What is actually seen is a "work-function shadow" brought about by the change of electron emission at the site of an adsorbed species.

(b) Work function changes can be deduced from the emission current-voltage relationship and related to coverage if it is assumed that

$$\frac{\theta}{\theta_{\max}} = \frac{\Delta\Phi}{\Delta\Phi_{\max}} \tag{333}$$

* The derivation of this approximate relationship is given in Gomer (39). It follows published methods of calculating tunneling permeability coefficients.

where max indicates the maximum value of θ or $\Delta\Phi$ obtained at relatively high pressures.

(c)   Analytical applications can be made; e.g., traces of H_2 in CO can be detected at a low partial pressure on account of the characteristic field-emission patterns which are associated with H adsorption on tungsten.   Quantitative mobility and desorption-temperature measurements can confirm the presence of H_2 in CO and other gases.   Oxygen can also be detected by formation of characteristic oxide patterns. Dissociative chemisorption can be characterised in some cases, e.g., where carbides are formed as intermediates.

4.   FIELD IONISATION

(i) Phenomenology of Field Desorption.   Müller (319) was the first to make observations of field ionisation when reversed voltage was applied to a field-emission tip in the presence of hydrogen. Mass-spectrometric analysis showed that H_2^+ and H^+ were the ions formed.   Many ions of various molecules have now been identified at field-ionisation sources.

The formation of ions occurs at varying distances from the tip (up to 100 Å at high fields) and involves tunneling of an electron to the tip from an atom or molecule near the tip or adsorbed at its surface.   The situation is thus analogous to oxidation of a reductant at an electrode-solution interface.   The diagrams (Fig. 53) illustrate the situation.

The dashed line in Fig. 53a shows the cross-section of the coulomb potential of, for example, the $1s$ electron of the H atom without the applied field $\mathscr{E}$.   The field $\mathscr{E}$ deforms this potential as shown by the solid lines, so that the electron sees a barrier of finite height and width, which, if of suitable dimensions, will be permeable to the electron, and electron transfer to the metal (Fig. 53b) can occur.

At low fields, ions are formed by electron tunneling across this barrier from atoms or molecules only at short distances from the tip (the case shown in the diagram is for H at 5 Å from the metal).   At higher fields, tunneling can occur without the help of the image potential, and ions can be formed at greater distances from the surface.

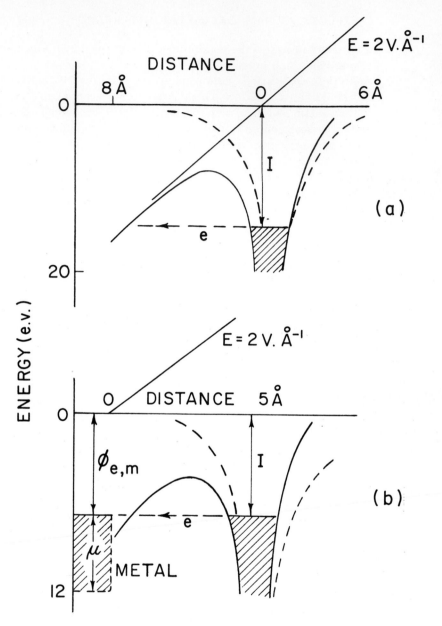

Fig. 53. (a) Coulomb potential for 1s electron in H in the presence of a field. (b) Field ionisation at a metal due to tunneling through field-modified coulomb-potential barrier for H. (After Gomer, 39.)

278

If $I > \Phi$, for example, as is the case for H at all metals, the field must raise the electron being transferred to a level at least equal to the Fermi level since other states below this level are occupied. This can occur if the field operates over a minimum distance x^0, so that

$$x^0 = \frac{I - \Phi}{e\mathscr{E}} \tag{334}$$

where $I - \Phi - e\mathscr{E}x^0 = 0$, i.e., the energy gained by passage down the field is $e\mathscr{E}x^0$.

If the image potential is included, then

$$e\mathscr{E}x^0 = I - \Phi - \frac{3.6q^2}{x^0} \tag{335}$$

where the image term arises from the fact that the total energy of the system after tunneling includes the attraction of the resulting ion (charge q) to the surface. (It will be noted that a quite analogous situation is involved in the energetics of electrochemical metal dissolution or deposition, or electrochemical H ionisation.)

(ii) **Applications to Adsorption: Field Desorption.** In addition to ionisation near the tip in the gas phase, direct desorption of adsorbed species can occur at high fields (*cf.* electrochemical oxidation of adsorbed H atoms). The desorbed species are usually ionic as may be shown by mass spectrometric experiments. The ionic products depend on the pretreatment of the tip. Desorption can be made the predominant ion-producing process by operating at low pressures and short field-pulse times.

Further potential-energy diagrams will be considered first for field ionisation and then with application to field desorption.

Figure 54 shows the potential energy for approach of an interacting atom A to the metal M as a function of distance x, and also the corresponding potential profile for M^- (electron in metal) $+ A^+$(ionised atom)—the potential profile is the image potential and differs at large distances from that for $M + A$ by the energy $I - \Phi$. When no field operates at the interface, the potential curves for $M + A$ and $M^+ + A^-$ will generally not cross.

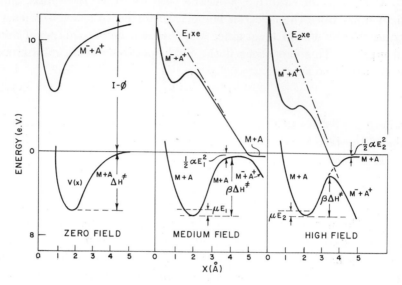

Fig. 54. Potential-energy diagrams for field-desorption ionisation at a metal. (a) zero-field case; (b) low-field case; (c) high-field case. (After Gomer, 39.)

When a strong field is applied, the curve for $M^+ + A^-$ is deformed and that for $M + A$ is displaced downward by a polarisation energy $\frac{1}{2}\alpha\mathscr{E}^2$. (The energy of the state $M^- + A^+$ in the field will also involve a polarisation term as well as the main simple coulombic one, but the polarisability of A^+ will of course be rather less than that of A.)

Field ionisation therefore occurs at x_c in the adiabatic transition, and x_c is, in fact, identical in significance with the minimum separation x^0 defined by the equation above.

When the field $\mathscr{E}$ is applied, the curve for $M^- + A^+ *$ is deformed and that for $M + A$ slightly shifted, and intersection

---

* For adsorption of most atoms at metals, the ionic state M^-, A^+ is an excited one with respect to that corresponding to covalent chemisorption in the state MA. However, for some adsorbates, e.g. the alkali metals at tungsten where $I < \Phi_{e,\text{W}}$ the chemisorbed state involves cations of the adsorbate.

occurs at x_c. Adiabatic transitions (see Chapter 8) of an atom A moving away from the surface will lead to ionisation at a critical distance x_c, and the particle will then follow the lower curve $M^- + A^+$, which gives the most stable species when $x > x_c$ at high fields. Non-adiabatic transitions, corresponding to the crossing of the curves near x_c (broken lines), can occur if the motion of A is too rapid for electron tunneling; this is unlikely. Vibrational desorption along MA requires the zero-field activation energy $\Delta H^{\ddagger}$ (except for dipole-field and polarisation energy terms), but can be followed by ionisation at x_c along the path $M^- + A^+$ when $x > x_c$; i.e. field-ion-desorption will have occurred (i.e. desorption of A as a cation under the influence of the field). At very high fields, when x_c falls within the "attractive part" of the M + A potential curve, the situation is as shown in Fig. 54c. The activation energy for desorption is then reduced from $\Delta H^{\ddagger}$ to $\beta \Delta H^{\ddagger}$, where $\beta < 1$ and β has a significance similar to that in solution electrode kinetics. The situation, however, is not qualitatively different from that for low-field conditions, except that the rate constant for field desorption will be higher.

(iii) Experimental Determination of the Potential Function for Adsorption of A at M by field-ionisation measurements.

Field-desorption studies at various field strengths can lead to quantitative information on the shape of the potential profile for adsorption of an atom at a metal.

Under high-field conditions, the activation energy $\beta \Delta H^{\ddagger}$ for desorption (see above) will be dependent on the shape of the potential function for M + A in so far as $\beta \Delta H^{\ddagger}$ will be determined by the magnitude of the M + A potential energy at various x_c values corresponding to changing field intensity.

When the field strength is high, only partial vibrational desorption along M + A is necessary for the saddle point to be reached (x_c) and for the M + A to go over to the state $M^- + A^+$. The critical distance x_c is then given (cf. Equation 335) by

$$e\mathscr{E} x_c = I - \Phi - \frac{3.6q^2}{x_c} - V(x_c) \qquad (336)$$

where $V(x_c)$ is the value of the desorption energy at $x = x_c$ on the M + A potential curve.

Evaluation of $\beta\Delta H^{\ddagger}$ $[= V(x_c)]$ as a function of field,* and hence of x_c, then leads to an *experimental evaluation* of the potential curve for adsorption of A at M. Such a curve has been evaluated (on the attractive side) for CO desorption at tungsten and is closely similar to a Morse curve. (It may be noted that this is the *first direct experiment* which verifies the form of the Morse p.e. function, previously developed empirically to represent anharmonicity effects in vibrational levels.)

(iv) Ion-Emission Microscopy. The field-ionisation principle can be used in a microscope which operates similarly to the electron-emission type except that the field is reversed. The resolution is much better, however, and the instrument is more versatile than the electron-emission microscope. Field desorption of metal atoms from the tungsten tip can be followed and movements of individual atoms detected and quantitatively measured; defects in the lattice can be localised; e.g., screw dislocations can be seen. Helium is usually used as the ionisable gas in these applications. Lattice geometry of the metal surface can be seen in astonishing detail. The intensity of ionisation near the tip is a sensitive function of local field, and the latter is related to the detailed geometry of atomic arrangements on various crystal planes. The image hence reproduces the microscopic field profile at the surface. Like the development of infra-red spectroscopy at interfaces, quantitative application of field-ionisation techniques must be regarded as one of the most important recent developments in electrochemical surface chemistry, in this case at the gas–metal-electrode interface.

---

* Experimentally, desorption rates are determined as a function of temperature at various field strengths. The values of $V(x_c)$ thus obtained are correlated with x_c by means of Equation 336 for $e\mathscr{E}x_c$.

Appendix

Basic Types of Mechanisms for Organic Electrode Processes [*]

1. Reduction
$$\begin{cases} \text{Electron transfer} + \text{proton transfer} \\ \quad R + e \to R^-; \quad R^- + H^+ \to RH \\ \quad RH + e \to RH^-; \quad RH^- + H^+ \to RH_2 \\ \text{Electrochemical hydrogenation} \\ \quad H_3O^+ + M + e \to MH + H_2O \\ \quad H_2O + M + e \to MH + OH^- \\ \quad R + M \to RM; \quad RM + 2MH \to RH_2 \end{cases}$$

2. Oxidation
$$\begin{cases} \text{Electron transfer} + OH^- \text{ transfer} \\ \quad R \to R^+ + e; \quad R^+ + H_2O \xrightarrow{rapid} ROH + H^+ \\ \text{Electrochemical catalytic oxidation} \\ \quad H_2O + M \to MOH + H^+ + e \\ \quad MOH + R \to ROH \\ \quad R + M \to R' + MH \text{ (dehydrogenation)} \\ \quad R' + MOH \to R'OH + M \end{cases}$$

3. Coupling at anode:
$$RCOO^- \to R + CO_2 + e$$
$$2R \to R_2 \text{ (Kolbe)}$$

4. Substitution at anode:
$$RCOO^- \to R + CO_2 + e$$
$$R + XH \to RX$$
$$RCOO + XH \to X.OOCR$$

5. Halogen substitution at anode:
$$Ha^- + M \to M.Ha$$
$$XH + M.Ha \to X.Ha$$
(molecular attack by Ha_2?)

---

[*] See p. 241.

Basic Types of Mechanisms for Organic
Electrode Processes (Continued)

6. Coupling at cathode via carbanion intermediate:

$$2CH_2{=}CH.CN + 2H^+ + 2e \rightarrow [{-}CH_2{-}CH_2{-}CN]_2$$

7. Coupling at cathode by ion discharge:

$$R'R_3N^+ + e \rightarrow R'_2$$

(*cf.* tetraphenyl borate reaction)

Example:

8. Anodic methoxylation (KOH/MeOH/Pt)

$$\rightarrow \text{polymethoxylated derivatives}$$

References

1. W, NICHOLSON and S. CARLISLE, *Nicholson's J. (J. Nat. Phil.)*, **4**, 179 (1800).
2. M. FARADAY, *Phil. Trans.*, **123**, 23 (1833); **124**, 77 (1834).
3. L. GALVANI; e.g., see *Effects of Electricity on Muscular Motion* (1791), transl. M. G. Foley, Burndy Lib., Norwalk, Conn., 1953.
4. A. VOLTA; e.g., see B. D. DIBNER, *Galvani-Volta*, Burndy Lib., Norwalk, Conn., 1952.
5. G. J. JOHNSTONE-STONEY, *Trans. Roy. Dublin Soc.*, 1891.
6. J. J. THOMSON; e.g., see LORD RAYLEIGH, *Sir J. J. Thomson*, Cambridge University Press, London, 1942.
7. J. O'M. BOCKRIS and B. E CONWAY, *Record Chem. Progr.*, **25**, 31 (1964).
8. B. E. CONWAY and J. O'M. BOCKRIS, *Modern Aspects of Electrochemistry*, vol. 1 (eds. J. O'M. BOCKRIS and B. E. CONWAY), Academic Press, New York, 1954. Chap. 2.
9. B. E. CONWAY, J. E. DESNOYERS and A. C. SMITH, *Phil. Trans. Roy. Soc. London*, **A256**, 389 (1964).
10. J. D. BERNAL and R. H. FOWLER, *J. Chem. Phys.*, **1**, 515 (1933).
11. T. R. ROSEBRUGH and W. LASH-MILLER, *J. Phys. Chem.*, **24**, 816 (1910); D. MacGILLAVRY and E. K. RIDEAL, *Rec. Trav. Chim.*, **56**, 1013 (1937).
12. H. S. SAND, *Phil. Mag.*, **1**, 45 (1900); *Z. Physik. Chem.*, **35**, 641 (1900); *Trans. Faraday Soc.*, **1**, 1 (1905).
13. V. LEVICH, *Discussions Faraday Soc.*, No. 1, 37 (1947).
14. C. F. BROCKMAN, *Electro-organic Chemistry*, John Wiley and Sons, New York, 1926.
15. J. A. V. BUTLER, *Trans. Faraday Soc.*, **19**, 734 (1924).
16. M. VOLMER and T. VON ERDEY-GRUZ, *Z. Physik. Chem.*, **A150**, 203 (1930).
17. M. BAARS, *Sitzber. Naturw. Marburg*, **63**, 213 (1928).
18. R. W. GURNEY, *Proc. Roy. Soc. London* **A134**, 137 (1932).
19. A. N. FRUMKIN, *Z. Physik. Chem.*, **A164**, 121 (1933); see also *Acta Physicochim. U.R.S.S.*, **6**, 502 (1937).

20. J. Horiuti and M. Polanyi, *Acta Physicochim. U.R.S.S.*, **2**, 505 (1935).
21. J. A. V. Butler, *Proc. Roy. Soc. London*, **A157**, 423 (1936).
22. R. J. Marcus, B. J. Zwolinsky and H. Eyring, *J. Phys. Chem.*, **58**, 432 (1952).
23. K. J. Laidler, *Can. J. Chem.*, **37**, 138 (1959).
24. J. E. B. Randles and K. W. Somerton, *Trans. Faraday Soc.*, **48**, 937 (1952); *cf.* also ref. 264.
25. V. Levich, *Dokl. Akad. Nauk SSSR*, **67**, 309 (1949).
26. B. E. Conway, *Can. J. Chem.* **37**, 178 (1959).
27. St. G. Christov, *Z. Elektrochem.*, **62**, 567 (1958); **64**, 840 (1960); see also *Electrochim. Acta*, **4**, 306 (1961).
28. E. Lange and B. Miscenko, *Z. Physik. Chem.*, **149**, 1 (1930); see also *Z. Elektrochem.*, **55**, 76 (1951); *Wien-Harms Handbuch Exptl. Phys.*, **12** (2), 267 (1933).
29. N. K. Adam, *Physics and Chemistry of Surfaces*, 3rd ed., Oxford University Press, London, 1941. P. 300.
30. R. Parsons, *Modern Aspects of Electrochemistry*, vol. 1 (eds. Bockris and Conway), Academic Press, New York, 1954. Chapter 2.
31. J. A. V. Butler, *Proc. Roy. Soc. London*, **A112**, 129 (1926); see also E. A. Guggenheim, ref. 42.
32. C. Herring and M. H. Nichols, *Rev. Mod. Phys.*, **21**, 185 (1949); *Seminar on Metal Interfaces* (Cleveland), American Institute of Metals (1951), p. 1.
33. D. D. Eley and M. G. Evans, *Trans. Faraday Soc.*, **34**, 1093 (1938); B. E. Conway and J. O'M. Bockris, Chapter 3 in ref. (30).
34. K. J. Laidler and M. Pegis, *Proc. Roy. Soc. London*, **A241**, 80 (1957).
35. J. E. B. Randles, *Advan. Electrochem. Electrochem. Eng.* (eds. Delahay and Tobias), **3**, 1 (1963).
36. J. Bardeen, *Phys. Rev.*, **58**, 727 (1940).
37. R. G. Sachs and D. C. Dexter, *J. Appl. Phys.*, **21**, 1304 (1950).
38. F. Seitz, *Modern Theory of Solids*, McGraw-Hill Book Co., New York, 1940.
39. R. Gomer, *Field Emission and Field Ionization*, Harvard University Press, Cambridge, Mass., 1961.
40. J. A. V. Butler, *Electrocapillarity*, Methuen, London, 1940.
41. I. Langmuir, *Trans. Am. Electrochem. Soc.*, **29**, 125 (1916).
42. E. A. Guggenheim, *J. Phys. Chem.*, **33**, 842 (1929); **34**, 1540 (1930).
43. H. L. F. von Helmholtz, *Wiss. Abhandl. Physik-tech. Reichsanstalt*, **1**, 925 (1879).
44. G. Gouy, *J. Phys.*, **9**, 457 (1910).
45. D. L. Chapman, *Phil. Mag.*, **25**, 475 (1913).
46. P. Debye and E. Hückel, *Physik. Z.*, **24**, 185, 305 (1923).
47. O. Stern, *Z. Elektrochem.*, **30**, 508 (1924).
48. B. E. Conway, Ph.D. thesis, London (1949).
49. B. E. Conway, J. O'M. Bockris and I. A. Ammar, *Trans. Faraday Soc.*, **47**, 756 (1951).

50. D. C. GRAHAME, *J. Chem. Phys.*, **18**, 903 (1950).
51. F. BOOTH, *J. Chem. Phys.*, **19**, 391 (1951); *cf.* J. C. WEBB, *J. Am. Chem. Soc.*, **48**, 2589 (1926).
52. M. A. V. DEVANATHAN, J. O'M. BOCKRIS and K. MÜLLER, *Proc. Roy. Soc. London*, **A274**, 55 (1963).
53. A. N. FRUMKIN, *Phil. Mag.*, **40**, (6) (1920).
54. D. C. GRAHAME, *Chem. Rev.*, **41**, 441 (1947).
55. G. GOUY, *Ann. Phys. (Paris)*, **7**, 163 (1917).
56. A. N. FRUMKIN, *Trans. Faraday Soc.*, **36**, 117 (1940).
57. R. H. FOWLER and E. A. GUGGENHEIM, *Statistical Thermodynamics*, Cambridge University Press, London, 1949.
58. J. O'M. BOCKRIS and B. E. CONWAY, *Trans. Faraday Soc.*, **48**, 724 (1952); *cf.* ref. 139.
59. D. C. GRAHAME, *J. Electrochem. Soc.*, **98**, 343 (1951); **99**, 370C (1952).
60. D. C. GRAHAME, *J. Am. Chem. Soc.*, **76**, 4819 (1954); **79**, 2093 (1957).
61. D. C. GRAHAME, *Z. Elektrochem.*, **59**, 773 (1955).
62. D. C. GRAHAME and B. SODERBERG, *J. Chem. Phys.*, **22**, 449 (1954).
63. D. C. GRAHAME, M. POTH and J. CUMMINGS, *J. Am. Chem. Soc.*, **74**, 4122 (1952).
64. O. A. ESIN and V. SHIKOV, *Zh. Fiz. Khim.*, **17**, 236 (1943).
65. B. V. ERSHLER, *Zh. Fiz. Khim.*, **20**, 679 (1946).
66. S. LEVINE, G. M. BELL and D. CALVERT, *Can. J. Chem.*, **40**, 518 (1962).
67. R. PARSONS, *Advan. Electrochem. Electrochem. Eng.* (eds. DELAHAY and TOBIAS), **1**, 1 (1961).
68. A. N. FRUMKIN and A. TITIEVSKAJA, *Zh. Fiz. Khim.*, **31**, 385 (1957); **32**, 157 (1958).
69. B. DAMASKIN, N. NIKOLAJEVA-FEDOROVICH and A. N. FRUMKIN, *Dokl. Akad. Nauk SSSR*, **121**, 129 (1958); F. DEANE, A. HIGINBOTHAM and D. C. GRAHAME, *Trans. Symp. Electrode Processes, Philadelphia, Pa.*, 1959 (1961), 39.
70. A. OBRUCHEVA, *Zh. Fiz. Khim.*, **32**, 2155 (1958); *Dokl. Akad. Nauk SSSR*, **120**, 1072 (1958).
71. J. MALSCH, *Physik. Z.*, **29**, 770 (1928).
72. J. E. DESNOYERS, Ph.D. thesis, Ottawa (1961); see also B. E. CONWAY, J. E. DESNOYERS and A. C. SMITH, *Phil. Trans. Roy. Soc. London*, **A256**, 389 (1964).
73. M. J. SPARNAAY, *Rec. Trav. Chim.* **77**, 872 (1958).
74. J. E. DESNOYERS, R. VERRALL and B. E. CONWAY, *J. Chem. Phys.* **43**, 243 (1965).
75. H. S. FRANK, *J. Chem. Phys.*, **23**, 2023 (1955).
76. J. R. MACDONALD, *J. Chem. Phys.*, **22**, 1859 (1954).
77. D. C. GRAHAME, *J. Chem. Phys.*, **23**, 1725 (1955).
78. N. F. MOTT and R. J. WATTS-TOBIN, *Phil. Mag.*, **7**, (8) 483 (1962).
79. G. H. NANCOLLAS and P. VINCENT, in course of publication; see P. VINCENT, Ph.D. thesis, Glasgow (1963).
80. F. O. KOENIG, *Z. Physik. Chem.*, **154**, 421, 454 (1931); **156**, 38 (1931); **157**, 96 (1931); *J. Phys. Chem.*, **38**, 111, 339 (1934).

81. S. R. Craxford, M. Gatty and St. J. Philpot, *Phil. Mag.*, **16**, 849 (1933); **17**, 54 (1934); **19**, 965 (1935); **22**, 359, 402 (1936).

82. J. A. V. Butler, *Proc. Roy. Soc. London*, **A113**, 594 (1927); see also *Electrocapillarity*, Methuen, London, 1940, and ref. 102.

83. A. N. Frumkin, *Z. Physik. Chem.*, **103**, 55 (1923).

84. J. A. V. Butler, *Proc. Roy. Soc. London*, **A122**, 399 (1929).

85. G. Lippmann, *Pogg. Ann.*, **149**, 547 (1878); *Ann. Chim. Phys.*, **5**, 494 (1875); **12**, 265 (1877).

86. G. Kucera, *Ann. Physik*, **11**, 529, 698 (1903).

87. S. R. Craxford and H. A. C. McKay, *J. Phys. Chem.*, **39**, 545 (1935).

88. R. K. Schofield, *Phil. Mag.*, **1**, 641 (1926).

89. E. A. Guggenheim, *J. Chem. Soc.*, **1940**, 106, 128.

90. D. C. Grahame and R. Parsons, *J. Am. Chem. Soc.*, **83**, 1291 (1961); see also M. A. V. Devanathan and S. G. Canagaratna, *Electrochim. Acta*, **8**, 77 (1963).

91. M. Proskurnin and A. N. Frumkin, *Trans. Faraday Soc.* **31**, 110 (1935); see also T. Borissova and M. Proskurnin, *Acta Physicochim. U.R.S.S.*, **4**, 819 (1936).

92. B. E. Conway, J. O'M. Bockris and B. Lovrecek, *Proc. Meeting Intern. Comm. Electrochem. Thermodyn. Kinet. 6th Royaumont Poitiers* 1954 (1955), 207.

93. E. Blomgren and J. O'M. Bockris, *J. Phys. Chem.*, **63**, 1475 (1959).

94. B. E. Conway and R. G. Barradas, *Electrochim. Acta*, **5**, 319, 349 (1961).

95. R. S. Hansen, R. E. Minturn and D. A. Hickson, *J. Phys. Chem.*, **60**, 1185 (1956); **61**, 953 (1957).

96. D. Leikis; see A. N. Frumkin, *J. Electrochem. Soc.*, **107**, 461 (1960).

97. N. A. Balashova, *Dokl. Akad. Nauk SSSR*, **103**, 639 (1955); see also *Z. Physik. Chem. (Leipzig)*, **207**, 340 (1957).

98. N. Hackerman and S. J. Stephens, *J. Phys. Chem.*, **58**, 904 (1954).

99. H. Wroblowa and M. Green, *Electrochim. Acta*, **8**, 679 (1963).

100. J. O'M. Bockris, D. A. J. Swinkells and M. Green, *Rev. Sci. Inst.* **33**, 18 (1962).

101. B. E. Conway, T. Zawidzki and R. G. Barradas, *J. Phys. Chem.*, **62**, 676 (1958); see also *J. Electroanal. Chem.*, **6**, 314 (1963).

102. O. Warburg, *Ann. Physik*, **41**, 1 (1890).

103. A. N. Frumkin, *Zh. Fiz. Khim.*, **5**, 240 (1934); see also *Z. Phys. Chem.*, **136**, 215, 451 (1928).

104. L. I. Antropov, *Zh. Fiz. Khim.*, **25**, 1494 (1951).

105. P. Ruetschi, *J. Electrochem. Soc.*, **104**, 176 (1957); cf. *J. Electrochem. Soc.*, **110**, 835 (1963).

106. B. V. Ershler, *Usp. Khim.*, **21**, 237 (1952).

107. O. A. Esin and B. E. Markov, *Acta Physicochim. U.R.S.S.*, **10**, 353 (1939).

108. D. C. Grahame, *Ann. Rev. Phys. Chem.*, **6**, 337 (1955).

109. R. Parsons, *Proc. Intern. Congr. Surface Activity*, 2nd, *London*, 1957 (ed. G. H. Schulman), **3**, 38.

110. J. O'M. BOCKRIS, B. E. CONWAY, W. MEHL and L. YOUNG, *J. Chem. Phys.*, **25**, 776 (1955).

111. P. REHBINDER and E. WENSTRÖM, *Zh. Fiz. Khim.*, **19**, 1 (1945); *Dokl. Akad. Nauk SSSR*, **68**, 329 (1949).

112. J. O'M. BOCKRIS and J. PARRY-JONES, *Nature*, **171**, 930 (1953).

113. A. GORODETZSKAYA and A. N. FRUMKIN, *Physik. Z. Sowjetunion*, **1**, 255 (1932); **5**, 418 (1934).

114. B. JAKUSZEWSKI and Z. KOZLOWSKI, *Roczniki Chem.*, **36**, 1873 (1962).

115. J. LEGRAN and I. I. LEVINA, *Acta Physicochim. U.R.S.S.*, **12**, 243 (1940).

116. A. N. FRUMKIN and N. BALASHOVA, *Dokl. Akad. Nauk SSSR*, **20**, 449 (1938); I. VOROPAJEVA, *ibid.*, **128**, 981 (1959).

117. T. BORISSOVA, B. V. ERSHLER and A. N. FRUMKIN, *Zh. Fiz. Khim. U.S.S.R.*, **22**, 925 (1948); **24**, 337 (1950); see also *J. Russ. Phys. Chem. Soc.*, **49**, 207 (1917).

118. N. BALASHOVA and N. S. MERKULEVA, *Proc. Conf. Electrochem. 3rd Moscow*, 1956 (1959), 48.

119. P. W. SHAPINCK *et al.*, *Trans. Faraday Soc.*, **56**, 415 (1960).

120. L. GIERST, *Trans. Symp. Electrode Processes Philadelphia, Pa.*, 1959 (1961), 109.

121. A. N. FRUMKIN, *Z. Physik*, **35**, 792 (1926).

122. M. A. V. DEVANATHAN, *Proc. Roy. Soc. London*, **A264**, 133 (1961).

123. R. PARSONS, *J. Electroanal. Chem.*, **5**, 397 (1963); see also H. A. LAITINEN and B. MOSIER, *J. Am. Chem. Soc.* **80**, 2363 (1958).

124. B. E. CONWAY and E. GILEADI, *Trans. Faraday Soc.*, **58**, 2493 (1962).

125. M. I. TEMKIN, *Zh. Fiz. Khim.*, **15**, 296 (1941); see also A. N. FRUMKIN, *Z. Physik. Chem.*, **116**, 466 (1925); *Z. Physik*, **35**, 792 (1926).

126. J. ZELDOWITCH, *Acta Physicochim. U.R.S.S.*, **1**, 961 (1935).

127. M. BOUDART, *J. Am. Chem. Soc.*, **72**, 3566 (1952).

128. E. GILEADI and B. E. CONWAY, *Modern Aspects of Electrochemistry*, vol. 3 (ed. J. O'M. BOCKRIS and B. E. CONWAY), Butterworths, London, 1964, Chapter 5.

129. M. I. TEMKIN, *Symp. Probl. Chem. Kinetics, Catalysis and Reactivity*, Akademiya Nauk, S.S.S.R., 1955.

130. E. A. MOELWYN-HUGHES, *Physical Chemistry*, Cambridge University Press, London, 1947.

131. I. LANGMUIR, *J. Am. Chem. Soc.*, **54**, 1252, 2798 (1932).

132. R. PARSONS, *Trans. Faraday Soc.*, **51**, 1518 (1955).

133. R. PARSONS, *Trans. Faraday Soc.*, **55**, 999 (1959).

134. W. LORENZ, F. MOCKEL, and N. MÜLLER, *Z. Physik. Chem.* **25**, 145 (1960); see also B. B. DAMASKIN, *Electrochim. Acta*, **9**, 231 (1964).

135. M. GEROWICZ and P. RYBALSCHENKO, *Zh. Fiz. Khim.*, **32**, 109 (1958).

136. M. GEROWICZ and P. RYBALSCHENKO, *Dokl. Akad. Nauk SSSR*, **86**, 543 (1954); **105**, 1278 (1955).

137. S. GLASSTONE, K. J. LAIDLER and H. EYRING, *Theory of Rate Processes*, McGraw-Hill Book Co., Inc., New York, 1940.

138. L. GIERST, *Trans. Symp. Electrode Processes*, Philadelphia, Pa. 1959 (1961), 109.

139. C. D. Russell, *J. Electroanal. Chem.*, **6**, 486 (1963).
140. H. Gerischer, *Z. Physik. Chem.*, **26**, 223, 325 (1960).
141. K. J. Laidler, *Can. J. Chem.*, **37**, 138 (1959).
142. L. Young, *Trans. Faraday Soc.*, **50**, 159 (1954).
143. G. E. Kimball, *J. Chem. Phys.*, 8, 199 (1940).
144. G. E. Kimball, S. Glasstone and A. Glassner, *J. Chem. Phys.*, **9**, 91 (1941).
145. J. A. V. Butler, *J. Chem. Phys.*, **9**, 279 (1941).
146. R. A. Marcus, *Trans. Symp. Electrode Processes, Philadelphia, Pa.*, 1959 (1961), 239.
147. K. Vetter, *Trans. Symp. Electrode Processes, Philadelphia, Pa.*, 1959 (1961), 47.
148. B. E. Conway and M. Salomon, *Electrochim. Acta*, **9**, 1599 (1964).
149. J. O'M. Bockris and I. A. Ammar, *J. Phys. Chem.*, **61**, 879 (1957).
150. A. N. Frumkin and N. Nikolajeva-Fedorovich, *Vestn. Mosk. Univ.*, **N4**, 169 (1957); see also *Wiss. Z. Tech. Hochsch., Dresden*, **7**, 847 (1957–58).
151. R. Parsons, *Trans. Faraday Soc.*, **47**, 1332 (1951).
152. J. O'M. Bockris, *Modern Aspects of Electrochemistry*, vol. 1 (eds. Bockris and Conway), Butterworths, London, 1954, Chapter 4.
153. A. C. Makrides, *J. Electrochem. Soc.*, **104**, 677 (1957); **109**, 256 (1962).
154. J. O'M. Bockris and E. C. Potter, *J. Electrochem. Soc.*, **99**, 169 (1952); *J. Chem. Phys.*, **20**, 614 (1952).
155. V. Losev and A. I. Molodov, *Zh. Fiz. Khim.*, **35**, 2487 (1961); see also G. M. Budov and V. Losev, *Dokl. Akad. Nauk SSSR*, **129**, 1321 (1959).
156. B. E. Conway and J. O'M. Bockris, *J. Chem. Phys.*, **28**, 707 (1958).
157. B. E. Conway, *Electrochemical Data*, Elsevier Publishing Co., Amsterdam, 1952.
158. J. Eastman, *J. Am. Chem. Soc.*, **50**, 283, 292 (1928).
159. M. I. Temkin, *Zh. Fiz. Khim.*, **22**, 1081 (1948).
160. H. F. Halliwell and S. C. Nyburg, *Trans. Faraday Soc.*, **59**, 1126 (1963); C. Herring and M. H. Nichols, *Rev. Mod. Phys.*, **21**, 185 (1949) (ref. 32).
161. B. E. Conway, *Trans. Roy. Soc. Can., Sect. III*, **54**, 19 (1960).
162. B. E. Conway and M. Salomon, *J. Chem. Phys.* **41**, 3169 (1964).
163. K. M. Joshi, W. Mehl and R. Parsons, *Trans. Symp. Electrode Processes, Philadelphia, Pa.*, 1959 (1961), 249.
164. H. Gerischer, *Z. Elektrochem.*, **62**, 256 (1958).
165. B. E. Conway and P. L. Bourgault, *Can. J. Chem.*, **38**, 1557 (1960).
166. C. A. Christiansen, *Z. Physik. Chem.*, **B33**, 145 (1936); **B37**, 374 (1937).
167. J. O'M. Bockris, *J. Chem. Phys.*, **24**, 817 (1956).
168. B. E. Conway and P. L. Bourgault, *Can. J. Chem.*, **37**, 292 (1959); *Trans. Faraday Soc.*, **58**, 593 (1962).
169. A. I. Krazil'shchikov, *Russ. J. Phys. Chem. (Engl. Transl.)*, **37**, 273 (1963).
170. R. Parsons, *Trans. Faraday Soc.*, **54**, 1053 (1958).

171. J. G. N. THOMAS, *ibid.*, **57**, 1603 (1961).
172. A. N. FRUMKIN, P. DOLIN and B. V. ERSHLER, *Acta Physicochim. U.R.S.S.*, **13**, 779 (1940); see also M. I. TEMKIN and S. PYZHEV, *ibid.*, **12**, 327 (1940).
173. J. P. HOARE and S. SCHULDINER, *J. Electrochem. Soc.*, **102**, 485 (1955).
174. J. O'M. BOCKRIS, N. PENTLAND and E. SHELDON, *J. Electrochem. Soc.*, **104**, 182 (1957).
175. B. V. ERSHLER and A. N. FRUMKIN, *Trans. Faraday Soc.*, **35**, 464 (1939).
176. B. E. CONWAY and P. L. BOURGAULT, *Can. J. Chem.*, **40**, 1690 (1962).
177. B. E. CONWAY and M. DZIECIUCH, *Can. J. Chem.*, **41**, 21, 38, 55 (1963).
178. B. E. CONWAY, E. GILEADI and M. DZIECIUCH, *Electrochim. Acta*, **8**, 143 (1963).
179. M. SIDDIQUI and F. C. TOMPKINS, *Proc. Roy. Soc. London*, **A268**, 452 (1962).
180. J. E. B. RANDLES, *Discussions Faraday Soc.*, No. 1, 11 (1947).
181. N. S. HUSH, *J. Chem. Phys.*, **28**, 962 (1958).
182. B. E. CONWAY and J. O'M. BOCKRIS, *J. Chem. Phys.*, **26**, 532 (1957); *cf.* P. RUETSCHI and P. DELAHAY, *ibid.*, **23**, 195 (1955).
183. B. E. CONWAY, E. BEATTY and P. A. D. DE MAINE, *Electrochim. Acta*, **7**, 39 (1962).
184. B. E. CONWAY and J. O'M. BOCKRIS, *Can. J. Chem.*, **35**, 1124 (1957).
185. J. O'M. BOCKRIS and R. PARSONS, *Trans. Faraday Soc.*, **47**, 914 (1951).
186. T. KEII and T. KODERA, *J. Res. Inst. Catalysis, Hokkaido Univ.*, **5**, 105 (1957); see also J. O'M. BOCKRIS and S. SRINIVASEN, *J. Electrochem. Soc.* **111**, 844 (1964).
187. B. E. CONWAY and J. O'M. BOCKRIS, *Electrochim. Acta*, **3**, 340 (1961).
188. G. OKAMOTO, J. HORIUTI and K. HIROTA, *Sci. Papers Inst. Phys. Chem. Res., Tokyo*, **29**, 223 (1936); see also **28**, 231 (1936) and ref. 302.
189. P. DOLIN and B. V. ERSHLER, *Acta Physicochim. U.R.S.S.*, **13**, 747 (1940).
190. B. E. CONWAY and E. GILEADI, *Can. J. Chem.*, **42**, 90 (1964); see also *J. Chem. Phys.*, **39**, 3420 (1963).
191. W. BOELD and M. BREITER, *Electrochim. Acta*, **5**, 145, 169 (1961).
192. O. BEECK, *Discussions Faraday Soc.*, No. 8, 118 (1950).
193. J. P. HOARE and S. SCHULDINER, *J. Phys. Chem.*, **61**, 705 (1957); see also M. OIKAWA, *Bull. Chem. Soc. Japan*, **28**, 626 (1955).
194. E. GILEADI, Ph.D. thesis, Ottawa (1963).
195. F. P. BOWDEN and E. K. RIDEAL, *Proc. Roy. Soc. London*, **A120**, 59, 80 (1928).
196. A. N. FRUMKIN and A. I. SLYGIN, *Acta Physicochim. U.R.S.S.*, **3**, 791 (1935); **4**, 991 (1936).
197. H. GERISCHER and W. MEHL, *Z. Elektrochem.*, **59**, 1049 (1955).
198. M. A. V. DEVANATHAN, J. O'M. BOCKRIS and W. MEHL, *J. Electroanal. Chem.*, **1**, 143 (1959–60); M. A. V. DEVANATHAN and K. SELVARATNAM, *Trans. Faraday Soc.*, **56**, 1820 (1960).

199. H. A. Kozlowska and B. E. Conway, *J. Electroanal. Chem.*, **7**, 109 (1964).
200. A. Eucken and B. Weblus, *Z. Elektrochem.*, **55**, 115 (1951).
201. M. Breiter, *Trans. Symp. Electrode Processes, Philadelphia, Pa.*, 1959 (1961), 307.
202. F. Will, *Abstr. Electrochem. Soc. Meeting, Toronto* (1964).
203. B. E. Conway and M. Salomon, *Ber. Bunsenges.*, **68**, 331 (1964).
204. O. Beeck, *Advan. Catalysis*, **2**, 151 (1950).
205. J. A. V. Butler and G. Armstrong, *Proc. Roy. Soc. London*, **A137**, 604 (1932); *Trans. Faraday Soc.*, **29**, 1261 (1933); *J. Chem. Soc.*, **1934**, 743.
206. H. B. Morley and F. E. W. Wetmore, *Can. J. Chem.*, **34**, 359 (1956).
207. V. I. Past and I. Jofa, *Zh. Fiz. Khim.*, **33**, 913, 1230 (1959); *Dokl. Akad. Nauk S.S.S.R.*, **106**, 1050 (1956).
208. P. D. Lukovstev and V. I. Temerin, *Tr. Akad. Nauk SSSR, Otd. Khim. Nauk* (1953), 494.
209. T. Anderson and H. Eyring, *J. Phys. Chem.*, **67**, 92 (1963).
210. P. Delahay, *J. Phys. Chem.*, **66**, 2204 (1962); see also P. Delahay and A. Aramata, *ibid.*, **66**, 2208 (1962).
211. A. Sevčik, *Collection Czech. Chem. Commun.*, **13**, 349 (1948).
212. M. Breiter, *Electrochim. Acta*, 8, 457 (1963); see also A. Kutschker, and W. Vielstich, *ibid.*, 8, 985 (1963); S. Gilman, *J. Phys. Chem.* **67**, 78 (1963).
213. B. E. Conway, E. Gileadi and H. A. Kozlowska, *J. Electrochem. Soc.*, **112**, 341 (1965).
214. B. E. Conway and A. Vijh, in course of publication.
215. H. Dahms and M. Green, *J. Electrochem. Soc.*, **110**, 1075 (1963).
216. A. Reddy, M. A. V. Devanathan and J. O'M. Bockris, *J. Electroanal. Chem.*, **6**, 61 (1963).
217. D. H. Geske and J. L. Ragle, *J. Am. Chem. Soc.*, **83**, 3532 (1961); A. Naki and D. H. Geske, *ibid.*, **83**, 1852 (1961); *J. Chem. Phys.*, **33**, 825 (1960).
218. B. E. Conway and P. Bourgault, *J. Electroanal. Chem.*, **1**, 8 (1959).
219. A. Mituya, *J. Res. Inst. Catalysis, Hokkaido Univ.*, **4**, 228 (1956–57).
220. J. O'M. Bockris, *ibid.*, **2**, 105 (1953).
221. A. N. Frumkin, *Discussions Faraday Soc.*, No. 1, (1947); *Trans. Symp. Electrode Processes, Philadelphia, Pa.*, 1959 (1961), 41.
222. J. O'M. Bockris and A. M. Azzam, *Trans. Faraday Soc.*, **48**, 145 (1952).
223. B. E. Conway and M. Salomon, *Proc. Symp. Electrolyte Solutions* (1964) John Wiley and Sons, New York, in press (1965).
224. C. G. Swain and R. F. W. Bader, *Tetrahedron*, **10**, 182, 200 (1960).
225. H. V. Buttlar, W. Vielstich and H. Barth, *Ber. Bunsenges.*, **67**, 650 (1963); see also W. Vielstich, T. H. Schuchard and M. von Stackelberg, *ibid.*, **67**, 1487 (1963).
226. G. R. Lewis and P. Ruetschi, *J. Phys. Chem.*, **66**, 1487 (1962).
227. M. Salomon and B. E. Conway, *J. Phys. Chem.*, **68**, 2009 (1964).
228. H. F. Walton and J. H. Wolfendon, *Trans. Faraday Soc.*, **34**, 436 (1938).

229. M. FUKUDA and J. HORIUTI, *J. Res. Inst. Catalysis, Hokkaido Univ.*, **10**, 43 (1962).

230. M. ROME and C. F. HISKEY, *J. Am. Chem. Soc.*, **76**, 5207 (1954).

231. J. MAYELL and S. LANGER, *J. Electrochem. Soc.*, **111**, 438 (1964).

232. H. A. LAITINEN and C. G. ENKE, *J. Electrochem. Soc.*, **107**, 773 (1960).

233. K. J. VETTER and D. BERNDT, *Z. Elektrochem.*, **62**, 378 (1958).

234. J. J. MACDONALD and B. E. CONWAY, *Proc. Roy. Soc. London*, **A269**, 419 (1962).

235. J. O'M. BOCKRIS and A. K. HUQ, *Proc. Roy. Soc. London*, **A237**, 227 (1956).

236. *Corrosion Handbook*, 1st Ed. (ed. H. H. UHLIG), The Electrochemical Society, John Wiley and Sons, New York, 1948.

237. U. R. EVANS, *Corrosion and Oxidation of Metals*, Arnold, London, 1960.

238. C. WAGNER and W. TRAUD, *Z. Elektrochem.*, **44**, 391 (1938).

239. W. FRAENKEL and H. HEINZ, *Z. Anorg. Chem.*, **133**, 167 (1924).

240. H. II. UHLIG, *Z. Elektrochem.*, **62**, 626, 700 (1958).

241. J. O'M. BOCKRIS and P. DRAZIC, *Electrochim. Acta*, **7**, 293 (1962); see also *J. Chem. Phys.*, **42**, 2246 (1965).

242. Y. M. KOLOTYRKIN, *Z. Elektrochem.*, **62**, 664 (1958); see also H. NORD, *Acta Chem. Scand.*, **18**, 681 (1964).

243. M. POURBAIX, *Thermodynamics of Dilute Aqueous Solutions*, Arnold, London, 1949.

244. M. STERN, *J. Electrochem. Soc.*, **104**, 559, 600 (1957); **105**, 638 (1958); **108**, 836 (1961).

245. B. E. CONWAY and E. GILEADI, *Can. J. Chem.* **40**, 1933 (1962); see also ref. 165.

246. B. E. CONWAY and J. O'M. BOCKRIS, *Proc. Roy. Soc. London*, **A248**, 394 (1958); see also *Electrochim. Acta*, **3**, 340 (1960).

247. N. F. MOTT and J. WATTS-TOBIN, *Electrochim. Acta*, **4**, 79 (1961).

248. J. O'M. BOCKRIS and W. MEHL, *J. Chem. Phys.* **27**, 817 (1957); *Can. J. Chem.*, **37**, 190 (1959).

249. M. VOLMER, *Elektrolytische Kristallwachstum, Herman, Paris*, 1934; *Kinetik der Phasenbildung*, Steinkopff, Dresden, 1939.

250. W. LORENZ, *Z. Naturforsch.*, **9a**, 716 (1954); see also H. BRANDES, *Z. Phys. Chem.*, **A142**, 97 (1929).

251. M. FLEISCHMANN and H. R. THIRSK, *Advan. Electrochem. Electrochem. Eng.* (eds. DELAHAY and TOBIAS), **3**, 123 (1963).

252. I. ENYO and J. O'M. BOCKRIS, *J. Electrochem. Soc.*, **109**, 48 (1962); I. ENYO, Ph.D. thesis, University of Pennsylvania (1960).

253. H. FISCHER, *Elektrolytische Abscheidung und Elektrokristallisation von Metallen*, Springer, Berlin, 1954. Pp. 324–326.

254. G. KORTÜM, *Lehrbuch der Elektrochemie*, Verlag Chemie, Weinheim/Bergstr., 1957. P. 519.

255. J. O'M. BOCKRIS and A. DAMJANOVIC, *Modern Aspects of Electrochemistry*, vol. 3 (eds. BOCKRIS and CONWAY), Butterworths, 1964. P. 224.

256. M. DESPIC, and J. O'M. BOCKRIS, *J. Chem. Phys.*, **32**, 389 (1960).

257. J. Barton and J. O'M. Bockris, *Proc. Roy. Soc. London*, **A268**, 485 (1962).

258. H. Seiter, H. Fischer and H. Albert, *Electrochim. Acta*, **2**, 167 (1960).

259. G. Wranglèn, *Trans. Roy. Inst. Technol., Stockholm*, no. 94 (1955); see also *Electrochim. Acta*, **2**, 130 (1960).

260. H. J. Pick, G. G. Storey and T. B. Vaughan, *Electrochim. Acta*, **2**, 165 (1960).

261. S. C. Barnes, G. G. Storey and H. J. Pick, *Electrochim. Acta*, **2**, 195 (1960).

262. O. Essin, L. Antropov and A. Levin, *Acta Physicochim. U.R.S.S.*, **6**, 447 (1937).

263. W. Rojter, W. Juza and E. Polujan, *ibid.*, **10**, 389, 845 (1939).

264. J. E. B. Randles and K. W. Somerton, *Trans. Faraday Soc.*, **48**, 951 (1952).

265. J. E. B. Randles, *Trans. Faraday Soc.*, **48**, 828 (1952).

266. N. S. Hush, *Trans. Faraday Soc.*, **57**, 557 (1961).

267. V. Levich and Y. Dogonadze, *Dokl. Akad. Nauk SSSR*, **124**, 123 (1959); **133**, 138 (1960).

268. W. Ehrenfest, *Ann. Physik*, **51**, 327 (1916); R. A. Marcus, *Ann. Rev. Phys. Chem.*, **15**, 155 (1964).

269. E. Sacher and K. J. Laidler, *Modern Aspects of Electrochemistry*, vol. 3 (eds. Bockris and Conway), Butterworths, London, 1964. Chapter 1.

270. R. W. Gurney and R. H. Fowler, *Proc. Roy. Soc. London*, **A134**, 137 (1931); **A186**, 378 (1932).

271. J. A. V. Butler, *Electrical Phenomena at Interfaces*, Methuen, London, 1951. P. 23.

272. W. H. Brittain and C. G. B. Garrett, *Bell System Tech. J.*, **34**, 129 (1955).

273. F. Beck and H. Gerischer, *Z. Elektrochem.*, **63**, 500 (1959); for reviews, see H. Gerischer, *Record Chem. Progr.*, **23**, 135 (1962); P. Delahay and Tobias (eds.), *Advances in Electrochemistry*, **1** (1961); M. Green, *Modern Aspects of Electrochemistry*, vol. 2 (ed. Bockris), Butterworths, London, 1959, P. 343.

274. H. Gerischer and F. Beck, *Z. Physik. Chem. Frankfurt, N.F.*, **13**, 389 (1957); *Z. Elektrochem.*, **63**, 943 (1959).

275. V. Levich, *Acta Physicochim. U.R.S.S.*, **17**, 257 (1942); **79**, 117, 133 (1944); see also D. Jahn and W. Vielstich, *J. Electrochem. Soc.*, **109**, 849 (1962).

276. P. Delahay, *New Instrumental Methods in Electrochemistry*, Interscience Publishers, Ltd., London, 1954.

277. P. Delahay and M. Berzins, *J. Am. Chem. Soc.*, **75**, 2486 (1953).

278. J. E. B. Randles, *Discussions Faraday Soc.*, No. 1, 11 (1947).

279. P. Dolin and B. V. Ershler, *Acta Physicochim. U.R.S.S.*, **13**, 747 (1940); **21**, 213 (1946).

280. J. O'M. Bockris and B. E. Conway, *J. Chem. Phys.* **28**, 707 (1958).

281. K. S. G. Doss and H. P. Agarwal, *J. Sci. Ind. Res. India*, **9B**, 280 (1950).

282. P. Delahay, *Advan. Electrochem. Electrochem. Eng.*, **1**, 233 (1961).
283. M. von Stackelberg and P. Weber, *Z. Elektrochem.* **56**, 806 (1952).
284. M. J. Allen and J. Corwin, *J. Am. Chem. Soc.*, **72**, 114 (1950).
285. H. Kolbe, *Liebigs Ann. Chem.*, **69**, 257 (1849).
286. S. Glasstone and A. Hickling, *J. Chem. Soc.*, **1934**, 1878; **1936**, 820.
287. B. C. L. Weedon, *Quart. Rev. London*, **6**, 380 (1952).
288. D. A. Fairweather and O. J. Walker, *J. Chem. Soc.*, **1926**, 3111; S. N. Shukla and O. J. Walker, *Trans. Faraday Soc.*, **27**, 722 (1931).
289. M. J. Allen, *Organic Electrode Processes*, Reinhold Publishing Corp., New York, 1958; see also P. J. Elving and B. Pullman, *Advan. Chem. Phys.*, **3**, 1 (1961).
290. M. Y. Fioshin and Y. B. Vasilev, *Dokl. Akad. Nauk SSSR*, **134**, 879 (1960).
291. C. Schall, *Z. Elektrochem.*, **3**, 83 (1896).
292. F. Fichter, *Trans. Electrochem. Soc.*, **75**, 309 (1939); **56**, 8 (1929).
293. S. Goldschmidt, W. Leicher and H. Haas, *Ann. Chem.*, **577**, 153 (1952).
294. A. Crum-Brown and J. Walker, *Ann. Chem.*, **261**, 107 (1891).
295. C. Wilson and W. J. Lippincott, *J. Am. Chem. Soc.*, **78**, 4290 (1956); *J. Electrochem. Soc.*, **103**, 672 (1956).
296. B. E. Conway and A. Vijh, in course of publication.
297. L. Young, *Anodic Films*, Academic Press, New York, 1961; see also *Trans. Faraday Soc.*, **50**, 159 (1954); J. F. Dewald, *J. Electrochem. Soc.*, **102**, 1 (1955); *J. Phys. Chem. Solids* **2**, 55 (1959).
298. N. F. Mott, *Trans. Faraday Soc.*, **36**, 472 (1940); H. Cabrera and N. F. Mott, *Rep. Progr. Phys.*, **12**, 163 (1948–49); see also M. J. Dignam, *Can. J. Chem.*, **42**, 1155 (1964).
299. D. A. Vermilyea, *Acta Met.*, **1**, 282 (1953); see also C. P. Bean, T. C. Fisher and D. A. Vermilyea, *Phys. Rev.*, **101**, 551 (1956).
300. R. F. Meyer, *J. Electrochem. Soc.*, **107**, 847 (1960).
301. J. O'M. Bockris and S. Srinivasen, *Electrochim. Acta*, **9**, 31 (1964).
302. B. E. Conway, *Proc. Roy. Soc. London*, **A256**, 128 (1960); see also J. O'M. Bockris and D. F. A. Koch, *J. Phys. Chem.*, **65**, 1941 (1961).
303. A. Eucken and K. Bratzler, *Z. Physik. Chem.*, **A174**, 273 (1935).
304. B. Topley and H. Eyring, *J. Chem. Phys.*, **2**, 217 (1934).
305. K. I. Rozental, P. Dolin and B. V. Ershler, *Acta Physicochim. U.S.S.R.*, **21**, 213 (1946).
306. M. L. Eidenhoff, *J. Am. Chem. Soc.*, **69**, 2507 (1949).
307. B. Post and C. F. Hiskey, *J. Am. Chem. Soc.*, **72**, 4203 (1950); *ibid.*, **73**, 161 (1951).
308. H. Gohr and E. Lange, *Z. Elektrochem.*, **63**, 673 (1958).
309. J. Horiuti, *J. Res. Inst. Catalysis, Hokkaido Univ.*, **1**, 8 (1948); J. Horiuti and M. Ikusima, *Proc. Imp. Acad. Tokyo*, **15**, 39 (1939).
310. R. Parsons, *Trans. Faraday Soc.*, **47**, 1332 (1951).
311. P. D. Lukovstev, *Zh. Fiz. Khim. U.S.S.R.*, **31**, 509 (1947); see also

J. O'M. Bockris and E. C. Potter, *J. Electrochem. Soc.*, **99**, 169 (1952).

312. A. C. Makrides, *J. Electrochem. Soc.*, **104**, 677 (1957).
313. H. G. Oswin and M. Salomon, *Can. J. Chem.*, **41**, 1686 (1963).
314. J. Prigogine, *Thermodynamics of Irreversible Processes*, Charles C Thomas, Publishers, Springfield, Ill.,1955.
315. M. Manes, L. J. E. Hofer and S. Waller, *J. Chem. Phys.*, **18**, 1355 (1950).
316. J. Horiuti, *Trans. Symp. Electrode Processes, Philadelphia, Pa.*, 1959 (1961), 17.
317. A. C. Makrides, *J. Electrochem. Soc.*, **109**, 256 (1962).
318. A. N. Frumkin, *Dokl. Akad. Nauk SSSR*, **119**, 318 (1958).
319. E. Müller, *Ergeb. Exakt. Naturw.*, **27**, 290 (1953).

Index

Absolute rate theory
  kinetic equations in, 93
  transmission coefficient in, 95
A.c. impedance
  in fast reactions, 238
  theory of, 239
Acid and base, electrode as, 181
Acid-base equilibria and adsorption, 59
Acids and bases, adsorption of, 59
Activated complex, 95, 96, 181
Activation
  apparent heat of, 108
  energies, calculation of, 133
  energy
    effects of potential on, 97, 98
    field effects on, 100
  entropy of, 108
  free energy, 93
  heat or enthalpy of, 106
Addition agents in metal deposition, 218
Adiabatic process, 222
Adions, in metal deposition, 205, 212
Adsorbed intermediates, 5, 8, 136
  in kinetics, 112, 116, 123, 136
  methods of study for, 150
Adsorption
  of acids and bases, 59
  activated and non-activated, 122
  and field emission, 276
  and field ionisation, 277
  of H, thermodynamics of, 154

immobile, 81
of ions, 44
methods for, summarised, 64, 66
of neutral molecules, 69
pseudocapacitance, 138, 141
of radio-labelled species, 61, 166
of reactants, 9, 10, 44
  in kinetics, 93, 94
standard free energy of, 82
theories of
  for ions, 28, 78
  for molecules, 71, 76
by u-v absorbance, 62
Alternative reactions, in kinetics, 109
Amines, adsorption of, 59
Anodic films
  growth of, 252
  inhomogeneous field at, 261
  mechanisms of growth of, 253
  space charge in, 258
  theory of growth of, 254
Applications of electrochemical kinetic and adsorption principles, 170

Band theory of semiconductors, 225
Barrier layer films, 185, 252; *see also* Anodic films
Bases, adsorption of, 59

Capacitance
  diffusional, 140, 239
  from open-circuit decay, 156

Capacity
  and components of charge, 51, 52, 56
  desorption effects on, 70
  double-layer, 25, 30, 51, 57
    dipole orientation contribution, 75
  from electrocapillary curves, 49
  hump, 39, 42
  integral, 35, 36, 42
  and isotherms, 76, 91, 162
Catalytic steps, 12, 114, 136
Cathodic protection, 191
Charge
  adsorption and surface, 77, 91
  components of, in double-layer, 49, 51, 55
  density, space, in double-layer, 28
  diffuse layer, 30, 55, 57
  inner Helmholtz layer, 55
Charge-transfer steps, 10
Charging
  component currents in, 152
  curves, 150, 184
    differential, 152
Chemical reaction steps, 12
Chemisorption
  effects at electrodes, 147, 149, 168
  of ions, 33, 37, 39
Chi-potential, 14, 15, 16, 19
Chronopotentiometry, 150, 152
Circuits, equivalent, 139
Closest approach, distance of, 29
Components of adsorbed charge, 48, 49, 56
  from capacities, 51, 52, 56
Components of charge
  contributions to, 55, 56
  and ionic equilibria, 59
Conduction
  early work, 3
  and electrode processes, 3, 7
Consecutive reactions
  in kinetics, 109
  in metal deposition, 109, 205
Contact potential difference, significance of, 22, 23

Coordination, effects in metal deposition, 208
Corrosion, 187
  current, 194, 196
  current-potential diagrams, 193
  inhibition, 200
  and pH-potential diagrams, 191
Coulostatic method, 159
Coverage
  intermediate, conditions for, 137
  in kinetics, 93
  relation between charge and capacitance for, 138
  relations, steady-state, 112
Critical current, in passivation, 190
Current density
  distribution in metal deposition, 214
  and rate, 92, 93
Current-potential curve, equation to polarographic, 234
Current-potential curves, polarographic, 234
Current-potential diagrams, for corrosion, 193, 196, 198, 199
Cyclic voltammetry, 160

Debye-Langevin theory, 72
Decay of e.m.f.
  coupled mechanism for, 158
  on open circuit, 155
Depolarisation, of dipoles, 17
Desorption
  field ionisation, 277
  and surface tension and capacity, 70
Deuterium evolution and separation factor, 177–182
Dielectric constant
  in double-layer, 28–29, 38, 40
  in surface-layer, 17
Diffusion
  control, 9, 232
  layer, 9, 11, 232
  limited current, 9, 232
Dipole potential difference, 14
Discreteness-of-charge effects, 37
Dislocation, screw, 213, 216

Dislocations, role of, in metal deposition, 212
Dissolution of metals, 204
Distance of closest approach, 29
Double-layer
  capacitance, 25
  capacity, dipole contribution, 75
  dielectric constant in, 28–29, 38, 40
  diffuse, 27, 32
  effects in kinetics, 94
  electrostriction in, 38
  field in, 29, 40
  Gouy-Chapman theory of, 27
  Helmholtz or compact, 27, 32, 57
  inner Helmholtz region, 32, 36, 55
  ion distribution function for, 28
  ion distribution in, 25
  models of, 26, 39, 41
  outer Helmholtz region, 32, 36
  solvent orientation theory of, 39, 41
  Stern theory of, 31, 33
  theory, relation to Debye-Hückel theory, 28
Dropping mercury electrode, 230

Electrocapillarity, 45
Electrocapillary curve, 49
Electrocapillary curves, for neutral molecules, 70
Electrocapillary maximum (e.c.m.) potential, 31, 65
  methods for study of, 66–67
  and work function, 67
Electrocapillary method, 45
  theory of, 46
Electrochemical kinetics, 92
Electrochemical potential, 14, 15, 20
Electrochemical reactions, fast, 236
Electrochemistry
  early work in, 3, 4, 5
  structure of, 3, 7
Electrode
  potential
    half-cell, 19
    and rate, 96, 101
    single, 19

potential difference
  in a cell, 21, 22
  measured, 22
potentials, thermodynamics of, 19
reactions
  organic, 240
  relation to other fields, 6, 7
surface charge on, 30
Electrodics, 3, 4
Electro-inorganic chemistry, 5, 6, 7
Electrolyte solutions, early work on, 4
Electron, 4
  energy distribution in semiconductors, 229
  gas, model at surface, 84
  number, 265
  spin resonance, 167
  transfer
    and activated complex, 96
    at semiconductors, 222, 223, 227
    by tunneling, 96
    tunneling in redox reactions, 96, 223
  work function
    in electrode equilibria, 21, 23
    in kinetics, 132; *see also* Work function
Electrons, field emission of, 273, 274
Electro-organic chemistry, 5, 6, 7, 240, 283
Electrostriction in double-layer, 38
Ellipsometry, 166, 253
E.m.f., decay of, 156, 158
Energetics
  of irreversible processes, 126
  of redox reactions, 219
Equilibrium
  chemical condition for, 20
  electrochemical condition for, 20
  electron work function in, 21
  energetics of electrochemical, 21, 22
  solvation energy in, 21
Equivalent circuits, 139
Exchange current
  density, 105
  and work function, 171

Exchange currents
  and H adsorption, 134
  for H and D, ratio of, 177
Extrinsic semiconductors, 225

Faraday's laws, apparent deviations
  from, 93
Field emission, 273
Field ionisation
  energetics of, 278
  and potential functions, 281
Franck-Condon principle, in redox
  reactions, 222
Free energy of activation, 93
Free radical intermediates, 8
Frequencies, vibrational, in acti-
  vated complexes, 182
Frequency factors, 106
  and proton tunneling, 109

Galvani potential, 17
Gas-metal interface, field effects at,
  273
Gauss's equation, 30, 40
Germanium, dissolution of, 227
Gibbs equation, 46

Half-jump distance, 97
Heat of activation, 106
Helmholtz equation, 17
Helmholtz layer, inner and outer,
  32, 36, 55
Henry's law isotherm, 35, 81
Heterogeneity
  in hydrogen adsorption, 154–155
  induced, 124
  intrinsic, 125
  of surface, 81
Hydrocarbons, adsorption of, 168
Hydrogen adsorption
  in kinetics, 112, 134
  at single crystals, 153
  thermodynamics of, 154
Hydrogen evolution reaction
  mechanisms of, 111, 112
  methods for study of mechanisms,
  172

Tafel slopes and reaction orders,
  174, 175
  and work function, 131

Ideal polarisable electrode, 27
  at mercury, 27, 45
  at platinum, 27
Ilkovič equation, 235
Image potential, 18, 38
Impedance, a.c.
  in fast reactions, 238
  theory of, 239
Inhibition
  of corrosion, 200
  self-, in organic oxidations, 201,
  203
Inner Helmholtz layer, 32, 36, 55
Inner potential, 17
Integral capacity, 35, 36, 42, 49
  and surface tension, 49
Intermediates, adsorbed, 5, 8, 150
  methods of study of, 150
Intrinsic semiconductors, 225
Ion-distribution function, for double-layer, 28
Ion emission microscopy, 282
Ion-pair formation, hydration in, 43
Ionic adsorption, 44
Ionic redox reactions, 170, 218
Ionisation potential and work function, relation to atomic number, 24
Ionisation potentials in electrochemical equilibria, 21, 23
Irreversible processes, energetics of,
  126
Isotherms
  dipole repulsion, 87, 89
  electrochemical, 85, 137
  interaction effects in, 85
  ion replusion, 85
  Langmuir and Temkin, 78, 81, 137
    comparison of, 83, 84
  in relation to capacity data, 76,
  91, 163
  in relation to surface tension, 87
  and surface pressure, 87
Isotope effects, in kinetics, 177–182

Kinetic rate equations, 93, 101
Kinetics
    double-layer effects in, 94
    electrochemical, 92
        under Temkin conditions, 118
    of redox reactions, 219
    at semiconductors, 223, 227
Kolbe reaction, 136, 185, 244
    free radicals in, 249
    mechanisms of, 247
    and oxygen evolution, 247
    periodic polarisation in, 250
    potentiostatic studies of, 251

Langmuir isotherm
    basis of, 78
    comparison with Temkin type, 83, 84
    in Stern theory, 34
Limiting current
    activation-controlled, 176
    diffusion-controlled, 232, 233
Lippmann equation, 48

Metal
    deposition, 204
        addition agents in, 218
        current density distribution in, 214
        distinction of steps in, 209
        morphology in, 214, 217
        step and facet growth in, 215, 216
        successive steps in, 203, 207
        transients in, 209
    dissolution, 204
    "interface," significance of, 42
Microscopy, field emission, 273, 282
Mixed potential, 194, 199
Morphology, of metal deposits, 214, 217

Nernst equation, 20, 22
Neutral molecules
    adsorption of, 69
    theories for adsorption of, 71
Nucleation, surface, 213

Ohm's law, transport of charge carriers, 225
Open circuit, gas evolution on, 167
Open-circuit decay of e.m.f., theory of, 155
Organic electrode processes, 5, 6, 7, 240, 283
Orientation
    distribution function for, 73, 74, 75
    effects, in double-layer, 39, 73, 74
Outer Helmholtz layer, 32, 36
Outer potential, 17
Overpotential, 102
    and work function, 130
Overvoltage; see Overpotential
Oxidation reduction; see Redox reactions
Oxidations, organic electrochemical, 242
Oxide film growth; see Anodic films
Oxides, surface, 117, 183
    passivation by, 201
Oxygen, reversible electrode potential for, 186
Oxygen evolution reaction, mechanisms for, 116, 183

Passivation effects, kinetic theory of, 201
Passivity, 187
Peroxide, 187
pH-potential diagrams, 191
Phase growth, 170
n-orbital interaction, with surfaces, 91
Poisson equation, 28
Polarisation
    electronic, and adsorption, 72
    orientation, 72
    total, 72
Polarographic current vs. potential curves, 234
Polarography, 230
    irreversible effects in, 235

Potential
　Galvani, 17
　image, 18, 38
　inner, 17
　outer, 17
　-pH diagrams, 191
　real, 17
　Volta, 17, 18
　of zero charge, 31, 65
　　methods for study of, 66–67
　　and specific adsorption, 68
　　and work function, 67
Potential difference at interfaces, 13
Potential electrolytes, 4
Potentiodynamic method, 160
Potentiostatic method in passivation, 194
Potentiostatic transient, 151
Pre-electrochemical steps, 12, 136
Pressure
　electrostatic, in double-layer, 38
　at ions in solution, 38
Proton
　discharge, 112, 171
　tunneling, 182
　　at low temperatures, 182
Pseudocapacitance, adsorption, 138, 141
　and isotherms, 163
　from kinetic equations, 142
　rate effects in, 147, 148
　relation to isotherm, 143, 145
Psi-potential in kinetics, 94

Quasi-equilibrium method for coverage relations, 115
Quinone electrode, 218

Radio-isotope labelling, methods for adsorption, 61, 166, 169
Rate constant, electrochemical, 107
Rate-controlling step, 110
Rate equations, electrochemical, 101
Rates and electrode potential, 96, 101
Reactant adsorption, 44

Reaction orders
　double-layer effects and, 103, 104,
　electrochemical, 103, 104
　for hydrogen evolution, tabulated, 175
Real potential, 17
Rectification, faradaic, 240
Redox reactions, 8, 218
　at dropping mercury electrodes, 231
　energetics of, 219, 220
　ionic, 170, 218
　kinetics of, 219
　at semiconductors, 227
　tunneling in, 223
Reductions, organic electrochemical, 241
Reversible potential for oxygen, 186

Salting-out, relation to desorption, 72
Screw dislocation, 213, 216
Semiconductors
　intrinsic and extrinsic, 225
　n and p type, 226
　redox reactions at, 223, 227
Separation factor, 177
　and mechanism, 178
　values of, tabulated, 179
Single crystal faces, H adsorption at, 153
Single electrode potential, 19
Solvation
　free energy of, 18
　in redox reactions, 221
Solvent
　adsorption, surface potential and, 65
　orientation
　　in double-layer, 39, 41
　　and e.c.m., 65, 72
Space charge
　density, in double-layer, 28
　effects, in oxide films, 258
Specific adsorption of ions, 32, 37, 39
Steady state
　in electrochemical kinetics, 112
　method for coverage relations, 112

Step and facet growth, 215
Stern theory of double-layer, 31, 33
Stoichiometric numbers, 101, 262
  problems in significance of, 266, 267
  for processes near equilibrium, 268
  and reaction mechanism, 265
Structure of electrochemistry, 3, 7
Successive steps in electrode processes, 10, 11, 101
Super-equivalent adsorption, of ions, 34, 39, 57
Surface
  charge, 30
    and adsorption, 77, 91, 138
  coverage
    conditions for intermediate, 137
    effects in kinetics, 118
  diffusion, in metal deposition, 207
  excess, 46, 47
    of bases and their ions, 59
    for individual ions, 51
  oxide species, 117
  potential, 14, 15, 16
    at liquid-gas interface, 18
  pressure, and isotherms, 87, 88
  tension
    and adsorption, 45
    from integration of capacity data, 58
    and isotherms, 87
Symmetry factor (β), 98, 99
  and half-jump distance, 99

Tafel equation, 102
  for anodic film processes, 256, 257
Tafel slope and e m f decay slopes, 157
Tafel slopes
  and alternative reactions, 110, 112
  and consecutive reactions, 110, 112
  for hydrogen evolution, tabulated, 174
  at intermediate coverage, 118, 120, 176

and reaction mechanisms, 113, 117
Temkin isotherm, 81, 118, 123
  and electrochemical kinetics, 118, 123, 124
Temkin parameters, deduction of, 76, 91, 164
Thermodynamics of electrode potentials, 19
Transition time in fast reactions, 237
Transmission coefficient, significance of, 95
Trans-passive processes, 197
Triangular voltage sweep, 160, 162, 184
Tunneling
  of electrons, 96
  of protons, 182

U-v absorption method for adsorption study, 62

Van der Waals forces, effects of, 85
Vibrational frequencies and H/D separation factor, 181
Vibrational modes in activated complex for proton transfer, 181
Volta potential, 17
Voltammetry, cyclic, 160, 162, 184

Work function
  and e.c.m. potential, 67
  electron, in electrochemical equilibrium, 21, 23
  and exchange current, 132
  in field emission, 274, 277
  and H adsorption energy, 133
  and hydrogen evolution reaction, 132
  in kinetics, 127, 132
  and single electrode equilibria, 21, 23

Zero charge, potential of, 31, 65
  relation to surface tension, 31, 49, 65, 66
  relation to work function, 67